LOIS
LENSKI

TWENTY-TWO
SHORT STORIES
OF AMERICA

Selected and Arranged by
Edith Mirrielees, Stanford University

ILLUSTRATED BY LOIS LENSKI

D. C. HEATH AND COMPANY

NEW YORK   BOSTON   CHICAGO
ATLANTA   SAN FRANCISCO   DALLAS   LONDON

TO

*The boys and girls and teachers
far too many for separate naming
who have given me help in the
making of this collection of
stories*

FOREWORD TO TEACHERS

IF YOU should chance to break a long-standing tradition and read this foreword, you would find in it three things — first, an explanation of why twelve of the stories are placed in pairs; second, a set of suggestions for using the equipment attached to each story; and third, a statement of the plan which has governed the selection of material for the book.

The pairing of twelve of the stories is done in answer to two conditions existent in every classroom. In all classes, the members differ widely both in reading speed and in reading comprehension, and yet if one great value of fiction reading is not to be sacrificed, it is essential that each reader enjoy what he reads. In all classes too, as every teacher knows without telling, it is easier to make a point by contrast than by direct analysis and assertion; and the search for surface differences and then for deep-lying likenesses between two stories is at once a source of interest in reading and an aid later in class discussion.

Within the pairs here given, there are differences either in the lengths of the stories paired or in the amount of concentration and imaginative capacity which the reading of the story calls for. The same variation in amount of difficulty is to be found in the topics for discussion following each pair. By different assignments of story and topic, the teacher can offer levels of effort suited to the several levels of reading ability in her class. By reversing the assignment following a first discussion, she can the more easily induct reluctant readers into a story about which they already know something. At the same time, she can give the experienced readers opportunity to widen their reading and some exercise in the formulating of literary judgments. For an example of how paired stories may be so used, let us consider one of the pairs, "Growing Up" and "The Night Hunter."

If I were dealing with this pair, I should ask one section of my class to read both stories, reading them as quickly as was compatible with grasping the thought. A second section I should ask to read "Growing Up," and a third, "The Night Hunter" — in each case carefully. After one class discussion, I should reverse the assignment for sections two and three, and ask section one either to read another story by whichever of the two authors the reader preferred or to make a written comment or comparison concerning the stories already read. (Where practicable, reference is given in the foreword to other stories by the same writer appearing in books or magazines likely to be easily available.) When everyone had read the two stories and some of the class had read more, discussion would be possible in which each pupil could take an intelligent part. After two or three pairs had been read in this fashion, readers would be ready to make their own combinations, emphasizing likenesses and differences among the unpaired stories and finding new combinations among the paired ones.

Unless the context makes their meaning clear, words likely to be unfamiliar are given, with their definitions, at the end of the story in which they appear. If the definition is not all-inclusive — and few definitions are — the phrase in which the word is used is repeated and only that meaning given which fits that usage.

Apart from definitions, the equipment which accompanies the stories is of two kinds, "Questions for Self-Testing" and "Topics for Themes or Discussion." Perhaps the most important thing to say about this equipment is that the questions marked "For Self-Testing" are not meant to be used for inquiry on the teacher's part into whether or not reading has been done. They are meant for exactly what they are named — a means of helping the reader to find out for himself how far he recalls what he has read. A story read without enjoyment does nothing towards the establishment of a reading habit; and it is difficult to enjoy reading if, while you read, your mind is occupied with snatching at details for fear of being tripped up on them later. To reassure readers that no later tripping up is here intended, there is put at the end of the book a set of page references showing where the material for answer to each of the self-testing questions is to be found.

But since these questions are not for examination purposes, and since the answers to them are made easy to find, why include them at all? If classes were made up only of natural-born readers, they would not be included. Under conditions as they now exist, they are put in with the purpose of appealing to the play impulse and thus attaching to reading some of the entertainment which has so long provided an audience for the *Ask Me Another* books. The questions may be used in class in any of a dozen ways or not used at all. Out of their possible uses I am setting down three.

1. The class has read the story, read the self-testing questions, answered them in mind, or not, as each member chose. The assignment, made in class and to be fulfilled within a strict time limit, is, "Write three self-testing questions of your own." The questions, collected and read at once, serve as a foundation for story discussion and for inquiry into what constitutes a really testing question.

2. Following the reading of a story, the class is divided into groups, one member of the group propounding the questions and a secretary checking on who first can find the actual words from which the answer is drawn. If this exercise degenerates

into a nervous attempt to satisfy a requirement, it is useless. If it remains a game, it provides admirable practice in rapid reading.

3. The questions themselves are brought to trial: Is this a good question for its purpose? Are there other answers to it besides the answer indicated? How many of these questions can you replace with better ones? Here, of course, the whole matter of what is or is not important in the story can hardly fail to be opened up for discussion.

The self-testing questions deal necessarily with details. "Topics for Themes or Discussion," on the other hand, deal with analysis or contrast of characters and situations and with the ideas which underlie the stories. Frequently, too, some one of the questions calls for an imaginative carrying on of the action, for a replacement of one action by another, or for an application of the story's main idea to some situation possible in the reader's own life. Here, as with the self-testing questions, the topics given should be open to class criticism and to additions by means of class suggestions.

So far we have spoken only of individual stories and their uses. What of the book as a whole? It is made up, as is evident, of stories concerned with American life. As is evident, too, its bent is markedly historical — if, that is, "historical" be interpreted widely enough to mean not chiefly battles and diplomatic efforts but also the external struggles and the emotional adjustments peculiar to our American situation. "The White Dogs of Arran," for example, with its picture of ranch life in Montana, is quite as certainly an historical story as is "For Peace and Concord." The folktales could have grown to their present form nowhere except on the American continent.

But, though the stories have an historical bearing, that

bearing is not the chief bond of union among them. Their chief bond is this: Every one, even the least realistic, contains an emotional situation which boys and girls can recognize as real, and which, to the extent that they do recognize it, provides them with understanding and power of adjustment in the situations they must themselves meet. Reading is vicarious living; these stories, however different their settings or their placing in time, have been chosen with a view to making the vicarious living they offer relate closely and truthfully to the lives of the readers. With most of the stories, the phase of action or feeling illuminated is obvious beyond need of explanation. Where there has seemed any possibility of its not being obvious to an inexperienced reader, it has been suggested in the accompanying foreword.

The order in which the stories are best used is necessarily a thing to be decided by each teacher. For convenience, they are placed in the book not in the order of their publication but roughly in the order of the time they deal with, beginning with a pre-Colonial story and ending with those laid in the 1930's. For convenience, too, paired stories are placed at either end of the book, so that they may be used both by the teacher who prefers to begin with colonial days and move forward in time, and by the one who prefers to begin with today and move backward.

EDITH MIRRIELEES
Associate Professor of English,
Stanford University

ACKNOWLEDGMENT

For permission to use copyrighted material grateful acknowledgment is made to:

Harper's Magazine and Mr. Gouverneur Morris for "Growing Up."

The American Boy and Mr. Alexander Key for "The Night Hunter."

D. Appleton-Century Company, Publishers, New York, New York, for the story "For Peace and Concord," from *A Patriot Maid and Other Stories*, by Emilie Benson Knipe and Alden Arthur Knipe.

Alfred A. Knopf, Inc., and Mr. James Stevens for "Shanty Boy," from his book, *Paul Bunyan*.

Mrs. Susan K. Branner for "How the Cat Came to Have Nine Lives," from *How and Why Stories*, by John Casper Branner, published by Henry Holt and Company.

Miss Cornelia Meigs for "Guests in the Smokehouse," published in *St. Nicholas*.

D. Appleton-Century Company, Publishers, New York, New York, for "The Rip Van Winkle Man-O'-War," by Mr. H. Irving Hancock, from *Patriotism and the Flag Retold from St. Nicholas*.

Mrs. Eliza London Shepard for "That Spot," by Jack London.

Mr. Booth Tarkington for "Bingism" from his book, *Penrod and Sam*, published by Doubleday, Doran and Co., Inc., Garden City, New York.

Mr. James Thurber for "Snapshot of a Dog," published in *The New Yorker*.

Houghton Mifflin Company for the story "Semaphore," from *America at Work*, by Joseph Husband.

Mr. John D. Morse for "Ocean Gold," published in *St. Nicholas*.

The Macmillan Company and Miss Cornelia Meigs for "The White Dogs of Arran," from *The Pool of Stars*, published by Macmillan Company.

Mr. Bigelow Neal for "Tamerlane," from *American Boy Adventure Stories*, published by Doubleday, Doran and Company, Inc., Garden City, New York.

Miss Elsie Singmaster for "Mr. Brownlee's Roses," published in *St. Nicholas*.

Mrs. Josephine Daskam Bacon for her story "For What We Have Just Received," published in *St. Nicholas*.

Doubleday, Doran and Company, Inc., Publishers, Garden City, New York, for "After Twenty Years," from *The Four Million*, by O. Henry.

Mr. Lupton Wilkinson for "Miss Letitia's Profession," published in *North American Review*.

Efforts have been made by the author to communicate with Miss Mary Wells for permission to use "The Silver Snuffbox," and with Mr. John Schoolcraft for permission to use "The 'Coon and Dog Logan," from *American Boy Adventure Stories*, published by Doubleday, Doran and Company, Inc., Publishers, Garden City, New York.

CONTENTS

TWENTY-TWO
SHORT STORIES
OF AMERICA

GROWING UP

By GOUVERNEUR MORRIS

Indians are the Americans who have been longest in America. All the rest of our ancestors came from somewhere else, even though, with some of them, the coming happened as early as 1607 or 1620. But if Indian ancestors came originally from somewhere else, it was so long ago that no clear record of their coming exists.

In "Growing Up," Gouverneur Morris pictures an Indian village as it may have been when there were no whites anywhere about to interfere with its customs. Living in that village are Indian boys and girls whose hopes and wishes and affections are much the same as those that boys and girls have always had, whatever their location or the color of their skins.

Almost any volume of the Magazine Index *from 1900 to 1936 provides a list of stories by Gouverneur Morris.*

THE CHILDREN were all down in the salt marsh playing at marriage-by-capture. It was a very good play.
You ran just as fast after the ugly girls as the pretty ones,
and you didn't have to abide by the result. One little
girl got so excited that she fell into the river, and it was
Andramark who pulled her out, and beat her on the back
till she stopped choking. It may be well to remember
that she was named Tassel Top, a figure taken from the
Indian-corn ear when it is in silk.

Andramark was the name of a boy. He was the seventh
son of Squirrel Eyes, and all his six brothers were dead,
because they had been born in hard times, or had fallen
out of trees, or had been drowned. To grow up in an
Indian village, especially when it is traveling, is very
difficult. Sometimes a boy's mother has to work so hard
that she runs plumb out of milk; and sometimes he gets

playing too roughly with the other boys, and gets wounded, and blood poisoning sets in; or he finds a dead fish and cooks it and eats it, and ptomaine poisoning sets in; or he catches too much cold on a full stomach, or too much malaria on an empty one. Or he tries to win glory by stealing a bear cub when its mother isn't looking, or a neighboring tribe drops in between days for an unfriendly visit, and some big, painted devil knocks him over the head and takes his scalp home to his own little boy to play with.

Contrariwise, if he does manage to grow up and reach man's estate he's got something to brag of. Only he doesn't do it; because the first thing that people learn who have to live very intimately together is that bore and boaster are synonymous terms. So he never brags of what he has accomplished in the way of deeds and experiences until he is married. And then only in the privacy of his own lodge, when that big hickory stick which he keeps for the purpose assures him of the beloved one's best ears and most flattering attention.

Andramark's father was worse than dead. He had been tried in the council lodge by the elders, and had been found guilty of something which need not be gone into here, and driven forth into the wilderness which surrounded the summer village to shift for himself. By the same judgment the culprit's wife, Squirrel Eyes, was pronounced a widow. Most women in her position would have been ambitious to marry again, but Squirrel Eyes' only ambition was to raise her seventh son to be the pride and support of her old age. She had had quite enough of marriage, she would have thanked you.

So, when Andramark was thirteen years old, and very swift and husky for his age, Squirrel Eyes went to the Wisest Medicine-man, and begged him to take her boy in hand and make a man of him.

"Woman," the Wisest Medicine-man had said, "fifteen is the very greenest age at which boys are made men, but seeing that you are a widow, and without support, it may be that something can be done. We will see."

That was why Owl Eyes, the Wisest Medicine-man, invited two of his cronies to sit with him on the bluff overlooking the salt marsh and watch the children playing at marriage-by-capture.

Those old men were among the best judges of sports and form living. They could remember three generations of hunters and fighters. They had all the records for jumping, swimming under water, spear-throwing, axe-throwing, and bow-shooting at their tongues' ends. And they knew the pedigree for many, many generations of every child at that moment playing in the meadow, and into just what sort of man or woman that child should grow, with good luck and proper training.

Owl Eyes did not call his two cronies' attention to Andramark. If there was any precocity in the lad it would show of itself, and nothing would escape their black, jewel-like, inscrutable eyes. When Tassel Top fell into the river the aged pair laughed heartily, and when Andramark, without changing his stride, followed her in and fished her out, one of them said, "That's a quick boy," and the other said, "Why hasn't that girl been taught to swim?" Owl Eyes said, "That's a big boy for only thirteen — that Andramark."

In the next event Andramark from scratch ran through a field — some of the boys were older and taller than himself — and captured yet another wife, who, because she expected and longed to be caught by some other boy, promptly boxed the air where his ears had been. Andramark, smiling, caught both her hands in one of his, tripped her over a neatly placed foot, threw her, face down, and seated himself quietly on the small of her back and rubbed her nose in the mud.

The other children, laughing and shouting, rushed to the rescue. Simultaneously Andramark, also laughing, was on his feet, running and dodging. Twice he passed through the whole mob of his pursuers without, so it seemed to the aged watchers on the bluff, being touched. Then, having won some ten yards clear of them, he wheeled about and stood with folded arms. A great lad foremost in the pursuit reached for him, was caught instead by the outstretched hand, and jerked forward on his face. Some of the children laughed so hard that they had to stop running. Others redoubled their efforts to close with the once more darting, dodging, and squirming Andramark, who, however, threading through them, for the third and last time, in the most mocking and insulting manner, headed straight for the bluff a little to the right of where his elders and betters were seated with their legs hanging over, leaped at a dangling wild grape-vine, squirmed to the top, turned and prepared to defend his position against anyone insolent enough to assail it.

The children, crowded at the base of the little bluff, looked up. Andramark looked down. With one hand

and the tip of his nose he made the insulting gesture which is older than antiquity.

Meanwhile, Owl Eyes had left his front-row seat, and not even a waving of the grasses showed that he was crawling upon Andramark from behind.

Owl Eyes' idea was to push the boy over the bluff as a lesson to him never to concentrate himself too much on one thing at a time. But just at the crucial moment Andramark leaped to one side, and it was a completely flabbergasted old gentleman who descended through the air in his stead upon a scattering flock of children. Owl Eyes, still agile at eighty, gathered himself into a ball, jerked violently with his head and arms, and managed to land on his feet. But he was very much shaken, and nobody laughed. He turned and looked up at Andramark, and Andramark looked down.

"I couldn't help it," said Andramark. "I knew you were there all the time."

Owl Eyes' two old cronies grinned behind their hands.

"Come down," said Owl Eyes, sternly.

Andramark leaped and landed lightly, and stood with folded arms and looked straight into the eyes of the Wisest Medicine-man. Everybody made sure that there was going to be one heap big beating, and there were not wanting those who would have volunteered to fetch a stick, even from a great distance. But Owl Eyes was not called the Wisest Medicine-man for nothing. His first thought had been, "I will beat the life out of this boy." But then (it was a strict rule that he always followed) he recited to himself the first three stanzas of the Rain-Maker's song, and had a new and wiser thought. This he spoke aloud.

"Boy," he said, "beginning tomorrow I myself will take you in hand and make a man of you. You will be at the medicine lodge at noon. Meanwhile go to your mother's lodge, and tell her from me to give you a sound beating."

The children marveled, the boys envied, and Andramark, his head very high, his heart thumping, passed among them and went home to his mother and repeated what the Wisest Medicine-man had said.

"And you are to give me a sound beating, mother," said Andramark, "because after today they will begin making a man of me, and when I am a man it will be the other way around, and I shall have to beat you."

His back was bare, and he bent forward so that his mother could beat him. And she took down from the lodgepole a heavy whip of raw buckskin. It was not so heavy as her heart.

Then she raised the whip and said:

"A blow for the carrying," and she struck; "a blow for the bearing," and she struck; "a blow for the milking," and she struck; "a blow for lies spoken," and she did *not* strike; "a blow for food stolen," and she did *not* strike.

And she went through the whole litany of the beating ceremonial and struck such blows as the law demanded, and spared those she honestly could spare, and when in doubt she quibbled — struck, but struck lightly.

When the beating was over they sat down facing each other and talked. And Squirrel Eyes said: "What must be, must. The next days will soon be over."

And Andramark shuddered (he was alone with his

mother), and said, "If I show that they hurt me, they will never let me be a man."

And Squirrel Eyes did her best to comfort him and put courage in his heart, just as modern mothers do for sons who are about to have a tooth pulled or a tonsil taken out.

The next day at noon sharp Andramark stood before the entrance of the medicine lodge with his arms folded; and all his boy and girl friends watched him from a distance. And all the boys envied him, and all the girls wished that they were boys. Andramark stood very still, almost without swaying, for the better part of an hour. His body was nicely greased, and he resembled a wet terra-cotta statue. A few mosquitoes were fattening themselves on him, and a bite in the small of his back itched so that he wanted very much to squirm and wriggle. But that would have been almost as bad an offense against ceremonial as complaining of hunger during the fast, or shedding tears under the torture.

Andramark had never seen the inside of the medicine lodge; but it was well known to be very dark, and to contain skulls, and thigh-bones of famous enemies, and devil-masks, and horns and rattles and other disturbing and ghostly properties. Of what would happen to him when he had passed between the flaps of the lodge and was alone with the medicine men, he did not know. But he reasoned that if they really wanted to make a man of him they would not really try to kill him or maim him. And he was strong in the determination, no matter what should happen, to show neither surprise, fear, nor pain.

A quiet voice spoke suddenly, just within the flaps of the lodge:

"Who is standing without?"

"The boy Andramark."

"What do you wish of us?"

"To be made a man."

"Then say farewell to your companions of childhood."

Andramark turned toward the boys and girls who were watching him. Their faces swam a little before his eyes, and he felt a big lump coming slowly up in his throat. He raised his right arm to its full length, palm forward, and said:

"Farewell, O children; I shall never play with you any more."

Then the children set up a great howl of lamentation, which was all part of the ceremonial, and Andramark turned and found that the flaps of the lodge had been drawn aside, and that within there was thick darkness and the sound of men breathing.

"Come in, Andramark."

The flaps of the lodge fell together behind him. Fingers touched his shoulder and guided him in the dark, and then a voice told him to sit down. His quick eyes, already accustomed to the darkness, recognized one after another the eleven medicine men of his tribe. They were seated cross-legged in a semicircle, and one of them was thumbing tobacco into the bowl of a poppy-red pipe. Some of the medicine men had rattles handy in their laps, others devil-horns. They were all smiling and looking kindly at the little boy who sat all alone by himself facing them. Then old Owl Eyes, who was the central medicine man of the eleven, spoke.

"In this lodge," he said, "no harm will befall you. But lest the women and children grow to think lightly of manhood there will be from time to time much din and devil-noises."

At that the eleven medicine men began to rock their bodies and groan like lost souls (they groaned louder and louder, with a kind of awful rhythm), and to shake the devil-rattles, which were dried gourds, brightly painted, and containing teeth of famous enemies, and one of the medicine men tossed a devil-horn to Andramark, and the boy put it to his lips and blew for all he was worth. It was quite obvious that the medicine men were just having fun, not with him, but with all the women and children of the village who were outside listening — at a safe distance, of course — and imagining that the medicine lodge was at that moment a scene of the most awful visitations and terrors. And all that afternoon, at intervals, the ghastly uproar was repeated, until Andramark's lips were chapped with blowing the devil-horn, and his insides felt very shaky. But between times the business of the medicine men with Andramark was very serious, and they talked to him like so many fathers, and he listened with both ears, and pulled at the poppy-red medicine pipe whenever it was passed to him.

They lectured him upon anatomy and hygiene; upon tribal laws; and always they explained "why" as well as they could, and if they didn't know "why" they said it must be right because it's always been done that way. Sometimes they said things that made him feel very self-conscious and uncomfortable. And sometimes they became so interesting that it was the other way round.

"The gulf," said Owl Eyes, "between the race of men and the races of women and children is knowledge. For, whereas many squaws and little children possess courage, knowledge is kept from them, even as the first-run shad of the spring. The duty of the child is to acquire strength and skill, of the woman to bear children, to labor in the cornfield, and to keep the lodge. But the duty of man is to hunt, and to fight, and to make medicines, to know, and to keep knowledge to himself. Hence the saying that what man betrays the secrets of the council lodge to a squaw is a squaw himself. Hitherto, Andramark, you have been a talkative child, but from henceforth you will watch your tongue as a warrior watches the prisoner that he is bringing to his village for torture. When a man ceases to be a mystery to the women and children, he ceases to be a man. Do not tell them what has passed in the medicine lodge, but let it appear that you could discourse of ghostly mysteries and devilish visitations and other dread wonders — if you would; so that even to the mother that bore you you will be henceforward and forever a thing apart, a thing above, a thing beyond."

And the old medicine man who sat on Owl Eyes' left cleared his throat and said:

"When a man's wife is in torment, it is as well for him to nod his head, and let her believe that she does not know what suffering is."

Another said:

"Should a man's child ask what the moon is made of, let that man answer that it is made of foolish questions, but at the same time let him smile, as much as to say that he could give the truthful answer — if he would."

Another said:

"When you lie to women and children, lie foolishly, so that they may know that you are making sport of them and may be ashamed. In this way a man may keep the whole of his knowledge to himself, like a basket of corn hidden in a place of his own secret choosing."

Still another pulled one flap of the lodge a little so that a ray of light entered. He held his hand in the ray and said:

"The palm of my hand is in darkness, the back is in light. It is the same with all acts and happenings — there is a bright side and a dark side. Never be so foolish as to look on the dark side of things; there may be somewhat there worth discovering, but it is in vain to look because it cannot be seen."

And Owl Eyes said:

"It will be well now to rest ourselves from seriousness with more din and devil-noises. And after that we shall lead the man-boy, Andramark, to the Lodge of Nettles, there to sit alone for a space and to turn over in his mind all that we have said to him."

"One thing more." This from a very little medicine man, who had done very little talking. "When you run the gantlet of the women and children, from the Hot Lodge to the river, watch neither their eyes nor their whips; watch only their feet, lest you be tripped and thrown at the very threshold of manhood."

Nettles, thistles, and last year's burdocks and sandspurs strewed the floor of the lodge to which Andramark was

now taken. And he was told that he must not thrust
these to one side and make himself comfortable upon the
bare ground. He might sit, or stand, or lie down; he
might walk about; but he mustn't think of going to sleep,
or, indeed, of anything but the knowledge and mysteries
which had been revealed to him in the medicine lodge.

All that night, all the next day, and all the next night he
meditated. For the first six hours he meditated on knowledge, mystery, and the whole duty of man, just as he had
been told to do. And he only stopped once, to listen to a
flute-player who had stolen into the forest back of the
lodge, and was trying to tell some young squaw how much
he loved her and how lonely he was without her. The flute
had only four notes, and one of them was out of order;
but Andramark had been brought up on that sort of music,
and it sounded very beautiful to him. Still, he listened
with only one ear, Indian fashion. The other was busy
taking in all the other noises of the night and the village.
Somebody passed slowly and softly. "A man," thought
Andramark, "would not make any noise at all. A child
would be in bed."

The slow, soft steps were nearing the forest back of the
lodge, quickening a little. Contrariwise, the flute was
being played more and more slowly. Each of its three
good notes was a stab at the feelings, and so, for that
matter, was the note that had gone wrong. An owl hooted.
Andramark smiled. If he had been born enough hundreds
of years later he might have said, "You can't fool me!"

The flute-playing stopped abruptly. Andramark forgot all about the nettles and sat down. Then he stood up.

He meditated on war and women, just as he had been

told to do. Then, because he was thirsty, he meditated
upon suffering. And he finished the night meditating upon
an empty stomach.

Light filtered under the skirts of the lodge. He heard
the early women going to their work in the fields. The
young leaves were on the oaks, and it was corn-planting
time. Even very old corn, however, tastes very good prepared in any number of different ways. Andramark
agreed with himself that when he gave himself in marriage
it would be to a woman who was a thoroughly good cook.
But quite raw food is acceptable at times. It is pleasant
to crack quail eggs between the teeth, or to rip the roe
out of a fresh-caught shad with your forefinger and just
let it melt in your mouth.

The light brightened. It was a fine day. It grew warm
in the lodge, hot, intolerably hot. The skins of which it
was made exhaled a stuffy, meaty smell. Andramark was
tempted to see if he couldn't suck a little nourishment out
of them. A shadow lapped the skirts of the lodge and
crawled upward. It became cool, cold. The boy, almost
naked, began to shiver and shake. He swung his arms as
cab drivers do, and tried very hard to meditate upon the
art of being a man.

During the second night one of his former companions
crept up to the lodge and spoke to him under its skirts,
"Sst! Heh! What does it feel like to be a man?" —
chuckled and withdrew.

Andramark said to himself the Indian for "I'll lay for
that boy." He was very angry. He had been gratuitously
insulted in the midst of his new dignities.

Suddenly the flaps of the lodge were opened and some

one leaned in and set something upon the floor. Andramark did not move. His nostrils dilated, and he said to
himself, "Venison — broiled to the second."

In the morning he saw that there was not only venison,
but a bowl of water, and a soft bearskin upon which he
might stretch himself and sleep. His lips curled with a
great scorn. And he remained standing aloof from the
temptations. And meditated upon the privileges of being
a man.

About noon he began to have visitors. At first they
were vague, dark spots that hopped and ziddied in the
overheated air. But these became, with careful looking,
all sorts of devils and evil spirits, and beasts the like of
which were not in the experience of any living man. There
were creatures made like men, only that they were covered
with long, silky hair, and had crybaby faces and long tails.
And there was a vague, yellowish beast, very terrible,
something like a huge cat, only that it had curling tusks
like a very big wild pig. And there were other things that
looked like men, only that they were quite white, as if they
had been most awfully frightened. And suddenly Andramark imagined that he was hanging to a tree, but not by
his hands or his feet, and the limb to which he was hanging broke, and, after falling for two or three days, he
landed on his feet among burs and nettles that were spread
over the floor of a lodge.

The child had slept standing up, and had evolved from
his subconsciousness, as children will, beasts and conditions that had existed when the whole human race was a
frightened crybaby in its cradle. He had never heard of a
monkey or a saber-tooth tiger; but he had managed to

see a sort of vision of them both, and had dreamed that he was a monkey hanging by his tail.

He was very faint and sick when the medicine men came for him. But it did not show in his face, and he walked firmly among them to the great Torture Lodge, his head very high and the ghost of a smile hovering about his mouth.

It was a grim business that waited him in the Torture Lodge. He was strung up by his thumbs to a peg high up the great lodgepole, and drawn taut by thongs from his big toes to another peg in the base of the pole, and then, without any unnecessary delays, for every step in the proceeding was according to a ceremonial that was almost as old as suffering, they gave him, what with blunt flint-knives and lighted slivers of hot pine, a very good working idea of hell. They told him, without words, which are the very tenderest and most nervous places in all the human anatomy, and showed him how simple it is to give a little boy all the sensations of major operations without actually removing his arms and legs. And they talked to him. They told him that because he came of a somewhat timorous family they were letting him off very easily; that they weren't really hurting him, because it was evident from the look of him that at the first hint of real pain he would scream and cry. And then suddenly, just when the child was passing through the ultimate borderland of endurance, they cut him down, and praised him, and said that he had behaved splendidly, and had taken to torture as a young duck takes to water. And poor little Andramark found that under the circumstances kindness was the very hardest thing of all to bear. One after another great lumps rushed up his throat, and he began to tremble and totter and struggle with the corners of his mouth.

Old Owl Eyes, who had tortured plenty of brave boys in his day, was ready for this phase. He caught up a great bowl of ice-cold spring water and emptied it with all his strength against Andramark's bloody back. The shock of that sudden icy blow brought the boy's runaway nerves back into hand. He shook himself, drew a long breath, and, without a quiver anywhere, smiled.

And the old men were as glad as he was that the very necessary trial by torture was at an end. And, blowing triumphantly upon devil-horns and shaking devil-rattles, they carried him the whole length of the village to the base of the hill where the Hot Lodge was.

This was a little cave, in the mouth of which was a spring, said to be very full of Big Medicine. The entrance to the cave was closed by a heavy arras of bearskins, three or four thick, and the ground in front was thickly strewn with round and flat stones cracked and blackened by fire. From the cave to the fifteen-foot bluff overhanging a deep pool of the river the ground was level, and worn in a smooth band eight or ten feet wide, as by the trampling of many feet.

Andramark, stark naked and still bleeding in many places, sat cross-legged in the cave, at the very rim of the medicine spring. His head hung forward on his chest. All his muscles were soft and relaxed. After a while the hangings of the cave entrance were drawn a little to one side, and a stone plumped into the spring with a savage hiss; another followed — another — and another and another. Steam began to rise from the surface of the spring, little bubbles darted up from the bottom and burst. More hot stones were thrown into the water. Steam, soft and caressing, filled the cave. The temperature rose by leaps and bounds. The roots of Andramark's hair began to tickle — the tickling became unendurable, and ceased suddenly as the sweat burst from every pore of his body. His eyes closed; in his heart it was as if love-music were being played upon a flute. He was no longer conscious of hunger or thirst. He yielded, body and soul, to the sensuous miracle of the steam, and slept.

He was awakened by many shrill voices that laughed and dared him to come out.

"It's only one big beating," he said, rose, stepped over the spring, pushed through the bearskins, and stood gleaming and steaming in the fading light.

The gantlet that he was to run extended from the cave to the bluff overhanging the river. He looked the length of the double row of grinning women and children — the active agents in what was to come. Back of the women and children were warriors and old men, their faces relaxed into holiday expressions. Toward the river end of the gantlet were stationed the youngest, the most vigorous, the most fun-loving of the women, and the larger boys, with only a negligible sprinkling of really little children. Every woman and child in the two rows was armed with a savage-looking whip of willow, hickory, and even green brier, and the still more savage intention of using these whips to the utmost extent of their speed and accuracy in striking.

Upon a signal Andramark darted forward and was lost in a whistling smother. It was as if an untrimmed hedge

had suddenly gone mad. Andramark made the best of a
bad business, guarded his face and the top of his head
with his arms, ran swiftly, but not too swiftly, and kept
his eyes out for feet that were thrust forward to trip him.

A dozen feet ahead he saw a pair of little moccasins that
were familiar to him. As he passed them he looked into
their owner's face, and wondered why, of all the little
girls in the village, Tassel Top alone did not use her whip
on him.

At last, half blinded, lurching as he ran, he came to the
edge of the bluff, and dived, almost without a splash, into
the deep, fresh water. The cold of it stung his overheated,
bleeding body like a swarm of wild bees, and it is possible
that when he reached the Canoe Beach the water in his
eyes was not all fresh. Here, however, smiling chiefs and
warriors surrounded the stoic, and welcomed him to their
number with kind words and grunts of approval. And
then, because he that had been but a moment before a
naked child was now a naked man, and no fit spectacle
for women and children, they formed a bright-colored
moving screen about him and conducted him to the great
council lodge. There they eased his wounds with pleasant
greases, and dressed him in softest buckskin, and gave him
just as much food as it was safe for him to eat — a couple
of quail eggs and a little dish of corn and fresh-water
mussels baked.

And after that they sent him home armed with a big
stick. And there was his mother, squatting on the floor
of their lodge, with her back bared in readiness for a good
beating. But Andramark closed the lodge-flaps, and
dropped his big stick, and began to blubber and sob.

And his mother leaped up and caught him in her arms; and then — once a mother, always tactful — she began to howl and yell, just as if she were actually receiving the ceremonial beating which was her due. And the neighbors pricked up their ears and chuckled, and said the Indian for "Squirrel Eyes is getting what was coming to her."

Maybe Andramark didn't sleep that night, and maybe he did. And all the dreams that he dreamed were pleasant, and he got the best of everybody in them, and he woke next morning to a pleasant smell of broiling shad, and lay on his back blinking and yawning, and wondering why of all the little girls in the village Tassel Top alone had not used her whip on him.

UNUSUAL WORDS

arras — (The entrance was closed by a heavy arras) a heavy curtain

crucial — (just at the crucial moment) the most important moment of all

gratuitously — (He had been gratuitously insulted) insulted without cause

inscrutable — (their black, jewel-like, inscrutable eyes) eyes which betrayed nothing to the person who looked into them

precocity — (If there was any precocity in the lad) any unusually early bodily or mental development

sensuous — (He yielded to the sensuous miracle of the steam) to the miracle which soothed his senses

stoic — (smiling chiefs and warriors surrounded the stoic) the person who bore suffering without showing any sign of pain

ziddied — (vague dark spots that hopped and ziddied) *ziddied* is a made-up word, its sound suggesting the way the spots moved

QUESTIONS FOR SELF-TESTING

1. Why were Owl Eyes and his cronies sitting on the bluff watching the children at their play?
2. What was Owl Eyes' method for preventing himself from acting hastily?
3. What had become of Andramark's father?
4. For what reason did the medicine men make hideous noises inside the medicine lodge?
5. What was inside the devil-rattles?
6. After Andramark had meditated on many things, with what meditations did he finally finish the night?
7. In Indian belief, what made the gulf between men on the one hand and women and children on the other?
8. How does the writer account for Andramark's dreams when at last he went to sleep in the Lodge of Nettles?
9. Against what is Andramark warned to guard himself when he runs the gantlet?
10. How does Owl Eyes protect Andramark from breaking down when he is kindly spoken to at the end of the torture?
11. Why is the Hot Lodge so named?

TOPICS FOR THEMES OR DISCUSSION

1. Discuss the writer's statement as to what is "the first thing that people learn who have to live very intimately together."
2. What were Owl Eyes' reasons for deciding to make a man of Andramark?
3. "And she took down from the lodgepole a heavy whip of raw buckskin. It was not so heavy as her heart." Since Squirrel Eyes had asked to have Andramark promoted to man's estate, why was her heart heavy?

4. Explain the system whereby the men were to keep the squaws and children in awe of their knowledge.
5. Write a dialogue, or invent a situation, in which the same system is successfully used, but this time by a woman to make men and boys feel her superior knowledge.
6. How does this story explain the phrase "running the gantlet"?
7. "And the old men were as glad as he was that the very necessary trial by torture was at an end." Does the writer give us any reasons why trial by torture was necessary?
8. Write Andramark's account of some one day (not one of the days shown in the story) which he has particularly enjoyed.
9. Write Tassel Top's account of the same day.

THE NIGHT HUNTER

By ALEXANDER KEY

"The Night Hunter" is set in the year 1777, the second year of the Revolutionary War. In almost any year, however, from soon after Jamestown was settled in 1607 down to the completion of the first great railroad in 1868, the dangers shown in this story were being faced somewhere within what is now the United States. And no matter where the struggle between whites and Indians went on, the conditions of the struggle were about the same. On the one side were the whites, trying to conquer the new land for farming and trade; on the other were the Indians, trying to protect their hunting grounds and keep themselves from starvation.

"The Night Hunter" is written from the standpoint of the whites, and just as Gouverneur Morris, in "Growing Up," made us sympathize with Andramark, so here the writer makes all our sympathy go to James Ray and the hard-pressed people inside the fort.

Alexander Key's stories — nearly always exciting ones — appear usually in The American Boy.

Jᴀᴍᴇꜱ ʀᴀʏ crouched upon the lookout platform above the great log gates, thin face wedged into a loophole, his spare young body doubled like a bent reed. A hundred times that night his keen blue eyes had studied the dim slope to the creek and the black edge of the woods beyond. As his ears strained for some signal of Kirby's return, his lips prayed soundlessly. Men stood by the bars below him ready to slide them instantly open. Farther back, long rifles primed and ready in their hands, stood other men, their faces hard as gray granite in the shadow of the palisade.

It would soon be dawn. Already cabin doors were creaking, and gaunt, silent figures gathered in the common. Ray could feel their eyes upon him, reproachful and a little cold. It was as if they held him responsible for the man outside, just as they'd done that day when he was out with Bill. They should have let him go with Kirby last evening.

The sky paled, reddening above the trees beyond the field. Ray gave the woods a last, minute inspection, then turned slowly, dreading this moment of finality. He glanced at the silent group below and shook his head.

"Hain't no sign o' him yet."

A woman stared up at him, her face dull white and expressionless. She was the one who had been standing there nearly all night.

"Iffen he hain't come by now," she said in a strange, low voice, "I reckon he hain't never comin' — ever." He could see her hands clenched under her apron as she moved to her cabin.

No one spoke. Ray heard the click of the latch as her door swung shut. Bunches of muscle knotted in his cheeks and he rubbed his palms upon his grimy buckskins.

He wouldn't have thought they'd get Kirby too. Kirby was the stoutest of the Long Knives, and there wasn't a hunter in Kentuck — excepting Boone, maybe — who had a keener or a swifter hand. But somehow Kirby had failed. Out there in those black woods, now, were four men who'd slipped past the gates at night looking for meat. Four men who'd never see Fort Harrod again. And for another day the cookpots would remain empty.

A lean, bearded man crawled up beside him. "Better git some rest, lad. I'll take yo' place for a spell."

Ray nodded, but made no move to go down the ladder. He stared across the field where the stalks of last year's corn showed above the weeds, and in his mind he saw a spot five miles beyond. He recalled painted, half-naked figures leaping like panthers from the cane, and beside him a boy stumbling with an arrow in his back. He'd had to leave Bill behind that day.

"Stop thinkin' o' Shawnee Run, lad," said the bearded man.

Ray brushed a hand through his sandy hair. Lines showed in his thin, pleasant face, and his wide mouth tightened. "There's things, Mr. Bush, you cain't forget. H — hit's been three weeks now, an' I've had to sit here the whole endurin' time, thinkin' —"

"Yo' brother died like a man," began Bush. "An' you runned a great race with the Shawnee that day, e'en though there be some what whisper. Five miles hit was, an' you outstripped all o' Blackfish's devils."

"I hyeared Harrod a-sayin' my heart's in my heels."

"Harrod's a good man with a load o' worry on him this spring." Bush spat and his voice grew harsh. "But enough o' that, an' enough o' the dead. 'Tis the livin' we must be a-thinkin' of now. They got to be fed — somehow." He cursed and his big fist slammed against his knee and he looked ruefully at his leg. "That's what's holdin' me back! I'd a-been out there with Kirby last night iffen hit warn't for the lead in my leg. But they'd a got me 'fore I could e'en fetch the woods."

"Mr. Bush, I'm a-goin' to sneak out tonight iffen . . ." Ray slid down the ladder, a tall, gangling youth in his late teens whose taut muscles seemed stretched to the utmost to cover the man's frame beneath them. Bush squinted after him, eyes hard, speculative.

A hound bayed hungrily at the moon rising like a thin slice of melon high over the fort. Someone cursed and

turned from the group in the center of the common to deal
it a kick. The cabins, a score of them lying against the
palisade walls, were dark. A big man, half a head taller
than the others, spoke:

"Four dead's enough. An' they were the best hunters
in Kaintuck. No, not another man goes out."

"Harrod, we cain't be a-holdin' out much longer without vittles," Bush said. "Here's a lad —"

Harrod glanced quickly from Bush to James Ray standing awkwardly beside him. When he spoke, his voice had
lost some of its usual heartiness.

"Didn't know you were a night hunter, too, James Ray.
Better trot back an' do your shift on the wall."

There was a rasping laugh. "Why not let the lad go
out, Mr. Harrod, iffen he's so almighty anxious to lose his
sculp?"

"Sho," a second man said. "An' I've hyeared tell he's
a mite fast on his feet. There was a turkey a-gobblin'
over in the cane — maybe he kin run hit down an' fetch
hit back."

"Shet yo' mouth." Bush's voice snapped out angrily.
"I notice you hain't a-rarin' to do no huntin'."

Ray opened his mouth, closed it, then tugged uneasily
at Bush's arm. "Let's go."

In the shadow of the logs they stopped, and the youth
put his hand on the other's shoulder. "You — you
watchin' the little east gate tonight, hain't you, Mr.
Bush?"

Bush nodded, but said nothing.

"Well, iffen someone was to slip through, there wouldn't
no one know nothin' about it except you and me."

Bush rubbed his beard, considering. "I'm a-thinkin' o' yo' ma. You're all she's got now."

"She's sick, an' goin' without vittles hain't a-goin' to make her better."

Bush was silent for some time, his hand tugging slowly at his beard. At last he straightened and Ray saw his eyes staring hard into his own. "Wait," Bush spoke in a voice scarcely audible. "Wait till the moon's an hour higher, then . . ." He winked solemnly and turned away.

The moon was over the peak of the west blockhouse when Ray slipped quietly around the corner of a cabin and approached the narrow east gate that Bush was guarding. No one else was near; he knew that Harrod was on the other side of the common, making the rounds of the sentinels. For a moment he was troubled at the thought of disobeying that bluff, kindly man whom they had followed westward over the mountains. Here in the fort that he had planned and built, Harrod's word was law, his judgment was respected.

They couldn't afford to lose any more men. Blackfish had murdered a lot — but the long winter had taken more. Half of those left were sick. Suppose the devils out there in the woods decided to rush the gates some night? It would take every fighting hand in the place to beat them back. He could see why Harrod thought as he did. The fort needed every man.

But — the fort also had to have meat.

"Ready?" Bush was whispering.

"Uh-huh. All I'm takin's my rifle an' knife."

Bush surveyed him dubiously. "You mean you're just countin' on one shot? Leavin' yo' powder an' stuff here?"

"Reckon I won't have time to shoot but once. After that hit'll be runnin'. A powder horn might catch on something."

"Now, lad, don't go where Kirby went — there's buffalo in the bottoms, but the place will be watched. Try beyondst the hill. Ought to be a buck there."

"That's what I was figurin'. Iffen I come back easy, I'll give you the whippoorwill call. Iffen I'm runnin', I'll whistle."

"I'll be here waitin', son, with my hand on the bar." Bush started to say more but broke off in a rumble. Something wet gleamed in the corner of his eye. He spat and cautiously opened the gate a few inches. Ray crawled through on his hands and knees and flattened himself to the ground.

The moon was brighter out here beyond the protection of the walls. The dark line of forest marking the ridge to the right was a far place to crawl, when so little cover lay between. Once there in the blackness of the trees he would have to be even more careful. But to gain the trees without being seen was important, for then he might be able to hunt for a while. After the sharp, telltale sound of the rifle he'd have to hurry!

He found a furrow and began worming along it to the end of the field. Here the weeds grew higher and he was able to turn and start upward. Within thirty yards of the first clump of hawthorns near the ridge, he stopped, listening. A turkey was gobbling in the cane an arrow's flight to the left. A turkey had gobbled there last night — and the night before.

A swift conviction came over him and he wondered why

he hadn't thought of it sooner. That turkey was an Indian, waiting for some fool to come close enough to have his hair lifted.

Ray lay still for a quarter of an hour while he studied every detail of the ground ahead. There would be scouts hidden at varying intervals entirely around the fort. But the hawthorn thicket seemed clear.

He crept ahead a few inches at a time, smelling the sweet scent of the hawthorn blooms and the dampness of the grass under his fingers. Branches closed over him and he rose to his knees. A few minutes later he stood upright under the tall trees beyond, filling his lungs with a long breath.

Farther on, now, he should find game. Deer and wood buffalo near the rank meadows, bear and turkey in the thickets. But the best hunting, and the safest, would be somewhere on the edge of the deeper woods where the animals came to drink. At that moment he remembered a small spring he'd once discovered bubbling in a ravine less than two miles from the fort. It lay beyond the rise to his left. There was good cover there for hiding, and the ravine might muffle the sound of a shot.

He worked slowly down through the black woods, slipping noiselessly from one great tree to another, carefully avoiding the open glades where moonlight streamed through the foliage overhead. It shouldn't be so hard finding the spring at night. Most of the way, the forest floor was nearly clear of underbrush and he'd have no trouble. It all depended on how shrewdly he could judge the distance. First, he'd have to go about a mile, following the gentle curve of the deeper woods. Then, beyond a low hill, he'd find where the ravine dipped away as if it had been cut with a knife. He remembered the well-worn game trail leading to the spring. He could make it!

But suddenly he felt the vastness of the woods at night, and he grew afraid. Blackfish's men hid somewhere in these black shadows, listening and waiting.

An hour later he stopped abruptly, his skin prickling with the breath of a sound that came from somewhere near. He froze against a tree and untied the leather guard on his gunlock that served to keep the priming dry. Just beyond was an open glade faintly illuminated by the moon. His eyes searched along the huge trunks enclosing it, seeking to distinguish some telltale difference in the deeper shadows.

The gray shape of a deer glided smoothly across the edge of the glade and stood still. He raised the rifle with infinite caution, sighted down the long barrel. His trigger hand tightened, then relaxed. He wasn't certain just how far he was from the fort. Half a thousand Shawnees would hear the shot — just as he'd heard Kirby's shot last night. It might be that before he could lug the carcass across the ridge, they'd have him bottled up like a pig in a pen.

He stood watching the deer with a curious longing, wondering if there could be some way to hunt without shooting. His father had told him how they did it in Carolina, only it took two men.

The deer was nervous. The cry of a screech owl came from beyond it. At the sound, the deer leaped, turned in mid-air, and fled past so close that Ray could have touched it with his barrel. Instantly he crouched, his heart hammering violently.

That cry was unnatural! He was wondering whether

to turn and crawl back the way he had come when a second owl call quavered behind him. He sank closer between the roots of the tree and his fingers sought the handle of the long knife fastened at his back. Shawnee signals! But what were scouts doing here so far beyond the ridge? Had he blundered somewhere along the way — had Blackfish's braves been following him all the time?

Wondering, he squatted immovable upon his haunches, the rifle across his knees, one hand still clasping the knife. He heard rustlings in the leaves and small furtive movements along the ground. But these were explainable sounds, as natural as the piping of frogs in the bottoms and the *rak*, *rak* of a coon somewhere in the distance. There was no sign of danger near him.

He remained motionless for an hour, every sense strained. His fear changed to a dull rage of bafflement. He couldn't fail Bush, who had faith in him — and who would be blamed for his absence. He owed it to Harrod to get back. But whether he returned or not, he wouldn't go back without meat.

In sudden apprehension he realized that the glade was growing darker. A fresh wind moaned high up in the trees and with it came the low rumble of thunder. For tonight, at least, he'd have to forget the ravine and the spring. He'd save that spot for later, and maybe — his eyes lightened with a sudden idea — maybe he could figure a way of giving the fort a steady supply of meat. A new plan was forming in his mind, but not for tonight. This night he'd have to take his chances here in the woods while there was still light enough to shoot — and then trust to his speed afterward.

Belly flat to the ground, he began crawling from the tree, feeling his way ahead with his fingers. The rumblings of thunder drowned out the sound of his moving body. He must have covered thirty yards from the tree when the first flash of lightning came, illuminating a game trail leading toward the glade. He gave a low exclamation.

Now he knew where he was! Somehow in his erratic journey through the woods, he'd circled too far to the left — the fort was only a fifteen-minute walk away! The ravine lay nearly a mile straight to the right.

But he knew with a horrible certainty why Kirby and the others had died. Within easy reach of the fort were half a dozen places like the glade behind him, places where game trails forked or crossed — all logical spots for hunters to lie in wait. The Shawnees, shrewd hunters themselves, had searched out every likely point near by and were keeping guards stationed there at night. No wonder Kirby had failed. The places were traps!

He thought of the ravine. None of the trails around the fort led to it, nor was it known to any of the hunters. He'd stumbled upon it by accident; it was hardly likely that it would come under the suspicion of Blackfish's men. The place was ideal for the kind of hunting his father had told him about. Two men could go there with only their knives—and they could return night after night with deer. The Shawnees would hear no shot, never guess . . .

He would have to get back, explain the plan to Harrod. But first he must find meat.

The rain was beginning to patter on the leaves overhead when he decided he was far enough from the glade to walk upright. It would soon be pouring and he'd have to hurry.

A dozen paces to the left was the deer path leading in the general direction of the fort and the creek. He placed the leather guard back over the gunlock, picked his route to parallel the path whenever the lightning flashed, then ran quickly from one tree to the next in the darkness.

He stopped at last when the ground began to slope upward to the ridge again. Beside him was a log commanding a narrow view of the trail ahead. The rain worried him. He'd been wrong to come out without an extra round of powder. What if the priming should become dampened?

Then the thought left him as he remembered the glade, barely three hundred yards behind him. At the crack of the rifle, grim figures would spring out of the shadows, running. And there would be others beyond the ridge guarding the approach to the field. He'd have to work fast —

The rain stopped for a moment and the moon shone briefly. For an instant it silhouetted a moving form ahead. A deer. He could almost reach out and touch it.

He snapped the rifle to his shoulder, snatched the guard away, and prayed for a crash of thunder to drown the shot. But the heavens were silent — the rifle spoke with deadly clearness.

Ray reached the trail in a bound. He dropped the weapon, sprang upon the form threshing in the underbrush, and whipped out his knife. It was a buck, a big one. Too heavy to carry. He worked furiously, slashing, stabbing, dividing the carcass below the ribs.

Already he thought he could hear swift movements behind him, in front of him. He seized the hindquarters, gave them a twist, and pulled them free. Abruptly he dropped them and snatched up the rifle by the barrel.

He ducked instinctively and something scored his breast. Immediately after the roar of the musket, a flicker of lightning outlined the half-naked figure hurtling upon him. He jumped sidewise, swinging the rifle with all the power in him.

Bush watched silently by the gate for an hour, his eye fastened to a peephole between the logs. Harrod had made the rounds once, but thus far Ray's absence had not been discovered.

"I shouldn't a-let the kid go," he kept repeating over and over. Sure, it was his own weakness that had made him do the thing — that and the fact that he'd have given a hundred prime beavers to be out there himself.

As the minutes dragged slowly by, his hands began to twitch and he struck absently at the unwilling leg. Finally he took out a corncob pipe and thrust it between his teeth. He chewed upon the stem with methodical viciousness until the reed crunched in two and the pipe fell to the ground.

The kid had been gone a long time now. Good kid, too. Too good a kid to be wasted. He listened for the high, whiplike note of Ray's rifle, but the sound didn't come. At the first roll of thunder he looked up toward the sky and his lips tightened when he saw that the moon was clouding over. He heard Harrod's light tread behind him.

"Seen Ray?" Harrod asked.

Bush didn't answer for a while. At last he spat out the pulp of the pipe stem. "Naw," he growled.

"He's gone," said Harrod. "You be the one what let him out?"

"I did — two hours an' more hit's been now." Bush waited for the other's outbreak of wrath, but none came. He knew, with so many sick, that the fort was short-handed, and that Harrod's only reason for stopping further hunting was his lack of faith in the remaining hunters. A man might be a wonder in the woods during the day — but a night hunter had to have a different set of instincts. He had to be good.

"Hit warn't lack o' respect fo' you that made him go," Bush continued. "I'll trust yo' jedgment in most everything — but in Ray's case you miscalc'lated on human nature. The kid's got the makin's o' somethin' but hain't never had the chance to show hit."

Harrod shook his head. "In this rain he'll get lost and blunder into a tommyhawk. They'll get him anyhow, ten minutes after he pulls the trigger. If Kirby died, what chance —"

He stopped suddenly. There was the sharp crack of a rifle somewhere in the darkness beyond.

Instantly Harrod wheeled, shouting orders as he ran. Figures darted across the common to the blockhouses. The big man was back in less than a minute, climbing to the tiny platform above the gate. He thrust his gun through a loophole and quickly primed the pan with fresh powder. For a moment the rain had ceased and the moon shone again. Cabin doors opened and a group collected around the east gate.

Bush opened his mouth to speak. It snapped shut as a second shot rang with dread finality in his ears.

"That — that's a musket!" someone spoke.

Bush clamped his hand tight upon the bar, feeling a limpness in his knees as if all strength had been drawn from them. "Yeah," he growled. "An' the first shot was Ray's. They both come from the same place."

For a second there was a stark silence as the group behind him grasped the full import of this information. Then the word spread, and he could hear it passing down the walls to his right and left, and on to the blockhouses.

"Hit's young Ray! Slipped out to hunt — they've jumped him!"

Bush eased back upon the bar a trifle, thrust his face tight against the peephole. The moon had clouded again; the field stretching from the logs faded into an empty blackness a dozen feet away. He tried to visualize what was taking place somewhere a half mile beyond, tried to catch the first faint echo of a whistle that would tell him Ray was approaching. But he heard only the breathing of those around him and the scattered drops of rain promising a cloudburst.

Thunder rolled like a regiment of drums. Lightning arched overhead, splitting the field with a white knife.

The watchers on the walls let out a shout.

"He's comin'!" Bush yelled. "Glory be! He's streakin' down the slope to the field like a colt gone wild!" He slammed back the bar, threw open the gate with a reckless abandon. Another flash illuminated the field.

"They's after him!" Bush screamed. "But look at him run — an' he's got meat!"

The storm was beginning to break; with the rapid flashes, the watchers could see him plainly. Ray was com-

ing like a bullet straight down the center of the field,
something bulky under his left arm, his gun hand pumping
furiously as if to pull him along.   A half-dozen black figures were bounding behind him, but they were not gaining.
Guns from the blockhouses rattled a warning.   Harrod
fired.   One of the pursuers spun around, dropped.   The
others halted.

Suddenly Bush yelled again, pointing to the right.   The
next flash illuminated a brave running doggedly across
the nearer corner of the field.   In a dozen more strides he
could intercept Ray, cut him off from the gate.   The
watchers waited, praying for another tongue of lightning
that would give the riflemen a chance.   But the night was
black now, and the rain came down in full force.

For a few seconds no one moved, then Bush snatched
a gun from the nearest pair of hands and ran out as fast
as his awkward leg would permit.   A form materialized
ahead.   He raised the weapon, then lowered it as recogni-
tion came.

"Look!" Bush cried gleefully, as they entered the fort
and the gate banged behind them.   "He's got meat —
an' he's got ha'r!"

"What eats me," Ray said dolefully, "is that I had to
leave another toler'ble good sculp a-layin' back yonder
in the woods with the other half o' the deer."

Later they sat in Harrod's cabin, the hunters pressing
close as Ray told of his discovery at the glade.   "That's
why we failed before," he explained.   "Blackfish had it all
figgered where a night hunter would go — and that's
where Kirby an' the others went.   But over at the ravine —"

"You're right," Bush interrupted. "The Shawnees wouldn't pay no attention to the ravine." Then he shook his head. "But the minute you start shootin' in the place, the varmints will catch on — an' be a-waitin' the next night."

"Not iffen we use poles with knives on the ends o' them. They used to do hit in the old days back in Caroliny. They say hit works better where the trees be thick — and the ravine's the place. One man takes a stand behind a tree where the path is narrow, the other sort o' scares the deer from behind so they won't be thinkin' o' nothin' in front. But the first man's got to be powerful quick."

Harrod smiled. "I used to do that twenty years ago, but hit's the first time I thought about hit since — or hyeard tell o' a spot where 'twould work. I reckon as how you an' me could go out every night and come back with enough meat to keep the fort a-rollin' in fat."

And history records that the founder of Harrodsburg and young James Ray, who could outrun the swiftest Shawnee brave, kept the fort supplied with meat all during that long siege of 1777.

UNUSUAL WORDS

blockhouses — log houses with holes in the walls through which to shoot

erratic — (in his erratic journey through the woods) in his journey which had not followed the expected path

gangling — (a tall, gangling youth) a tall, lean, awkward youth

intercept — (In a dozen strides he would intercept Ray) would get between Ray and his goal

palisade — a high fence or wall made of wooden stakes

silhouetted — (it [the moon] silhouetted a moving form)
   showed the form as a black outline against a lighter background

visualize — (he tried to visualize what was taking place) to
   make a picture in his mind of what was taking place

QUESTIONS FOR SELF-TESTING

1. Why had the four men, now lost, gone out from the
   fort?
2. Why did Harrod forbid any more to go?
3. Why was James Ray especially eager to try his luck
   outside?
4. By what means did he succeed in slipping out?
5. Why did Ray leave his powder horn behind, thus trusting
   to only one shot?
6. What warning did Ray have that Indians were all around
   him?
7. After he had discovered that there were Indians close at
   hand, why did he not slip quietly back to the fort?
8. Why did Ray believe the ravine he had in mind would
   be a comparatively safe place for hunting?
9. What was his plan for getting deer meat safely?
10. For what reason did the carrying out of the plan require
   two men?
11. Did the plan work?

TOPICS FOR THEMES OR DISCUSSION

1. When some of the men jeered at his wish to go outside
   the walls, why did not Ray answer them?
2. In the year 1777, while James Ray, on the frontier, was
   outwitting Indians, what was happening on the eastern
   rim of the United States?

3. We are told what Ray thinks while he lurks in the forest. Write out the thoughts of one of the Indians, a very young one, lurking in that same forest.

4. From the hints given in this story, describe the preparations and the progress of Harrod and Ray when, the next night, they start after deer.

5. In the first part of the story, the author keeps us almost constantly with Ray, telling us what he does and thinks. In the latter part, just when the action in which Ray is involved becomes most exciting, why does the author leave Ray and tell us what is being said and done inside the fort?

QUESTIONS ON
"GROWING UP" AND "THE NIGHT HUNTER"

1. In your opinion why are these two stories paired?

2. Contrast the impression of Indians that you get in "Growing Up" with that in "The Night Hunter."

3. Does James Ray or Andramark display the greater courage?

4. In "Growing Up," the writer makes Andramark the son of a despised father; in "The Night Hunter" the writer makes the men in the fort scornful and sarcastic toward James Ray because of what had happened three weeks earlier. Do you see any reason why the two writers should each want to give his hero an extra handicap?

THE SILVER SNUFFBOX

By MARY WELLS

The Boston Tea Party is one of the especially famous happenings in the years just preceding the Revolution. At the time of its happening, the oldest New England settlement was only a little more than a hundred and fifty years old. Boston was still younger, but it had grown into a city with an excellent harbor and a thriving sea trade. The throwing of the cases of taxed tea into Boston harbor was a gesture of defiance on the colonists' part against attempts in England to lay taxes on American trade, which was growing fast enough in some directions to rival England's own trade.

The author, Mary Wells, does not try to show us the political ins and outs of the colonists' relation with England. What she does show is, first, the serious discussion, among the solid men of the city, which preceded the Tea Party, and after that, the high excitement and patriotic feeling which accompanied the destruction.

THE OLD mahogany cabinet stands beneath the oil painting of my great-great-grandfather Prescott. This venerable gentleman has his powdered hair arranged to a nicety and wears the most correct of filmy neck-ruffles.

Within the cabinet is an object which has to do with one of the most exciting events of Joseph Prescott's life. This is a silver snuffbox, which, when opened, discloses — But to tell that at the beginning would be to spoil the story, which has to do with prerevolutionary times — to be exact, to the sixteenth of December in 1773.

Toward noon of that particular day, Master Joseph Prescott, then in his eighteenth year, was leaning over the palings in front of the Warren mansion, holding earnest converse with Miss Peggy Warren. Peggy, wearing a cherry-colored cape and hood which set off to advantage her dark hair and eyes, was listening with evident interest to Joseph's eager words.

"And the waistcoat is of pearl-gray satin with sprigs of forget-me-nots."

Peggy clasped her hands. "Oh, Joseph!" she cried, "you must run in to let us see you in your finery. Dinner and a ball besides! Would I were going!" Peggy sighed.

"Oh, your time will come," said Joseph, a little condescendingly.

"Thank you, Grandfather," Peggy laughed; "one would think you were an elderly gentleman instead of merely two years my senior." Then, eagerly, "Are you going to wear the silver buckles, Joseph?"

Joseph's face clouded. "The pumps came yesterday from Simmons'. They are too large by half a size and there is no time to change."

"Nobody will notice," said Peggy, consolingly; then, with a twinkle in her eye, "they will all be gazing at the waistcoat with the forget-me-nots."

"I wish you were going, Peggy," said Joseph, generously. "You dance the minuet far better than the older ones. I should like to have you for a partner."

Peggy swept him a courtesy. "Thank you, Master Joseph," she said.

On the other side of the street, several gentlemen passed in earnest conversation. Peggy's face grew suddenly grave. "'Tis Mr. Samuel Adams," she said with respectful awe, "and Mr. Quincy and Mr. Hancock with him." She lowered her voice. "They say that Governor Hutchinson refuses to let the tea ships sail."

"Yes, and the collector of customs has also refused papers. Master Rotch, of the *Dartmouth*, will interview the Governor again today; but they say he is obdurate."

"Father says the masters of the tea ships are between the devil and the deep sea," quoth Peggy.

"They were told eighteen days ago that entry at the customhouse would be at their peril. Now let them look to it. There is to be a meeting this afternoon at Old South Church with speeches by Samuel Adams, Josiah Quincy, and others. People have been pouring in from the country all the morning. Many will be there."

"What do you think they will do, Joseph?" asked Peggy, eagerly.

"Nobody knows; but mark my words, Peggy Warren, that tea will never be landed."

Peggy grew pale. "I hope there will be no fighting."

Joseph's boyish lips set firmly. "If there is, it will not be our fault. Loyal Bostonians are of one mind. Have you seen the broadside against William Jackson, importer at the Brazen Head, north side of the town house?"

"Yes, and rightly it says that those who buy from him will bring disgrace upon themselves forever. We will drink liberty tea all the days of our life before we pay their tax!" Peggy's eyes flashed.

"Amen!" said Joseph.

"And they thought that the cheapness would tempt us to forget principle! Little they know of the temper of Americans!" Peggy's voice was scornful.

"Tonight will tell the tale," said Joseph. "No penny of tax will be paid on that tea."

"Let us hope that the Governor will listen to reason and that tomorrow we shall see the ships weigh anchor. There is our black Amanda beckoning me to lunch, so good-by, Joseph."

As Peggy tripped up the steps she called back, "Do not forget to let us see you in your ball costume, and, Joseph — bring me something from the party. Promise!"

"I promise," said Joseph, with hand on heart.

That December afternoon, Peggy Warren was restless. After the midday meal, her father had departed for the meeting, grave and silent. She stood at the window and watched the men go hurrying by, all bound for Old South Church. The slow hours passed and Mr. Warren did not return. What was happening?

Early December twilight fell. In the kitchen, black Amanda was busy preparing the evening meal. Upstairs, Mrs. Warren was putting Baby John to bed. Peggy was alone in the big parlor, lighted only by the blazing logs on the hearth. She wandered over to the harpsichord and, seating herself, ran her fingers idly over the keys, dreamily watching the flames.

The door from the big hall opened quietly. Peggy looked up, then sprang to her feet in terror. There, before her, awful in war paint and feathers, stood a stalwart Indian. He held a tomahawk in his right hand. The expression on his face was terrifying.

Peggy opened her lips.

"Do not scream, Peggy. It is only I."

The voice was familiar. "Joseph Prescott!" gasped Peggy. Then severely, "What mean you, sir, ·coming here like this to scare a poor girl out of her wits?"

"I looked through the window and saw you were alone," said Joseph, calmly, "so I ventured in. I thought you would like to see me in this guise."

"Well, I do not. You are simply horrible," said Peggy,

witheringly. "What is this masquerade, and what of the dinner and the ball?"

"The dinner and the ball can wait," said Joseph, briefly. "We have more important business on hand. Governor Hutchinson has definitely refused to let the tea ships sail. Master Francis Rotch is even now on his way to Old South with the Governor's answer. Daniel Oldfield came to warn me. He is waiting outside."

"But what are you going to do, Joseph? I trust you do not intend to tomahawk poor Master Rotch."

Joseph ignored Peggy's flippancy. "We are going to have a party of our own." He spoke grimly.

Peggy's glance fell upon his feet. "Why, Joseph Prescott, you are wearing your pumps!"

"I was dressing when Daniel came and there was no time to change; but it matters little."

A shrill whistle came from without. "It is Daniel," said Joseph; "I must be off."

"Joseph, tell me —"

But Joseph was gone.

For a moment Peggy stood motionless, then, hurrying into the hall, she snatched up the red cape and, drawing it about her, ran out into the darkness.

"They will be shocked and I shall be roundly scolded, but I am going nevertheless."

In the dim light ahead, she could make out Joseph and his companion. With their cloaks drawn about them, there was no trace of Indian attire. So fast they walked that Peggy had almost to run to keep them in view.

Soon she found that others were running in that same direction; then at last, candlelight gleamed faintly from the windows of Old South Church. Caught in the crowd, Peggy lost sight of Joseph, and found herself swept helplessly to the very portal of the church.

"It is John Hancock speaking," said someone near her; and another, "Master Rotch has just arrived with the Governor's answer."

The door opened to admit a portly gentleman in a big cloak. Scarce knowing what she did, Peggy slipped in behind him and into a dark corner. No one noticed her, for in the dimly lighted room all eyes were fixed on John Hancock, who, bending from the pulpit, was talking in low tones to Master Rotch. After a few whispered words, he straightened himself. His face was very pale.

"Gentlemen," he said, "the Governor refuses to permit the *Dartmouth* to sail. This meeting can do nothing more to save the country."

Scarcely had the words left his lips when a terrifying war-whoop resounded from the porch. At the evident signal a band of fifty or more men dressed as Indians filed swiftly from the church.

Peggy shrank farther into her dark corner, fearing lest Joseph should see her.

"To Griffin's Wharf!" came the cry; "the Mohawks are going to the wharf!"

The masqueraders swung along, followed by the crowd. Peggy found herself outside the church running with the rest. In the excitement of the moment everything else was forgotten.

At the wharf lay the tea ships, dim lanterns swinging from their prows. The Mohawks swarmed over the wharf and up the sides. They disappeared into the hold. Peggy

waited breathless. Would they scuttle the ships? It was
evident that they had met with no resistance. Every
nerve tense, she stared into the darkness.

A moment later, a group appeared on the *Dartmouth's*
deck carrying a huge case. Tomahawks descended, packing was strewn about. There was a splash, and into the
water of Boston harbor fell the contents of the first of
three hundred and forty-two chests of tea!

"They are dumping the tea into the harbor," said
Peggy. "Rightly Joseph said there would be no tax
paid on this cargo."

A strange joy surged up in her heart. Tears were in
her eyes. She wondered which of the dimly moving
figures was Joseph. How still the crowd was! There was
almost a solemnity about the silence. Another case was
emptied and a third.

A hand fell upon Peggy's shoulder and a stern voice
said, "This is no place for women."

Peggy turned quickly. "Father!" she cried.

"Peggy Warren!" Her father's voice came amazed.
"What means this? What are you doing here?"

Peggy faced him bravely. "I followed Joseph Prescott,
Father!"

"Followed Joseph Prescott!"

"He came in, dressed as a Mohawk, and he went without telling me what was to be done. I know it was unmaidenly, but I had to come. I'm an American, too, Father."

At sight of Peggy's eager, pleading face, Mr. Warren's
stern countenance relaxed.

"Come, daughter," he said, "they will be three hours
at this task, for it is to be thoroughly done. Your mother

will be anxious about us both. Mayhap we may meet the town crier."

Peggy clung to her father's arm as he elbowed his way through the crowd. Despite her escapade, there seemed a new bond between them. For a time they walked in silence, then Peggy said timidly, "Father, what will England do?"

"God knows, my child; but whatever she does, we Americans must be united. As freemen we must be exempt from tyranny; but liberty is sometimes a costly thing, Peggy. Mr. Hancock's speech was a solemn setting forth of that."

"Oh, Father, think you there will be war?"

"It will not come unless they force it upon us, but if it does come, we shall be ready. Heretofore we have protested in vain; now we have acted with both dignity and effectiveness." There was pride in Mr. Warren's voice. "They can have no doubt of our determination now."

He spoke more lightly. "Some day, Peggy, you may be proud to say that you were at the Boston Tea Party. But look, there is your mother in the doorway. Think how you are going to make your peace with her."

The next morning, Peggy Warren was at the fireplace, demurely knitting, when Joseph Prescott arrived.

"Good morning, Master Mohawk!" she cried saucily, "give an account of yourself, sir, and of your Indian prank!"

"Of my Indian prank, as you call it, Mistress Peggy, no account is needed, since all Boston knows the story, you as well as another."

"Mayhap I know it better than another," said Peggy, with a smile.

"What mean you by that?"

"Merely that I speak with the positiveness of an eye-witness," said Peggy, nonchalantly. "Others than Mohawks may go to Old South Church and to Griffin's Wharf as well."

"Certainly others were there, but never you, Peggy Warren! You are trying to mystify me, that is all."

"But I was there," cried Peggy, "and it is you who must bear the blame of my unmaidenly conduct! Did you think, after so arousing my curiosity, that I could rest till I knew what was to be done? Listen, sir," and Peggy launched into a spirited narrative of her adventures.

Joseph listened with gratifying interest. When she paused for breath he queried, "And had you no fear, Peggy?"

Peggy laughed. "I must own that I shook in my shoes when Father appeared, but that was only for a little, for he was so kind and understanding. It was all wonderful. When I heard that first splash, Joseph, I almost clapped my hands for joy. I was so proud to think that you were there. How orderly it all was!"

Joseph nodded. "After it was all over, actors and spectators dispersed quietly; but this morning, Paul Revere was off to carry the news to New York and Philadelphia. It is the beginning of great things."

"The only drawback," said Peggy, a little later, "was your missing the ball. I was counting on your description of all the splendors."

"But I haven't missed it," said Joseph. "It is to be tonight. Our host was among the Mohawks."

"Then you may still wear the forget-me-not waist-coat; but the pumps, Joseph, were they not ruined?"

"They will pass, but since you mention pumps, Peggy, I am reminded."

He drew from his pocket a small box tied with ribbon and handed it to Peggy.

"What is it, Joseph?"

"Did I not promise to bring you something from the party?"

With trembling fingers Peggy untied the ribbon and lifted the cover. Her cheeks grew pink. "Oh, Joseph, it is tea from the Boston Tea Party."

"When I reached home," said Joseph, "my pumps were full of it, and with good reason since I tramped the tea-strewn deck of the *Dartmouth* for hours and the pumps were loose. Does the gift please you, Peggy?"

"Oh, Joseph!" was all she could say.

Peggy's father entered just then and Peggy proudly displayed her gift. Mr. Warren said nothing, but he went to a mahogany cabinet, opened it, took from a drawer a little silver box, and laid it in Peggy's lap.

"Oh, Father," she cried in awe, "your silver snuffbox!"

"The receptacle must be worthy of the contents," he said smiling.

Peggy turned to Joseph with sparkling eyes. "I am glad the pumps were large, Joseph. I shall keep the tea always, and when I am a white-haired old lady, I shall tell the story of the Boston Tea Party to my grandchildren, and always I shall finish by saying, 'Children, my friend and neighbor, Joseph Prescott, was one of those who threw the tea into the harbor.'"

Peggy's words were prophetic, for as **Peggy Prescott**, wife of Colonel Joseph Prescott, she lived to tell not only to her grandchildren, but to her great-grandchildren the story of the silver snuffbox and its contents.

QUESTIONS FOR SELF-TESTING

1. Why was Peggy not going to the ball?
2. What are the first words in the story which suggest to you that the colonists are facing difficulties?
3. What was Peggy doing when Joseph came in dressed as an Indian?
4. How did she manage to get into the church without being seen?
5. How did she feel when she saw the tea going into the water?
6. How did she show what she felt?
7. What does Peggy say was the only thing which frightened her when she went to the Boston Tea Party?
8. When Peggy left the house to follow Joseph, why did she not hurry and catch up with him?
9. What does Joseph bring Peggy as a souvenir of the destruction of the tea?
10. What do we learn of Peggy's future?

TOPICS FOR THEMES OR DISCUSSION

1. How long before the beginning of the Revolutionary War was the year 1773?
2. Look up in some American history the story of the Boston Tea Party and be prepared to give the historical version of what happened that night.
3. What do you find out from this story about the way girls were expected to behave in the Boston of 1773?

4. If the colonists did not want the tea, why did not the ships' captains take it back to the place from which it came?

5. What is the reason for the reader's being told early in the story that Joseph's pumps do not fit?

FOR PEACE AND CONCORD

By EMILIE BENSON KNIPE
and ALDEN ARTHUR KNIPE

Concord and Lexington and Bunker Hill are names known to every American from the time that history begins to have a meaning for him. In "For Peace and Concord," we see the famous skirmish of Concord, not as it looks to our time, but as it looked to the eyes of the people who took part in it. Especially we see it as it appeared to the lonely and unhappy little girl who lived in Concord against her will and thought she had no interest in what happened to it. The way that she discovered herself to be a colonist and an American is quite as much the point of the story as is the way that she found for solving her personal difficulties. The two authors, Emilie Benson Knipe and Alden Arthur Knipe, have written many stories of Revolutionary times, a number of which have appeared, as did this one, in St. Nicholas.

W HEN I grow up, I'm going to marry the governor
of the Colony and wear naught meaner than satin." Reflect Davis smoothed her faded linsey-woolsey, as if already she felt the suavity of silk beneath her fingers.

"Then you'll have to be a high Tory, and we'll none
of us play with you," little Sally Saunders piped.

"This foolishness of Tories and Patriots — of Sons of
Liberty and Loyal Friends of King George — will all be
forgotten long ere I'm a woman," Reflect asserted. "I've
heard my father say so many a time."

"While my father says his ancestors came here in
search not of wealth or worldly gear but of liberty of
conscience, and if that is now denied us, he'll fight for it
till he drops — and so will I and my family after me."

The children sent up a shout of laughter at this, for
the speaker, Job Doughty, was a fat boy of no more than
twelve years and noted for the placidity of his disposition.

"Doughty's his name and doughty his deeds — in the

future!" Cyrus Davis said scoffingly. "Meanwhile, let's play at soldiers."

"No, Indians," Reflect amended. "I'll be the beautiful maiden about to be carried away captive, and one of you shall rescue me."

"Let Verity Wythe be the beautiful maiden. She's much prettier than you," Reflect's candid brother suggested.

"Verity doubtless has work to do within doors." Reflect usually was kind to Verity. Now Cyrus had touched her vanity and she did not stop to think that she was being cruel and that there were tears in the eyes of the bound girl as she turned and ran to the house. Indeed, Verity's morning tasks were done, and she was now at liberty to play. It was the fear that Reflect did not want her that had hurried her away.

Her position in the household was peculiar. Her father was a hunter and fur-trader. For years he had taken his motherless child with him on his trapping expeditions, carrying her on his back when she was little and, later, proud of her strength and endurance when she had grown able to follow at his side and help him with his traps and deadfalls.

Then, on one of his returns to civilization, the good people of Concord had pointed out to David Wythe that Verity was a daughter, not a son, and should be given the benefit of such womanly education as their town afforded. Unwillingly he had yielded to the conviction that they were right, and when next he departed for the woods, he left behind him his rebellious and weeping daughter, and in the hands of the minister a supply of money to pay his child's expenses until the date of his return, the time for which came and went, while from David Wythe there was no word.

Verity, entirely taken up with her fears for her father's safety, had given no thought to the practical fact that she must continue to eat and live even though the funds for her support had been exhausted. The woman with whom she had been placed, however, was not one to lose sight of realities. As a paying guest, the Widow Dunning had been willing to be responsible for Verity, but she was not troubled with a tender heart and felt in no way bound to maintain the girl without ample recompense.

"'Tis no belief of mine that her father ever meant to come back," she said to the minister. "He's settled the chit on us for the town to support."

"I pray you to be more charitable, mistress!" Mr. Emerson protested. "Wythe only left the maid here at our insistence. I greatly fear he has met with ill-hap."

"Say naught of that to Verity, or she will be off into the woods to hunt for him," Mrs. Dunning warned him hastily. "She's somewhat tamed from what she was at the start; only, having no wholesome fear of the wilderness such as our town-bred children confess, she would never stay contented an she thought he was endangered."

"True," the minister nodded his head. "She is a valiant child."

"That she is," Mrs. Dunning wagged her cap in assent. "Not to call her bold. But I'm a lone widow woman with little substance to fill one mouth, let alone two. I tell you plainly I cannot be answerable for her keep an there is no more money forthcoming."

"I shall take the matter under advisement," the minister promised. "I see your difficulty, and doubtless a subscription, circulated around the town by the girl, will bring pledges to the full amount of her small expenses."

And doubtless it would have, had Verity fallen in with the plan. When it was broached to her, she had first reddened, then paled alarmingly. She could not humble herself to beg, nor did she think her father would wish her to do so. She did not, however, need to be told that his continued absence was alarming. Indeed she would have been off after him long before had she had any idea of the route he had traveled. This he had carefully concealed from her, fearing that in her first revolt against the restraints of life in a New England village, she might be tempted to run away to follow him if she were aware of his destination.

Verity knew to the full the hopelessness of attempting to trace him after the lapse of even a short time. Now that the snows of the second winter were on the land, it was nothing short of impossible. She must stay in Concord in the forlorn hope that he might yet return. Silently she laid the paper on the table between them and looked up at the minister, suffering beyond her years in her eyes.

"What is it, my child?" he asked anxiously. "You must own that it is only equitable that all in the town contribute each his mite to your support, rather than that the whole expense should fall on one household."

"Sir, I see no reason that all or any should pay my expenses. My father will defray them —"

"Yes, yes," Mr. Emerson cut in hastily, having long

given David Wythe up for lost; "assuredly — but, till
his return, you must be fed —"

"And I am a lusty feeder," Verity acknowledged sadly.
"I restrain my appetite, so that I am ever hungry. I
sometimes think that could I but eat my fill just once,
I should never be so empty again."

"Yes, yes," Mr. Emerson said again. He had heard
whispers of the parsimony of Mrs. Dunning even when
she was being well paid for Verity's keep; but he did not
feel it fitting to discuss his elder parishioner with the
young girl. "Since this plan is distasteful to you, have
you any other to suggest?"

"Two," Verity smiled. "The plan I like the better
you will at once reject. I am skilled in woodcraft as any
Indian. I should prefer to go into the woods as my father
did, and earn my own living trapping."

"Impossible!" Mr. Emerson sputtered. "Out of the
question! A young girl, alone? We will not discuss it.
Clearly 'tis impossible."

"Said I not that you would reject this plan? There remains then my second thought: I have been here now for
over a year under an exacting taskmistress. I am not the
useless maid I was. I can go as a servant for my keep."

Mr. Emerson looked at her with a full appreciation
of the quality of a pride that preferred to work even as a
menial rather than to live on charity.

"You realize that, at your age, you will have to be
bound out?"

"Aye," Verity answered unhesitatingly. "I beg that
you will receive this money for my father and pay Mistress
Dunning aught that is her due. I would not be beholden

to her for one crust. One event only I ask you to arrange for. Should my father return, he must be privileged to buy back my services."

"My child, surely, in these circumstances, no one would deny a parent such a right."

"Perchance not," Verity answered. "At all events, let us run no risk but have it wrote down in the bond."

Thus it had been settled, and Verity had been bound out in the family of Israel Davis, where she was as happy as she could ever be in such a position. Cyrus liked her and befriended her on every occasion; Reflect was indifferent; the younger children were no part of her work; indeed Verity saw surprisingly little of them. Mr. Emerson had selected this household because Mrs. Davis was a kindly woman, but she was too absorbed in the rearing of her own numerous brood to bestow much thought on her youngest handmaid. Consequently, while Verity now had plenty of food for her body, her affections continued to be starved, and on Cyrus alone did she bestow her friendship.

The lad felt that Reflect's thoughtlessness had hurt Verity, and ere long he left the others at their play to seek her out. He found her seated on the step at the kitchen door, her face supported on her hands, staring out at the landscape that now, in April, although the day was warm, showed few of the signs of spring.

"What think you of all this talk of oppressive British soldiery?" he asked, slipping down on the step beside her. His wish was more to divert the girl's thoughts than to discuss the politics of the day, although, like most boys of fourteen at that date, he was something of a politician.

"I think of it not at all," Verity answered listlessly. "I've no love for a country that separates me from my father. Whatever comes is no concern of mine. Nor do I mean to mix in it."

"Why, Verity Wythe!" exclaimed Cyrus, surprised and beginning to find himself more of a patriot than he had suspected. "You astound me. Dost mean to say you would make no move to hold your town against invaders?"

"Not I!" Verity declared. "Concord is no town of mine. I'm here against my will, alone and quite unfriended. Why should I meddle in what concerns me not?"

She got up in response to a summons from the kitchen and turned to go in, leaving Cyrus quite dismayed at such wrongheadedness.

"At all events, Miss," he called after her, "there's one thing you said that's not entire truth; for how can you be unfriended when you have me?"

Verity did not answer this, but just before she closed the door, turned and gave Cyrus a strange, trembling little smile.

Bedtime came early for all in the town. A light in a window later than ten o'clock was almost certain evidence of illness in the house, candles and good whale oil both costing money.

At two o'clock the next morning Verity was awakened by the mad galloping of a horse which was checked almost beneath her window.

"Within there!" a man's voice bawled. "The regulars are coming to seize our stores. Sound the alarm. To arms! To arms!"

In an instant, as it seemed, the sleeping town woke to vigorous life.

Not quite knowing why she did so, Verity hurried on her clothing, hearing the while the slamming of doors and the footfalls of men running swiftly to the meeting-house, the bell of which was soon sending peal on peal across the country to warn all who heard it that there was danger afoot.

When she went downstairs it was to find others of the household before her, and all vastly excited.

"William Dawes and Paul Revere, the silversmith, who made my granddam's candlesticks, have been taken by the British," Reflect told her, anxious to spread the news.

Verity saw in this no excuse for waking a whole town from its sleep, and turned to go upstairs again.

"If they've done no wrong, doubtless they'll loose them shortly," she said with a huge yawn.

"Call it wrong or right, they have roused Lexington and warned Mr. Adams and Mr. Hancock that troops are on the way to punish them for their patriotism." Reflect was proud of her superior knowledge.

"An these messengers were captured, how is it Concord is alarmed?"

"Dr. Prescott was with them. He had been visiting in Lexington and was too quick for the soldiers. When they tried to stay him, he leaped his horse over a stone wall and galloped here across country. He is my idea of a brave man!" Cyrus was greatly stirred. "I would there were something I could do —"

"There is!" His father, who had just come in, interrupted him grimly. "There's work for all hands. We must hide our provisions, both for peace and war. You are too young to carry a musket, Cyrus, but you can be useful in driving oxen and drawing our provender to safety. You maids, too, are stout enough to prove your patriotism. Carry the goods out into the wood lots and conceal them under the slashings." Mr. Davis was busily filling his powderhorn and ball-pouch while he talked, and ran out through the doorway on his last words. Reflect followed him importantly, saying:

"I'll to the barn and arm myself with an ox-goad."

"Come on, Verity! You and I will have out our dun oxen. Between us, we'll keep them trotting," Cyrus cried.

But Verity hung back.

"I told you this was none of my war," she said, stubbornly. "Why should I take sides in it?"

Cyrus stared at her in amazement.

"Does it not make your blood boil to have soldiers sent among us for pillage? Are we not free men that what has been paid for with hard-earned money is to be taken away from us at the will of King George's hirelings?"

"How do I know they mean to take aught?"

"I've no time to argle-bargle!" Cyrus interrupted almost angrily. "An you won't help, I'll make shift without you. But even Mr. Emerson is under arms, and 'tis my belief your own father would be ashamed of you were he here."

He left her standing as if stunned by his words. At last she turned and went silently upstairs. There was work in plenty to be done in the house. The young children, who had been awakened by the clanging of the alarm bell, had run to the windows expecting the spectacle of a fire, and now must be coaxed back to their warm beds. The chambers must be set to rights. Mr. Davis was nowhere to be seen, nor was the dairymaid, nor Hannah, the stout wench who did the heavy work of the family. Single-handed, Verity put room after room in order and had breakfast ready to set on the fire when the approach of daylight again wakened the little children. These were helped with their dressing, a task that was unfamiliar but which was gotten through at last, when she marshaled them downstairs to find that their father and mother had returned and were deep in consultation, while Hannah was busy heating the breakfast.

"Guards have been set to watch the approaches to the town. There is no doubt that the regulars have been sent against us to arrest Hancock and Samuel Adams at Lexington; and to seize our small store of powder and cannon here," Mr. Davis told his wife.

"How can we be sure, at this distance from Boston, that such is their intention? I'm certain that Mr. Hancock and Mr. Adams are worthy citizens." Mrs. Davis was twisting her apron in her fingers nervously, loath to credit that the peace of the countryside was to be shattered.

"To seize those gentlemen is to deny all of us the right to free speech, since that is their only offending," her husband told her firmly. "As to how we know, the signal that this movement was afoot was flashed from the North Church steeple in Boston, and an attempt was made to arrest Revere ere he passed Charlestown Neck — what's that?" Mr. Davis leaped from his seat and ran from the house, while all within fell silent, straining their ears to hear, but hearing nothing. The master of the house returned shortly.

"No one without heard aught," he said. "They can't conceive that I did. Yet I tell you that my ears have been keen since childhood, and I distinctly caught the crackle of a volley fired by trained men, not by our irregulars."

Verity said nothing, but, woods' child that she was, she too had noted a faint echo of the *feu de joie* fired at Lexington to celebrate a short-lived and unworthy triumph.

Mr. Davis swallowed a hasty breakfast and prepared to return to his duty with the minutemen.

"Have ready a good pot of soup for any who lack food," he said, on leaving; "for the rest, Hannah and you had better return to your task of hastening the removal of the supplies."

Reflect and Sue, the dairymaid, had come in, eaten, and gone again; but when Mrs. Davis gave the order to clear away, Cyrus had not been fed, and Verity hesitated.

"You did well to stay here and have a care over the house and children," Mrs. Davis said, tightening her apron strings and setting her cap more firmly on her head.

"Her's able," Hannah grunted in compliment. "Did as much as I could — or more!"

Verity flushed with pleasure at this commendation. Praise was a commodity of which the Widow Dunning had been very chary.

"Cyrus has not come to his breakfast," she hinted with a look toward the table. "Think you he has fed elsewhere?"

"'Tis unlikely," his mother replied. "The lads today are keyed to such a pitch of patriotism I doubt if they give a thought to their stomachs for once in life." She pulled up her netted mitts and prepared to go forth.

"He will fall ill an he goes empty," Verity cried. "You know the headaches he takes."

"True," Mrs. Davis paused. "Hannah must come with me. When the outposts send word the British are at hand, we will return and carry the little ones with us into the hills. Have ready a basket of food for us. There's a mutton-ham in the larder. You hear me, children? You are none of you to venture without the palings till Mother comes for you. But you, Verity, once you have set the soup kettle at the fire, do you clap together some slices of bread with meat between and take them to Cyrus."

"Where shall I find him?" Verity asked.

"We are filling the carts with valuables and sending them to the woods. I fancy Cyrus is hauling to our own lot, the way to which he knows best. Should I see him, I'll send him here."

Mrs. Davis and Hannah hurried away to join the excited throng of workers. Verity set to work briskly, but what with preparing the meal to be eaten in the open, and feeding sundry of the minutemen who now came seeking something to stay their appetites, she had not finished clearing away the meal when the two women came rushing back with news that the approach of the regulars was reported.

"Leave the work and come." Mrs. Davis had seized the baby on one arm and under the other she cherished a bundle containing her scraps of silver: one tankard, a snuffer, two candlecups, half a dozen teaspoons, a snuff-box, and tinder-case, wrapped about with a blanket; while the children, beginning to be alarmed they knew not why, clung either to her skirts or Hannah's. "Reflect has gone ahead with her young cousins."

"And Cyrus?" Verity asked.

"Drat the boy!" his mother exclaimed. "He should have let me know where he is. But all the lads are thinking themselves men now that there's fighting in the wind."

"Hurry, Dame Davis!" a neighbor called in passing. "I've word that our defenders are falling back before the regulars."

With a smothered exclamation, Mrs. Davis dropped her cherished silver, seized another of her little ones and, calling the rest to follow, joined the stampede into the hills.

Verity helped Hannah gather together the fallen silver, and handed her the basket of food which she had packed.

"Do you take these," she said; "I'm going to warn Cyrus of what is toward. Should he return with the oxen now, the soldiers would be able to follow his tracks and find all he has hidden."

"Will ye be runnin' into danger?" Hannah asked kindly.

"Not I!" Verity assured her. "I'm almost an Indian in training. I'll take to the woods should there be a need, while these town-bred, foreign soldiers will no doubt stick to the main road."

Hannah and the children who clung to her moved away, while Verity cast a glance around. It grieved her housewifely spirit to leave her work undone, but she felt it imperative that she should warn Cyrus of the nearness of the soldiery, so she snatched up the bread and meat she had ready and made off without a backward look. She, poor child, had no treasures to save, not so much as one least thin silver spoon, her most cherished possession being an old, worn hunting knife of her father's, which hung at her waist.

She hurried forward, possessed by a sudden joy. Was she not free and in the open? Almost she sang as she went onward lightly and soon was outside the town. Yet, of a sudden, she brought up with a start of dismay. Ahead of her, topping a hill scarce more than a quarter of a mile distant, the sun was glinting on the silver of bayonets and the scarlet of British uniforms.

Instinctively, as a deer might leap to shelter, Verity vaulted a stone wall and crept onward in its shadow. She was not far from the gap in the fence where the turn was made through the barway to reach the wood lot. When she found this opening, her heart sank in dismay. It was so plain, so entirely plain that many carts had passed in that way recently. The earth, out of which the frost was coming, was scored deep with wheel tracks. Since the British had elected to come by this back road, they could hardly miss such obvious signs of the business that had been toward all morning. What could she do to obliterate the traces? She was examining the lay of the land with a puckered brow when she was startled by a deep groan. Out in the field under a stunted juniper, a spot she had taken for a rock shifted slightly, and she recognized the gray homespun of Cyrus's jacket.

The soldiers were still on the far hilltop. Plainly a halt had been called, either to rest the men or for reconnaissance. Praying that the delay might be a long one, Verity stamped on a bush of laurel and snapped it off. Holding this over her as a screen in case their field should, haply, be under observation, she crept across until she was at the boy's side.

"Cyrus!" she cried, aghast at his pale cheeks and shut eyes. At the sound of her voice, however, he lifted his lids.

"Oh, Verity," he whispered. "I've caught a Tory spy — but I'm hurt. I could go no farther."

"Listen," said Verity, imperatively. "The British are on yonder hill. They're like to be here shortly. All you've done will go for naught an I cannot hide the ruts your cart has cut." She handed him the packet of food she had brought. "Eat something. 'Twill hearten you. My father always said a full stomach was a good comforter. Meanwhile, should the soldiers come by, do you lie still. Even I took you for a stone till you moved." She stuck the laurel bush she had broken off into the ground in such a way as to hide him better from the lane, and at once began to crawl off.

"What are you going to do?" Cyrus called after her, but she, in her haste to get away, vouchsafed no answer.

At the barway into the field she seized upon one of the rails and with it pried such of the stones as she could move from the wall down into the opening, letting them fall as they would so long as they effaced the cart tracks. She cared not that she lowered the wall at either side, although she repaired such gaps in a measure with the rails; but her operation was still incomplete when she glanced at the far hill to find that the soldiers were in motion. Straightway she ceased her work on the stones and feverishly broke with her feet or cut with her knife the laurel and other bushes bordering the wall, which she set in the ground among the fallen rocks so that they appeared to be growing, thus hiding the new gashes in the ground.

The rattling of accoutrements and tramp of marching feet at last warned her to desist, and, silent as a shadow, she vanished into the underbrush at the edge of the field, crawling close to the stone fence, from which position she could not see the road but watched anxiously to assure herself that Cyrus made no betraying movement. Minutes now passed like hours, but in tending traps and deadfalls for her father, Verity had learned patience. Finally, after the last straggler with a blistered heel had limped by, she waited for what she calculated as a full five minutes; then, wriggling along the fence toward the highest point of the land, she raised herself up slowly and took an observation in each direction. There were no soldiers in sight. Already they must be entering Concord to find private houses deserted and the tavern locked against them. Relieved of fear from that quarter, at least for the moment, Verity ran back to Cyrus. The boy sat up at her approach, making no attempt to rise.

"I think my leg is broken," he explained. "But as I trapped a spy and perchance saved all the stores which were carried hither from our house and Colonel Barrett's, I'm not complaining. The way of it was this: the last load I brought out here had few packages but heavy. We had been warned the time was short, and I did not stop to think how I was to get them off the cart and under cover, but made off as fast as I could, stirring the oxen to their best pace. Well, when I reached the wood, I couldn't budge 'em — the packages, I mean — so I was in a pickle; I knew I was needed back to carry away other things. Mayhap my plan was silly — it came to me that I had plenty of rawhide thongs and that if I couldn't lift the boxes, it might be possible to fasten them to a tree and pull the cart out from under them."

"That was an idea," Verity said. "Could you do it?"

"I don't know," Cyrus acknowledged. "I'd only begun to arrange things when I had my accident. First, I fastened a rawhide from the lashings of a box to the tree, then I thought that if I could tip it ever so slightly, it would make the packet more unsteady and the easier to slip out from under, so I set another rawhide under one side where fortunately the floor of the cart was uneven, and I climbed up into the tree with the idea of using a limb to lift the box in the direction I wanted. It sounds silly when I try to explain what I was hoping to do — you see, I was desperate. Once up in the tree, I caught sight of the British redcoats on the hill yonder, and I own I sat and gaped at them, for plainly there was no longer any haste about what I did and I was well hid in the wood. There was not time to make another trip to town, so there I perched, tired at the end of my job, when all at once I was aware of something moving in the fern and bushes beneath me. It was a man, and he was crawling from spot to spot where I had hidden kegs and boxes, counting them and writing out a list of all he found."

"The man was a spy!"

"Aye," Cyrus said. "I saw at once that 'twas the Tory, Job Hands. I couldn't think what to do. It was only a question of seconds till he must see me and I knew not what desperate measures he might take against me rather than be denounced to the town, where there was much talk this morning of the small mercy they would mete out to informers. Still less did I know how to cope with a man of his strength."

"What did you do?" Verity could hardly wait to hear.

"To be honest, I don't know that I did anything. Mayhap 'twas all chance. The man crept directly under me. He was not surprised to see the oxen. It was to be expected that all animals would be driven off to safety. What did surprise him were my rawhide lashings. He plainly could make neither head nor tail of them when he stopped and looked them over. And then it happened, and truly, Verity, I can't tell you at this moment whether the limb broke or whether I jumped on top of him. At all events I landed on his head with my stout new hobnailed boots and stunned him. Before he came to his senses, I had him trussed up tighter than I ever dared truss an Indian captive in our play. I had his pistol, too — and it was ready primed, Verity. I hid it in the rocks back a way. I was trying to crawl to the village when you found me."

Verity jumped to her feet.

"Where are you going?" Cyrus asked.

"To fetch the doctor for you," the girl answered in a matter-of-fact tone. "I have no skill with broken bones."

"You can't go back to the town," Cyrus said quietly. "The enemy has fired it."

Verity cast one quick glance in the direction of his pointing finger, then sank down on the ground as if overcome.

After a moment or two, however, she rose again, determinedly.

"I shall go and see for myself," she declared. "With most of the housewives hurried from the town, a fire may be accidental. Grease may have cooked over — anything! At least we have heard no gunshots." Even as she spoke, shots rang out in the distance, a desultory scattering as if fired at random, then a full-throated volley. There was a moment's silence, when there came a reply in kind.

"Those last were our men," Cyrus declared. "There is a difference in the sound of their muskets."

Verity nodded agreement, and the two faced each other, white-lipped and tense, waiting for the echo of more shots, which did not come. Then again the girl prepared for action.

"You're too near the road here," she said. "I must manage to draw you further back."

"Only one leg is hurt. I'll make shift to hop along, if you'll lend me your shoulder for a crutch."

"I wonder is there aught I could do for your poor leg? If it were an arm, now, it could be carried in a sling —"

"A sling would be a help," Cyrus owned. "The hurt is between knee and ankle, and it makes me feel queer when I joggle it."

"It's grown so hot you've no need for your muffler. We'll knot it over my arm and slip your leg through the loop. I'll hold that arm firm around your waist and you can support yourself on my shoulders."

In this way the two traversed the stony upland pastures and reached the shelter of the wood, having reclaimed the Tory's pistol on the way. But movement increased the pain of the lad's injury, and he was glad to come to rest. Verity was interested in the very thorough way his prisoner was tied up, but one fact she noted as unsatisfactory. He was not gagged, an omission she mentioned to Cyrus.

"Should the British come this way, he might call out to them," she suggested.

"He would, you mean," the Tory snarled.

"Then the thing for you to do is kill him should you see a redcoat," the girl told Cyrus quite calmly, making reassuring faces the while to advise him that her purpose was not really so bloodthirsty.

"Oh, I really couldn't!" Cyrus cried.

"'Tis war," declared Verity, again trying to make the boy see that her intention was to intimidate their prisoner. Cyrus, however, could not be made to understand.

"I don't like war!" he exclaimed, feelingly. "From this day on, I'll stand with you, Verity. I am a man of peace."

"Well, you can pretend you're going to shoot him, can't you?" Verity whispered, much annoyed at such denseness. "I don't think I could gag him so that he couldn't make any noise. And the British may come back."

"Don't you believe they are going to stop in Concord?" Cyrus asked.

"They would not burn the town if they meant to live in it," the girl said, wisely. "I don't imagine it would be a good place for them. Between the river and the hills, they'd be hemmed in. Anyhow, I'm going to spy out what they're up to."

This time she was really off, and when she returned it was with news:

"So far, there's little harm done in the village," she announced. "They've stolen food, mostly, and spoiled what they could not use. There are no houses burned. The smoke was from the wooden cannon wheels, the liberty pole, and some wooden utensils. The courthouse did catch fire, but Mistress Moulton put it out single-handed, and, if 'twas set, they were 'shamed to fire it again. But 'tis a sad day for some. Your father's cousin, Captain Isaac Davis, from over Acton way, was killed outright at the first volley, and there are others dead on both sides."

"Are there British soldiers slaughtered?" the Tory demanded. "'Tis treasonous — outrageous —"

"'Tis outrageous that they should have been sent to invade a peaceful countryside!" Verity turned on him. "As you will agree, Master Hands, when you set eyes on your house. Being told it was a good Tory's, they said: 'Tories' lying tongues brought us to this pass!' And they did not spare it, Master Hands."

"I would I could have been there to see," Cyrus spoke, regretfully.

"The British Colonel Smith — or it might be Major Pitcairn, I knew not how to tell them apart — is marching and countermarching his men about the town, to make a great show. He is wasting time that is worth more than money to him, for, if he is to escape, he must move swiftly."

"What is your meaning?" asked Cyrus.

For answer, Verity parted the branches so that he could look over the country.

"You can see the minutemen swarming from all directions."

"I see none." Cyrus's tone was disappointed.

"Then you must take my word for it that they are there. And the British know something of it, for here they come at the double — and not at ease as they marched in to the town, but with flanking parties thrown out on either hand — 'tis well you moved back here, Cyrus."

"Aye," the lad answered, craning his neck to look out between the branches of hemlock and laurel. "They would have found me for sure now that they have spread out beyond the stone walls."

Both boy and girl had forgotten the Tory in their excitement, and the man bided his time. From where he was lying, he could not watch the oncoming soldiers. When they had passed before, although he had caught echoes of their passing, he had held silent because he had made sure only Colonials would make use of this back road. Now he was forced to judge of their nearness by what the others said. And, fortunately for them, in his eagerness he cried out too soon:

"This way, British!" he yelled. "Help, help!"

"Set the pistol to his head, Cyrus," Verity said.

But Cyrus held back. "It might go off," he muttered.

"Give it to me, then," Verity snapped, measuring the distance to the advancing men with her eyes.

"Don't you understand, it might go off!" Cyrus protested, holding tightly to the weapon.

In another moment the soldiers would draw level with them — and then Verity remembered her hunting knife. With a bound she was at the side of the captive and had set it to his throat.

"If you so much as whisper, you know what to expect," she said.

And so the British passed.

When the last one was hidden by the dip in the land, Verity cast the weapon from her and burst into tears.

"Hey day, what's come to the brave lassie?" a man's voice asked. "Never did I see a needful deed more smartly done."

A stranger, dressed in hunting shirt, breeches, and moccasins of dressed deerskin, and armed with a long rifle, gravely picked up the knife and made to hand it back to her; but Verity made no move to take it from him, although she sat up and wiped the tears from her cheeks.

"I do not call it brave to threat to murder an unarmed man," she said with a sob. "Yet I had to keep him silent. I don't know why I cried unless 'twas from rage that Cyrus is such a zany he doth not seem to know that a pistol from which he has spilled the priming will not go off."

"Exactly," the hunter agreed gravely. "An empty pan or wet powder are alike useless, and I understand that this was an affair between Cyrus and you, and open to friendly settlement, while the altercation that is going on out there" — he waved a hand toward the open — "is but the beginning of greater things. I would gladly join myself to these," he continued to point to the fields, and the children saw to their surprise that each clump of laurel or juniper, each rock, each tree, each stone wall was now serving to cover the movements of minutemen who silently and relentlessly were following the enemies of their liberty and peace.

"I am here but by chance," the man continued, "having stepped aside to oblige a friend by conveying a packet to his daughter, who lives in the town yonder. Were I to fall in this fracas, which is unlikely — still accidents have befallen even skilled hunters — this might fail of reaching her hand did I carry it with me. I wonder do you know the maid, and will you perchance deliver this, leaving me free to let fly a shot or two in the good cause?"

He held out a packet, wrapped in birchbark, plainly inscribed, *For Verity Wythe at Concord in the Massachusetts Bay Colony.*

"But that is me!" cried Verity. "Ask Cyrus — or no! 'Tis my father's knife you hold in your hand. His name is burned into the haft. Oh, where is my father? And is he well?"

"He's well," the hunter answered. "His letter doubtless tells you all. Now I am on my way to strike a blow for peace, and, when I see your father, I shall tell him he has a daughter to be proud of." His moccasined feet making no noise, he slipped between the trees and was gone before she could say another word.

Verity, her precious packet clasped to her, moved off in the opposite direction.

"Where are you going?" Cyrus asked. He was feeling very humble. He wanted to tell Verity that he, too, admired her courage, and knew her father would be proud of her, but, boylike, he did not quite know how to go about it.

Verity paused and looked back at him.

"Why — to get you a doctor, to be sure," she said, "and to see what has come to the soup. 'Tis my hope that we are done with war here in Concord."

UNUSUAL WORDS

accoutrements — soldiers' equipment

chary — sparing

desultory — aimless

obliterate — wipe out

reconnaissance — examination of a piece of territory for military reasons

suavity — (felt the suavity of silk) the smoothness of silk

QUESTIONS FOR SELF-TESTING

1. How had Verity spent much of her early childhood?
2. Why had her father given up taking her with him?
3. How did the woman with whom she was left account for the prolonged absence of Verity's father?
4. What precautions had Verity's father taken to prevent her following him?
5. For what offense were Hancock and Adams siezed by the British?
6. In spite of the fact that William Dawes and Paul Revere had been captured by the British, how had news of the proposed raid on Concord been spread?
7. As the British approached the town, what became of the women and children?
8. How had Verity learned the patience which kept her lying perfectly still while the soldiers went past?
9. What plan did Cyrus make for moving the packages in the cart when he found them too heavy to lift?
10. How did Cyrus capture the Tory spy?

11. When the British approached the spot where Cyrus and Verity had their prisoner, how did Verity prevent the Tory from calling for help?
12. How did Verity prove to the stranger who joined them in the wood that she was the person for whom the package he carried was meant?

Topics for Themes or Discussion

1. Describe the preparations of the Concord people for the British approach.
2. So far as this story shows, what were the differences in manner of fighting between the British troops and the American settlers?
3. Find a historical account of the battle at Concord and contrast it with this fictional one.
4. For what person or persons in the story do you feel the most sympathy? Why?
5. Write the story of the return of Mrs. Davis to her house in the village — what she found and what she felt.

Questions on
"THE SILVER SNUFFBOX" and
"FOR PEACE AND CONCORD"

1. Contrast Peggy's feeling toward the Americans' fight for freedom with the feeling of the heroine of "For Peace and Concord."
2. In the two stories, which boy do you think is the more lifelike, Joseph or Cyrus?
3. How many years' difference in time is there between the action of the two stories?
4. Write a short scene showing how Peggy would have acted in one of the situations in which Verity found herself.

SHANTY BOY

A Paul Bunyan Story

By JAMES STEVENS

James Stevens, the author of "Shanty Boy," says that legends about Paul Bunyan had their beginning in Canada in 1837 when the French-Canadians revolted against English rule, and one of them, "a mighty-muscled, bellicose, bearded giant named Paul Bunyan," led his mates to battle. Later this same Paul Bunyan moved over into the United States — according, at least, to the stories about him — and there became the marvelous chief of a crew of marvelous loggers. Accounts of him and his crew and his great blue ox named Babe spread through all the logging country of the Northwest. Paul Bunyan himself was so huge that an elephant hide made only the toecap for his boot! His crew could perform the impossible, and as for his ox — but "Shanty Boy" shows one or two of the feats of which Babe was capable.

"Shanty Boy" is one of the stories in James Stevens' book Paul Bunyan.

In PAUL BUNYAN'S time, camp entertainment was of, by, and for the woodsmen. In Paul Bunyan's camp there were hypnotic storytellers, singers who could make you laugh and cry in the same moment, and steppers who could do a breakdown fit to shatter the frame of a bunkhouse. "Ol' Paul" knew the importance of social pleasures for his loggers, and he made natural provision for them. A good bunkhouse bard was marked by the great logger's especial favor; many a man who toiled poorly was saved from the lowly life of a farm hand by his ability to dance, whistle, and sing. Consequently Paul Bunyan's Bunkhouse Nights are as famous in history as his great feasts and labors.

Every night but Sunday, when the twelve hours of toil in the woods were ended and supper was over, the tired loggers would be cheered and consoled by the bunkhouse

86

bards. There was one for each shanty, and each one had his own particular virtues. There was Beeg An'tole, for example, who made his mates in Bunkhouse 999 hilarious as he told quaint tales about logging in "dat ver' fines' countree, which she's t'ree weeks below Quebec." Angus MacIlroy of Bunkhouse 1313 was made to sing "The Island Boys" a dozen times a night by his song-loving comrades. And Tinty Hoolan of Bunkhouse 6000 jigged with such violence and speed that a modern jazz band would have gone crazy trying to make music fast enough for him. The rattle of his jigging feet sounded like the buzz of a big bee. His bunkhouse cronies boasted that he could imitate any known sound with his feet except a tired logger's snore. And this, anyone admitted, defied imitation or description. Tinty Hoolan was a swamper, and a poor one; his feet, however, saved him from life among the scissorbills on Paul Bunyan's farm.

Now these were three of the greatest of Paul Bunyan's bards, and no one has ever found words to describe them or to give them fitting praise. And if words fail with them, how can they reveal the brightest star of all Paul Bunyan's performers? Indeed, Shanty Boy, of Bunkhouse 1, was more than a star; he was a constellation, for he was an entertainer with a thousand talents. What old logger does not feel his own soul dance as he hears, in the Bunyan histories, the soft, vibrant patter of Shanty Boy's right foot, the thunderous stamp of his left foot, the sharp rattle of his heel-cracking in a great breakdown? He not only danced with his feet, but with his hands and eyes; he had a dancing grin, too, which would shine now on the right side of his face, now on the left. Shanty

Boy put his whole soul into his dancing. And so he did with his stories. When he told a Swede story he *was* a Swede, and when he told a dirty story he *was* dirty. He was never content with mere pretending. He made entertainment of everything, and he did it naturally. A log would roll over his leg when he was at work. That night he would hobble down the bunkhouse aisle like an ailing old man, talking in the mournfullest way. "Oh, lawdy, boys! I 'low I ain't long fer *this* life. Thet new medicine I'm usin' don't 'pear to be doin' my rheumatiz no good, no good a-tall." Then he'd hobble back again, drawing his sore leg up like a string-halted horse, and groaning, "M-m-m! M-m-m! I 'low I feel worse'n any-one thet ever lived in this here world — an' lived." If somebody asked him what time it was, he would take out his old watch, hold it at arm's length, throw back his head and squint at the watch like he was looking at it through glasses. He claimed that "grandpap carried thet watch fer nigh on forty year, an' it won't tell the time onless I look at it just like he did." Sometimes he would sit down by the stove and eat an apple or a raw turnip. Then he would pull his hat down over his eyes, and while he chewed away, looking as solemn as a politician, he would make the hat bob up and down to keep time with his jaws. No one else could have done this without seem-ing foolish, but Shanty Boy always kept a kind of dignity when he was performing that made men respect him even when they were laughing at him.

But, it was his songs and stories which truly endeared him to the loggers. His renditions of "John Ross," "Jack Haggerty," "The Island Boys," and "Bung Yer

Eye," were so affecting and inspiring that the loggers,
what with laughing, crying, stamping, clapping, and cheering, often made so much sympathetic noise that the song
itself could not be heard. Shanty Boy only sang two
nights a week and then for no longer than four hours
at a time. The other nights he danced, and told true
but thrilling stories of life in the woods. The bards from
other bunkhouses would come to hear him and then give
imitations of his performances. His supremacy was un-
questioned, yet he remained unspoiled.

For he was more than mere entertainer. The mightiest
of Paul Bunyan's loggers lived in Bunkhouse 1, and as a
logger Shanty Boy was the peer of any of them. He
could notch a tree or work in white water with the best
of the fallers and rivermen. He held his own with even
Mark Beaucoup in the rough bunkhouse frolics. He was
Paul Bunyan's favorite faller, and the great logger often
carried him to the woods on his shoulder. He had an
equal rank with Hot Biscuit Slim, the chief cook, Shagline
Bill, the freighter, and Big Ole, the blacksmith. He was
a true hero. And a time came when he reached the greatest height of glory ever attained by a plain logger. Here
is how it came about.

The Year of the Two Winters had been disastrous for
Paul Bunyan. Winter had come again in the summer-
time that year, and the cold increased in the succeeding
months. At Christmas time there were fifty feet of ice
on Lake Michigan, and by the last of February the lake
was frozen to the bottom. Paul Bunyan was then en-
gaged in logging off the Peninsula country, and of course
his operations were halted. He cut the ice into blocks

and hauled them out on the lake shore with Babe, his big blue ox, who could pull anything that had two ends on it. This was done so that the ice would melt more quickly when normal summer weather returned. Then he moved his outfit to the old home camp in the Smiling River country, where severe weather was never experienced.

Paul Bunyan had done no logging around his old home camp for seven years. The remaining timber was so far from the river and on such steep hills that profitable logging seemed impossible. However, it was the best to be had, for elsewhere it would be weeks, even months, before the snowdrifts would melt away from the tree-tops. Paul Bunyan tackled the tough logging problems before him with characteristic courage. He was sure that his inventiveness and resourcefulness would, as always, triumph over every obstacle.

His most stubborn and difficult problem was that of getting the loggers to the woods in the morning in time to do any work and getting them home at night in time to do any sleep. One plan after another was tried and dropped, failures all. Paul Bunyan began with an attempt to work one day shift, but the loggers could not get to the woods before lunchtime; lunch finished, they had to start at once for the camp. Two shifts were then put on, but little work could be done at night, except when the moon was full. Paul Bunyan then sent the great Johnny Inkslinger, his timekeeper and man of science, to investigate the Aurora Borealis as a means of artificial lighting. Johnny reported that it was pretty but unreliable, and he doubted if even the blue ox could move it down from the North in less than six months.

The learned Inkslinger then sat down and figured desperately for a week, trying to devise a method of working three twelve-hour shifts a day. With such a routine one shift could be doing a day's work, while a second shift was coming to work, and a third was going to camp. Johnny Inkslinger was, beyond a doubt, the greatest man with figures that ever lived, but here his mathematics failed him. Paul Bunyan then thought of making a campsite in the timber, and he dug for water in the high hills. He succeeded in reaching a mighty vein, but it was so deep that it took a week to draw a bucket of water out of the well. It was out of the question as a water supply for the camp.

Now Paul Bunyan had to fall back on a last plan, a far-fetched one that seemed well-nigh hopeless. This was to build a great sled, something on the order of a lunch sled, and have Babe, the blue ox, haul the loggers to and from work each day. It was a desperate plan, and no one but Paul Bunyan would have had the courage to attempt it. It must be remembered that the blue ox measured forty-two ax handles and a plug of chewing tobacco between the horns; an ordinary man at his front had to use a telescope to see what he was doing with his hind legs, he was so long; he had so much energy and such delight in labor that no one could hold him when he started for the woods in the mornings; he was so fast that Paul Bunyan's foreman, the Big Swede, who was as tall as the trees, could not begin to keep up with him. Only Paul Bunyan could travel so fast. Whenever Babe moved the camp he traveled at a careful pace, but even then some of the loggers were made seasick; and all of them became so irritable when a move was being made that they fought constantly among themselves. If the comparatively slow camp-moving pace of the blue ox thus upset them, his timber-going gallop would be apt to ruin them completely. Paul Bunyan remembered how the Big Swede, hanging to Babe's halter rope, was hurled through the air, only striking the ground once in every quarter of a mile or so, when the blue ox rushed to his delightful labor each morning. A lunch sled full of loggers would be dragged by Babe in much the same fashion; it would be in the air most of the time, and when it did strike the ground loggers would be scattered like autumn leaves. The loggers who would hang on until the woods were reached would have the living daylights shaken out of them. A common lunch sled would not do; one must be invented that would hold the road.

So Paul Bunyan devised the serpentine bobsled. It was a long, low-built contraption; the runners were made in short sections, connected by double joints. When it was completed and lay in the road that led from camp, it looked like a squat fence, for it snugly fitted the contours of the hills and vales over which it extended.

"There's a rig that'll hold the road," said Paul Bunyan with pride. "Now I'll invent something equally good to hold Babe to a slow pace."

Several mechanical devices were tried without passing the first test. The sled lay idle. The loggers got sore feet, and they traveled so slowly that they began to take twelve hours to reach the woods. There was one shift on the road, going, and one coming all of the time. Not a tree was being felled.

"There's no way out of it but to try the grizzlies," Paul Bunyan told his timekeeper.

Among the other livestock on Paul Bunyan's farm, which was down the river from the old home camp, was a herd of grizzly bears. The great logger often amused himself by playing with them, and he had taught them many tricks. Not the least of their stunts was for each bear to hang from a tree with three paws and try to claw Paul Bunyan's mackinaw with the other paw as he dodged by.

"I'll station them at the trees which are left standing along the road," said Paul Bunyan, "and when Babe roars by they'll hook him. They may only frighten him into a faster run, but I think surely they'll slow him down."

The next morning the loggers, for the most part, joyfully crawled upon the serpentine bobsled. The timid and cranky among the loggers were pessimistic, of course, and declared noisily that this would be the end of them. But Shanty Boy and the other bards laughed at their fears, and at last every logger in camp was on the sled. Paul Bunyan ordered the Big Swede to hitch up the blue ox and start in half an hour, and he departed for the woods with his herd of grizzlies. He stationed one of them at every tree close to the road. When he reached the timber he straddled a hogback and sat down to wait for the outcome of his daring attempt.

In a short time he heard a faint thunder down in the valley, then he saw enormous balloons of dust twisting up in cyclonic bursts from the foothills, next he heard the crashing sound of hoofbeats that got louder and louder. . . . Through clouds of dust he saw Babe's tail brush lifted like a triumphal banner and the glitter of his horns. . . . The Big Swede, hanging to Babe's halter rope, soared and dived. . . .

The bears had failed. Indeed, they had failed terribly, for when Babe came to a halt in the timber Paul Bunyan saw bears' paws hanging from both sides of him. Only one bear had saved his paw, and he was holding a tree in a frenzied clutch. Babe had carried away bear, tree and all. Paul Bunyan rushed back over the road, and as he came to each unfortunate grizzly he mercifully dispatched him. He carried them all into camp.

"Bear meat for Sunday dinner," he said to Hot Biscuit Slim, as he threw the bears into the kitchen yard.

Paul Bunyan then had Johnny Inkslinger bring his medicine case, and the two hurried to the woods. But only a slight number of the loggers had been made truly ill by the terrific speed with which Babe had hauled them over the hills. The double-jointed sled runners had slipped over rocks, logs, and gullies as easily as a snake glides over a string. Not once had the sled bounded from the road. Not a logger had suffered a jolt. Some of them were dazed and breathless, others were choked with dust, but most of them were no more than badly scared by their terrific journey.

"Aye tal you it ban no use try hol' Babe down," said the Big Swede, with rare eloquence.

"The sled worked perfectly, at any rate," said Paul Bunyan. "We can depend on it. But those good bullies of mine are going to need a lot of encouragement to stand that ride every morning."

He was quite right. His loggers thought nothing of the perils of falling limbs, which are called "widow-makers" today in the woods. Breaking up log jams, jumping rolling logs, dodging butts of trees which bucked back from the stumps when they fell — all this was in the day's work. But even the serpentine bobsled could not banish the terrors of riding behind the blue ox each morning. "I'd ruther try ridin' a peavy handle down the West Branch." "I'll tell you Babe went so fast I acshuly *seen* the wind, an' I never seen anything more sickenin' in my life!" "What if Babe ud a throwed a shoe now? I bet it 'da tore through us like a cannon ball!"

Paul Bunyan frowned as he hearkened to their complaints. His loggers seldom thought of anything but their labor when they were in the woods. If they were complaining now, what would happen when the bunkhouse cranks got into action after supper? There would be much gloomy grumbling, and perhaps rebellious talk. When the loggers went to bed, they would brood over the cyclonic morning ride instead of getting fortifying sleep. Then they would soon balk against riding behind the blue ox. To avoid such an event he must call on his bards to cajole, humor, and inspire the men until he could devise new methods to solve his logging problems. With this idea in mind he took Shanty Boy aside, placed him on his knee, and explained the situation.

"I shore will do my best," said Shanty Boy. "But looky here, Mr. Bunyan, I 'low I'll have to lie to 'em right smart."

"How so, my lad?"

"Well, I've allus done the best I knowed how when

I set out to be amusin'. So, if I'm goin' to make my stories any thicker, I'll jest about have to stir a few lies into 'em.''

"Son, nobody loves a liar.''

"Thet's jest it, Mr. Bunyan. I got a powerful good reppytation fer truth, an' I can lie quite a spell afore I'm ketched. But if I do get ketched Mark Beaucoup an' them Rories'll chaw me up. You've learnt all the loggers to hate lyin' jest like you do yourself. I'd probably get spiled if I was ketched. Besides, I jest nacherly hate to lie. Yet, no lyin', no loggin', seems to be the fact o' the matter.''

Paul Bunyan pondered doubtfully for some time. Moral issues baffled him always. But at last he spoke with decision.

"Logging must go on. You may lie, if necessary, during the period of emergency.''

"Them's orders, Mr. Bunyan. But what if the gang gets hostile an' starts to chaw me up?''

Again Paul Bunyan hesitated. It was against his policy to interfere in the loggers' personal affairs. Then, firmly:

"A man with your talent should not have to lie, Shanty Boy, in order to entertain his mates. But you know best, of course. If you are discovered, tell the men that all complaints must be lodged with me before they act upon them. Be cautious and discreet, and honor and glory shall be yours.''

"I will, sir. Thank ye, sir, Mr. Bunyan.''

Shanty Boy went bravely to work carrying out the great logger's commands. For some time it was not necessary to tell more than two or three lies a week in order to take the logger's thoughts off their sickening morning rides. They were not great lies that he told, either, but only plausible exaggerations. Most of his stories were still true ones, and he told them better than ever. He inspired the visiting bards as never before. Each night he sent his mates smilingly to sleep, entirely forgetful of the ordeal that awaited them in the morning. But this was not natural, and of course it couldn't last. The loggers lost weight every day, and they began to complain of hurts in their innards. The bunkhouse cranks got their dismal chorus started, and Shanty Boy had to tell real big lies to hush it.

He lied wonderfully indeed, once he was well started. He got so funny that the loggers had to strap themselves into their bunks while they listened to him. They went to sleep laughing, as a rule, and the night long they would chuckle in their dreams.

Shanty Boy grew bolder with success. He told, with a bare face, stories about snakes that had many joints, and how they would separate into pieces and crawl a dozen ways at once. He called them joint snakes. He told stories about a snake that would put its tail in its mouth and roll down hill. He called it a hoop snake. When the loggers got a little tired of snakes, he told whoppers about possums, then about coons, and so on. At last he got around to fish, and he told so many good fish stories that the loggers would not let him switch to another subject. He ran out of ideas, but the loggers would not let him get away from fish.

One night as he was trying desperately to invent a

tolerable lie about fish he remembered a story of a whale that he had heard his grandfather tell, insisting that it was the gospel truth. It was the old story about Jonah and the whale, and the loggers had never heard it. They became indignant when Shanty Boy repeated it for the plain truth, and some of them began to shout at him. For the first time in his life he got stage fright. He felt that he was telling the gospel truth, but the memory of his previous lies overwhelmed him. He tried vainly to continue his narrative about Jonah's life in the whale's belly, but his tongue failed. He dropped his head, and he fixed a shamed gaze on his feet. First he heard nothing but the pounding of his heart; then an angry mutter ran along the bunks. It grew into a fierce growl. Then Shanty Boy heard the tramp of feet, and he looked up to see Mark Beaucoup and the bunkhouse cranks advancing upon him.

"She's lie!" yelled Mark Beaucoup. "*Sacre!* but she's tell a beeg wan."

He shook a huge brown fist under Shanty Boy's nose.

"Now you are feex yourself. Stan' up w'ile I knock you down!"

The loggers left their bunks and made a pressing crowd around their discomfited bard and his challenger.

"I was coun' for you stan' up. Wan — two — t'ree —"

Then Shanty Boy remembered Paul Bunyan's "All complaints must be lodged with me" and courage returned to him.

"You bunkhouse cranks shore give me a misery," he said contemptuously. "You jest go an' tell my story to ol' Paul an' see what *he* says about it."

The loggers stared at him with amazement.

"By gar!" exclaimed Mark Beaucoup. "De fool wan' me tell dees to ol' Paul! She's wan' me tell dees, dat crazy t'ing!"

"Thet's what I said," growled Shanty Boy. "Run along afore I get into one o' my tantrums."

Knowing Paul Bunyan's furious opinion of liars, the loggers were smitten with horror. Of course this story might not be a lie, but most likely it was, and what old Paul would do to him for telling it! Mark Beaucoup was triumphant. Soon Bunkhouse 1 would have another king; it should know a rule of iron instead of laughter.

"Come wit' me," he commanded his friends. The other loggers, except Shanty Boy, followed them to Paul Bunyan.

As Paul Bunyan listened to Mark Beaucoup he was struck with a powerful regret for having inspired his greatest bard to leave the path of truthful narration. Desperate circumstances had seemed to justify the step. But what a risk he had taken just to save a few weeks' logging! The faith his loggers had in him lay in the balance. Now it seemed that he must lose this faith or sacrifice a hero. He had never dreamed that Shanty Boy would recklessly tell such an incredible story. Surely he had not told it unthinkingly. No doubt he could explain it. Paul Bunyan sent for him.

It was with a heavy heart that the great bard walked through the lines of silent, accusing loggers. It looked like the end of everything for him. But he kept his courage, and, as he walked slowly on, his nimble mind was leaping from idea to idea, seeking a solid defense.

But what proof could he offer for such a story? His grandfather *knew* it was true, but the old man was far away in the Southern mountains. He alone must prove somehow that he had not lied. . . . Paul Bunyan's boots loomed before him. . . . He must think hard . . . hard. . . .

"This story must be explained," said Paul Bunyan in a stern voice, at the same time flashing him a look of the utmost sympathy.

"I 'low the story is beyond explainin', Mr. Bunyan, but I never lied whan I told it," said Shanty Boy, bravely.

"Prove it!" roared Mark Beaucoup and his followers.

Shanty Boy drew himself up pridefully and he fixed upon the multitude a gaze of lofty scorn.

"I never lied!" he declared. "I never lied, for when I lie my neck it swells! An' — now — look!"

He jerked open the collar of his shirt and exposed his muscular throat. There was not a sign of swelling about it. The loggers lifted a mighty cheer, and Mark Beaucoup, baffled, beaten, completely outwitted, could only swear:

"She's don' swell — by gar! — she's don' swell!"

Paul Bunyan could not restrain a windy sigh of relief. The trees bent before the blast and dust clouds rolled through the ranks of loggers. Now was the moment to complete the victory.

"Get to your bunkhouses!" Paul Bunyan roared.

Shanty Boy was carried on the shoulders of yelling admirers to Bunkhouse 1. Mark Beaucoup and the bunkhouse cranks did not venture to follow them until the lights had gone out. Then, humbled and quiet, they sneaked into their bunks.

As a result of his troubles Paul Bunyan came near to abandoning logging operations in the Smiling River country. But one night he got an idea, an idea so simple and sound that he was astonished at not thinking of it before. He put it into practice at once, and when the loggers awoke the next morning they saw wooded hills at the very door of the camp. Paul Bunyan had simply thrown a cable around each hill, and the blue ox, who could pull anything that had a top on it, had snaked every one into camp. So the logging then went on easily until the new summer had melted the ice and snow and Lake Michigan was filled with water once more, and had new fish in it.

Shanty Boy's triumph was complete. Not only did he have great honors from Paul Bunyan, but his mates now revered as well as admired him. His ventures from truth had held off revolt from the bunkhouses. He had convinced the loggers of the truth of the grand old story of Jonah and the whale. And he had made them all fear swelled necks as the result of lying. This last effect persists to this day, for everywhere loggers are still known as the most truthful of men.

UNUSUAL WORDS

Aurora Borealis — Northern Lights

hilarious — (who made his mates in Bunkhouse 999 hilarious) made them wildly amused

mackinaw — a short, heavy coat

pessimistic — (The timid and cranky among the loggers were pessimistic) were inclined to expect the worst

plausible — (but only plausible exaggerations) only exaggerations which were easy to believe

QUESTIONS FOR SELF-TESTING

1. What was one way in which Paul Bunyan showed that Shanty Boy was a favorite of his?
2. For what reason did Paul Bunyan cut the ice in Lake Michigan into blocks and haul it out to the shore?
3. What were the limits of Babe's hauling capacity?
4. What was the chief difficulty Paul Bunyan faced in logging at the home place?
5. How did he finally overcome this difficulty?
6. What plans did Johnny Inkslinger make for improving the logging schedule?
7. In what terms does the author explain how big Babe was?
8. What happened to the Big Swede when he accompanied Babe to work each morning?
9. By what device did Paul Bunyan try to slow down Babe's pace?
10. Why was the device unsuccessful?
11. What happened when Paul Bunyan sighed with relief?
12. Why are loggers today "known as the most truthful of men"?

TOPICS FOR THEMES OR DISCUSSION

1. Judging from the story here given, what should you say were the characteristics of the Paul Bunyan stories which have caused them to stay in circulation for already nearly a hundred years?
2. Make a suitable new adventure for one of the characters in this story.
3. The author says that Shanty Boy can "work in white water" as well as any of the men. What does he mean?

4. Find as many phrases as you can in which the author impresses on his readers the enormous size of Paul Bunyan.

5. What improvements can you suggest in the methods Paul Bunyan employs for taking his loggers on their daily rides?

HOW THE CAT CAME TO
HAVE NINE LIVES

By JOHN CASPER BRANNER

In the first chapter of How and Why Stories, *from which this story is taken, the author explains that the tales in the book are those he heard in the South "'fo' de wah" when, as a child, he was living surrounded by colored people. "To me they* [*the colored people*] *seemed vastly more interesting and more human than white folks — and it required a lot of parental authority and something else that I decline to name, to keep me away from their cabins. I managed to slip through the picket lines occasionally and sit for a few blissful minutes on the pile of pine knots at the corner of the fireplace." There "I first heard many of the folklore stories published later by Joel Chandler Harris, and a lot more besides."*

The author, John Casper Branner, was not only a writer but also a famous geologist and the president of a university. Though he published many professional books, he wrote no stories except those in How and Why Stories.

Eᴠᴀ'ʙᴏᴅʏ knows dat a cat's got nine lives, but it ain't eva'body dat knows jes' how he come by 'em. Hit was dis-a-way: an' I want you to tek notice at de staht dat when a mammy stan's by her childen an' de childen stan's by dey mammy, dey's a mighty ha'd lot to beat, des as sho's you's bawn.

At de staht an' up to de time o' de flood a cat didn't have but jes' one life, des like de othah crittahs. But at de time o' de flood when ole Mr. Noah went aroun' to drive de crittahs into de ark he foun' a tom cat an' a pussy cat an' he give 'em a invite to git ready an' come along wid him into de ark, 'cause dey's a gwine to be a powerful big rain an' a mighty big freshet. An' de tom cat he say he's all ready to go, an' de pussy cat say she's all ready 'cepn' she's got to take her kittens wid her, an' seein' as dey ain't yit got dey eyes open she's got to

tote 'em all de way by de back o' de neck, an' it's gwine
to tek some time 'cause dey's eight uv 'em. Den ole
Mr. Noah he tole 'em dat dey'd haf to leave de kittens
behime, 'cause dey wa'n't allowed to tek kittens wid 'em
into de ark. An' de pussy cat she low dat if dat was de
case dey'd hafter 'scuse her, 'cause she couldn' leave dem
childen widout any ma nohow, an' if Mr. Noah would
jes tek a look at 'em he'd see dat dey was jes' de fines'
lot o' kittens dat he evah sot his eyes on, an' he'd feel
obleege to tek 'em along. But Mr. Noah respon' dat de
boat didn' belong to him, an' dat he was a actin' undah
ordahs, an' de ordahs say dat dey wa'n't allowed to have
mo'n two cats on de boat. Den de pussy cat she 'splain
dat dese was jes kittens, an' if de ordahs didn't say nothin'
about kittens o' co'se — An' dar Mr. Noah stopped her
an' tole her she'd hev to 'scuse him 'cause he was mighty
busy an' dey wa'n't no time to lose, an' wid dat he hobble
off down de big road a lookin' fo' de othah crittahs an' a
tellin' 'em what to do, an' a growlin' 'cause de women
folks all want to argy an' 'splain so much.

Well, suh, dat pussy cat she mek up her min' dat she's
a gwine ter git dem kittens on bode whedder o' no; an'
she say dat it didn't hole to reason dat anybody could
be so low down triflin' dat he'd want to drown such a
fine lot o' kittens, an' dat too when dey didn' so much as
have dey eyes open. Wid dat she pick up one of 'em by
de back o' de neck an' ca'y it up close to whar de ark
was a standin', an' dar she put it down on de groun' by
de gangplank, an' tole de tom cat to stay dar an' min'
it while she go back atter de othahs. An' she kep' on a
fetchin' 'em ontil she had all eight uv 'em in one pile.

By dat time de crittahs was all a marchin' into de ark
two by two, wid de big ones in de front an' de little ones
behime accordin' to dey size, an' when it come time fo'
de cats to march in de pussy cat pick up one o' de kittens
by de back o' de neck an' stahted up de gangplank alongside o' de tom cat, a meanin' to git a pass an' come back
atter de othah ones. But jes' when she come up to de
big front do' whar dey all hatter go in, ole Mr. Noah was
a standin' dar a takin' de tickets, an' he say:

"Looky heah, Miss Cat, you'll hatter leave dat 'ar
kitten outside; I done tole you dat once befo'."

Well, suh, dat cat she want to argy de mattah, an'
she begins to talk so fas' dat Mr. Noah ain't have a chance
to say nothin', so he jes' call out:

"Don't block up de road dar!" an' wid dat he shove
de pussy cat an' her kitten offen de gangplank, an' de
tom cat he hatter go in by hisself 'cause de othah crittahs
was a crowdin' up behime.

Well, suh, de pussy cat 'low dat she ain't a gwine to
be beat out dat-a-way, but by de time she git back whar
she lef' de kittens, all de crittahs o' her size was done
gone in an' it look like she's gwine to be lef' outen de ark
sho' nough.

An' 'twan't long befo' de rain commence to rain and de
big watahs begin to come up ontil de cat an' de kittens
was lef a swimmin' aroun' de ark a meowin' an' a tryin'
to fin' a place whar dey could climb up an' git inside.

When de pussy cat tuk notice dat one o' de kittens
couldn' hol' out no longah she tuk it in her mouf, an'
when de kitten die, its life went down inside o' de ole cat.
Den when another was about to drown she drap de dead

one an' she took dat one up, an' when it die its life went down inside o' de ole cat too. An' dat went on ontil de kittens was all dade, all de whole eight ov 'em, an' de eight lives was all inside o' dey mammy.

Den de ole cat begin to meow, an' she make sich a moanful soun' dat ole Mr. Noah retch out his arm thu' a hole an' pull up de pussy cat, 'cause he remembah dat dey wa'n't no cat on bode 'cepn' de tom cat, an' he wa'n't no 'count nohow.

An' aftah de flood was all ovah an' de crittahs all come outen de ark, all de cats dat was bawn from dat time on had nine lives in 'em, 'ste'd o' jes one like dey stahted with.

An' dat's what mek me say dat when a mammy stick by her childen an' de childen stick by dey mammy, dey's mighty sho' to win in de long run.

Topics for Themes or Discussion

1. Write an introductory paragraph to this story showing the little boy coming into the cabin and settling down to be instructed.
2. The teller of this story tells the little boy twice what the moral of the story is. Does the story really illustrate all of the moral he gives? If not, why does he add the part not shown in the story itself?
3. Can you find a human situation which is like that of the mother cat arguing with Mr. Noah in favor of bringing her children with her on board the ark?
4. The writer of the *How and Why Stories* speaks of them as "folklore tales." Judging from this example, what should you say a "folklore tale" is?

QUESTIONS ON
"SHANTY BOY" AND "HOW THE CAT CAME TO HAVE NINE LIVES"

1. What reason can you see for pairing these two stories?
2. Can both of them properly be called American folklore? Explain your answer.
3. Write a paragraph showing how Paul Bunyan would have managed the loading of the ark.
4. Selecting one of Paul Bunyan's adventures, write out the moral which the teller of "How the Cat Came to Have Nine Lives" would probably have attached to it.

A TALE OF THREE TRUANTS

By Bret Harte

*Probably no author, not even Hawthorne or Poe, has in-
fluenced short-story writing in America more than has Bret
Harte. By his use of local color and by the flippant, humor-
ous wording of even his tragic narratives, he both made his
own stories highly popular and set a fashion for writers
who came after him.*

*"A Tale of Three Truants," given here with one section
left out (the section which shows the schoolmaster making
unsuccessful inquiries of the parents of the three truants),
comes from a volume called* Tales of Trail and Town.
*The story pictures the risks of life in the Sierras in the early
'60's and the indifferent fashion in which the settlers faced
those risks and immediately forgot about them.*

*The better known of Bret Harte's stories deal, all of them,
with California in the days of early settlement and gold
hunting. "The Luck of Roaring Camp" and "The Out-
casts of Poker Flat," both found in* The Luck of Roaring
Camp and Other Stories, *are two especially famous ones.*

THE SCHOOLMASTER at Hemlock Hill was troubled that morning. Three of his boys were missing. This was not only a notable deficit in a roll-call of twenty, but the absentees were his three most original and distinctive scholars. He had received no preliminary warning or excuse. Nor could he attribute their absence to any common local detention or difficulty of travel. They lived widely apart and in different directions. Neither were they generally known as "chums," or comrades, who might have entered into an unhallowed combination to "play hookey."

He looked at the vacant places before him with a concern which his other scholars little shared, having, after their first lively curiosity, not unmixed with some envy of the derelicts, apparently forgotten them. He missed the cropped head and inquisitive glances of Jack-

son Tribbs on the third bench, the red hair and brown eyes
of Providence Smith in the corner, and there was a blank
space in the first bench where Julian Fleming, a lanky
giant of seventeen, had sat. Still, it would not do to
show his concern openly, and, as became a man who was
at least three years the senior of the eldest, Julian Fleming,
he reflected that they were "only boys," and that their
friends were probably ignorant of the good he was doing
them, and so dismissed the subject. Nevertheless, it
struck him as wonderful how the little world beneath
him got on without them. Hanky Rogers, bully, who
had been kept in wholesome check by Julian Fleming,
was lively and exuberant, and his conduct was quietly
accepted by the whole school; Johnny Stebbins, Tribbs'
bosom friend, consorted openly with Tribbs' particular
enemy; some of the girls were singularly gay and con-
ceited. It was evident that some superior masculine op-
pression had been removed.

He was particularly struck by this last fact when, the
next morning, no news coming of the absentees, he was
impelled to question his flock somewhat precisely concerning them. There was the usual shy silence which follows
a general inquiry from the teacher's desk; the children
looked at one another, giggled nervously, and said nothing.

"Can you give me any idea what might have kept
them away?" said the master.

Hanky Rogers looked quickly around, began, "Playin'
hook —" in a loud voice, but stopped suddenly without
finishing the word, and became inaudible. The master
saw fit to ignore him.

"Bee-huntin'," said Annie Roker, vivaciously.

"Who is?" asked the master.

"Provy Smith, of course. Allers bee-huntin'. Gets lots o' honey. Got two full combs in his desk last week. He's awful on bees and honey. Ain't he, Jinny?" This in a high voice to her sister.

The younger Miss Roker, thus appealed to, was heard to murmur that of all the sneakin' bee-hunters she had ever seed, Provy Smith was the worst. "And squirrels — for nuts," she added.

The master became attentive — a clue seemed probable here. "Would Tribbs and Fleming be likely to go with him?" he asked.

A significant silence followed. The master felt that the children recognized a doubt of this, knowing the boys were not "chums"; possibly they also recognized something incriminating to them, and with characteristic freemasonry looked at one another and were dumb.

But the next morning he was both astounded and relieved, at the assembling of school, to find the three truants back in their places. His urgent questioning of them brought only the one and same response from each — "Got lost on the ridge." He further gathered that they had slept out for two nights, and were together all the time, but nothing further, and no details were given. The master was puzzled. They evidently expected punishment; that was no doubt also the wish of their parents; but if their story was true, it was a serious question if he ought to inflict it. There was no means of testing their statement; there was equally none by which he could controvert it. It was evident that the whole school accepted it without doubt; whether they were in possession of details gained from the truants themselves which they had withheld from him, or whether from some larger complicity with the culprits, he could not say. He told them gravely that he should withhold equally their punishment and their pardon until he could satisfy himself of their truthfulness and that there had been no premeditation in their act. They seemed relieved, but here again he could not tell whether their relief sprang from confidence in their own integrity or merely from youthful hopefulness that delayed retribution never arrived!

It was a month before their secret was fully disclosed. It was slowly evolved from corroborating circumstances, but always with a shy reluctance from the boys themselves, and a surprise that anyone should think it of importance. It was gathered partly from details picked up at recess or on the playground, from the voluntary testimony of teamsters and packers, from a record in the county newspaper, but always shaping itself into a consecutive and harmonious narrative.

It was a story so replete with marvelous escape and adventure that the master hesitated to accept it in its entirety until after it had long become a familiar history, and was even forgotten by the actors themselves. And even now he transcribes it more from the circumstances that surrounded it than from a hope that the story will be believed.

WHAT HAPPENED

Master Provy Smith had started out that eventful morning with the intention of fighting Master Jackson

Tribbs for the "Kingship" of Table Ridge — a trifling
territory of ten leagues square — Tribbs having infringed
on his boundaries and claimed absolute sovereignty over
the whole mountain range. Julian Fleming was present
as referee and bottle-holder. The battleground selected
was the highest part of the ridge. The hour was six
o'clock, which would allow them time to reach school
before its opening, with all traces of their conflict removed. The air was crisp and cold — a trifle colder than
usual — and there was a singular thickening of the sun's
rays on the ridge, which made the distant peaks in-
distinct and ghostlike. However, the two combatants
stripped, and Fleming patronizingly took position at the
"corner," leaning upon a rifle, which, by reason of his
superior years, and the wilderness he was obliged to trav-
erse in going to school, his father had lent him to carry.
It was that day a providential weapon.

Suddenly Fleming uttered the word "Sho!" The two
combatants paused in their first squaring off to see, to
their surprise, that their referee had faced round, with
his gun in his hand, and was staring in another direction.

"B'ar!" shouted the three voices together. A huge
bear, followed by its cubs, was seen stumbling awkwardly
away to the right, making for the timber below. In an
instant the boys had hurried into their jackets again, and
the glory of fight was forgotten in the fever of the chase.
Why should they pound each other when there was something to really *kill?* They started in instant pursuit,
Julian leading.

But the wind was now keen and bitter in their faces,

and that peculiar thickening of the air which they had noticed had become first a dark blue and then a whitening pall, in which the bear was lost. They still kept on. Suddenly Julian felt himself struck between the eyes by what seemed a snowball, and his companions were as quickly spattered by gouts of monstrous clinging snowflakes. Others as quickly followed — it was not snowing, it was snowballing. They at first laughed, affecting to fight back against these whirling, flying masses shaken like clinging feathers from a pillow; but in a few seconds they were covered from head to foot by snow, their limbs impeded or pinioned against them by its weight, their breath gone. They stopped blindly, breathlessly. Then with a common instinct, they turned back. But the next moment they heard Julian cry, "Look out!" Coming towards them out of the storm was the bear, who had evidently turned back by the same instinct. An ungovernable instinct seized the younger boys, and they fled. But Julian stopped with leveled rifle. The bear stopped too, with sullen, staring eyes. But the eyes that glanced along the rifle were young, true, and steady. Julian fired. The hot smoke was swept back by the gale into his face, but the bear turned and disappeared in the storm again. Julian ran on to where his companions had halted at the report, a little ashamed of their cowardice. "Keep on that way!" he shouted hoarsely. "No use tryin' to go where the b'ar couldn't. Keep on!"

"Keep on — whar? There ain't no trail — no nuthin'!" said Jackson, querulously, to hold down a rising fear. It was true. The trail had long since disappeared; even their footprints of a moment before were filled up by the piling snow; they were isolated in this stony upland, high in air, without a rock or tree to guide them across its vast white level. They were bitterly cold and benumbed. The stimulus of the storm and chase had passed, but Julian kept driving them before him, himself driven along by the furious blast, yet trying to keep some vague course along the waste. So an hour passed. Then the wind seemed to have changed, or else they had traveled in a circle — they knew not which, but the snow was in their faces now. But, worst of all, the snow had changed too; it no longer fell in huge blue flakes, but in millions of stinging gray particles. Julian's face grew hard and his eyes bright. He knew it was no longer a snow-squall, but a lasting storm. He stopped; the boys tumbled against him. He looked at them with a strange smile.

"Hev you two made up?" he said.

"No — o!"

"Make up, then."

"What?"

"Shake hands!"

They clasped each other's red benumbed fingers and laughed, albeit a little frightened at Julian. "Go on!" he said curtly.

They went on dazedly, stupidly, for another hour.

Suddenly Provy Smith's keen eyes sparkled. He pointed to a singular irregular mound of snow before them, plainly seen above the dreary level. Julian ran to it with a cry, and began wildly digging. "I knew I hit him," he cried, as he brushed the snow from a huge and hairy leg. It was the bear — dead, but not yet cold. He had succumbed with his huge back to the blast, the snow piling a bulwark

behind him, where it had slowly roofed him in. The
half-frozen lads threw themselves fearlessly against his
furry coat and crept between his legs, nestling themselves
beneath his still warm body with screams of joy. The
snow they had thrown back increased the bulwark, and,
drifting over it, in a few moments enclosed them in a
thin shell of snow. Thoroughly exhausted, after a few
grunts of satisfaction a deep sleep fell upon them, from
which they were only awakened by the pangs of hunger.
Alas! their dinners — the school dinners — had been left
on the inglorious battlefield. Nevertheless, they talked
of eating the bear if it came to the worst. They would
have tried it even then, but they were far above the belt
of timber; they had matches — what boy has not? —
but no wood. Still, they were reassured, and even delighted, with this prospect, and so fell asleep again, stew-
ing with the dead bear in the snow, and woke up in the
morning ravenous, yet to see the sun shining in their
faces through the melted snow, and for Jackson Tribbs
quickly to discover, four miles away as the crow flies,
the cabin of his father among the flaming sumacs.

They started up in the glare of the sun, which at first
blinded them. They then discovered that they were in
a depression of the tableland that sloped before them to
a deep gully in the mountainside, which again dropped
into the canyon below. The trail they had lost, they
now remembered, must be near this edge. But it was
still hidden, and in seeking it there was danger of some
fatal misstep in the treacherous snow. Nevertheless,
they sallied out bravely; they would gladly have stopped
to skin the bear, but Julian's mandate was peremp-

tory. They spread themselves along the ridge, at times scraping the loose snow away in their search for the lost trail.

Suddenly they all slipped and fell, but rose again quickly, laughing. Then they slipped and fell again, but this time with the startling consciousness that it was not *they* who had slipped — but *the snow!* As they regained their feet they could plainly see now that a large crack on the white field, some twenty feet in width, extended between them and the carcass of the bear, showing the glistening rock below. Again they were thrown down with a sharp shock. Jackson Tribbs, who had been show-ing a strange excitement, suddenly gave a cry of warning. "Lie flat, fellers! but keep a-crawlin' and jumpin'. We're goin' down a slide!" And the next moment they were sliding and tossing, apparently with the whole snow field, down towards the gullied precipice.

What happened after this, and how long it lasted, they never knew. For, hurried along, with increasing speed, but always mechanically clutching at the snow, and bounding from it as they swept on, they sometimes lost breath, and even consciousness. At times they were half suffocated in rolling masses of drift, and again free and skimming over its arrested surface, but always falling, as it seemed to them, almost perpendicularly. In one of these shocks they seemed to be going through a thicket of underbrush — but Provy Smith knew that they were the tops of pine trees. At last there was one shock longer and lasting, followed by a deepening thunder below them. The avalanche had struck a ledge in the mountainside, and precipitated its lower part into the valley.

Then everything was still, until Provy heard Julian's voice calling. He answered, but there was no response from Tribbs. Had he gone over into the valley? They set up a despairing shout! A voice — a smothered one — that might be his, came apparently from the snow beneath them. They shouted again; the voice, vague and hollow, responded, but it was now surely his.

"Where are you?" screamed Provy.

"Down the chimbley."

There was a black square of adobe sticking out of the snow near them. They ran to it. There was a hole. They peered down, but could see nothing at first but a faint glimmer.

"Come down, fellows! It ain't far!" said Tribbs' voice.

"Wot yer got there?" asked Julian, cautiously.

"Suthin' to eat."

That was enough. In another instant Julian and Provy went down the chimney. What was a matter of fifteen feet after a thousand? Tribbs had already lit a candle, by which they could see that they were in the cabin of some tunnel-man at work on the ridge. He had probably been in the tunnel when the avalanche fell, and escaped, though his cabin was buried. The three discoverers helped themselves to his larder. They laughed and ate as at a picnic, played cards, pretended it was a robber's cave, and finally, wrapping themselves in the miner's blankets, slept soundly, knowing where they were, and confident that they could find the trail early the next morning. They did so, and, without going to their homes, came directly to school, having been absent about fifty hours. They were in high spirits — except for the thought of approaching punishment, never dreaming to evade it by anything miraculous in their adventures.

Such was briefly their story. Its truth was shown by the discovery of the bear's carcass, by the testimony of the tunnel-man, who found his larder mysteriously ransacked in his buried cabin, and, above all, by the long white tongue that for many months hung from the ledge into the valley. Nobody thought the lanky Julian a hero — least of all himself. Nobody suspected that Jackson Tribbs' treatment of a "slide" had been gathered from experiments in his father's "runs" — and he was glad they did not. The master's pardon obtained, the three truants cared little for the opinion of Hemlock Hill. They knew *themselves;* that was enough.

UNUSUAL WORDS

complicity — a sharing of guilt

controvert — deny

corroborating — (from corroborating circumstances) from circumstances which proved the thing to be true

deficit — lack, shortage

derelicts — persons who abandon their duty, or who have become incapacitated for doing it

incriminating — (something incriminating to them) something which caused them to be blamed

querulously — complainingly

retribution — punishment

transcribe — to copy in writing

Questions for Self-Testing

1. What effect does the absence of the three truants have on the rest of the school?
2. When the boys return, how do they account for their absence?
3. When the bear appears, how do the two younger boys act?
4. The trail being lost and the weather very cold, what keeps the boys from freezing to death in the snow?
5. When they wake after their night's sleep in the snow, what heartening sight do they see?
6. What does Jackson Tribbs warn the other two to do when they are caught in the snowslide?
7. Where has he learned what to do in a slide?
8. When the slide ended, what had become of Jackson?
9. How does he persuade his two companions to follow him?
10. When their story finally becomes known, what evidence proves it to be true?

Topics for Themes or Discussion

1. What, if anything, in this story lets you know that it was written half a century ago?
2. Why did Julian order the other two boys to shake hands?
3. What do you learn about the teacher?
4. Do the boys and girls in the schoolroom (not the absentees) seem to you lifelike? Has Bret Harte found the right reasons for their hesitation to answer the teacher?
5. Write Jackson Tribbs' account of his adventures as he tells them to his bosom friend, Johnny Stebbins.
6. Explain how the boys kept from being smothered in the snowslide.

GUESTS IN THE SMOKEHOUSE

By CORNELIA MEIGS

Before the Civil War slavery was recognized as lawful in the United States. There were, however, some people so opposed to it that they were willing to endanger their lives and property for the sake of helping runaway slaves to escape. The Underground Railway which is spoken of in this story was really not a railway at all but a series of hiding places maintained by these devoted people. Runaways were sent from one to the next till at last they could be slipped across the Canadian border into freedom.

In this narrative the persons in hiding are not colored; they are white Quakers who had endangered themselves by having helped escaping slaves. And the interest of the story lies as much in the way an indifferent boy is turned into a white-hot Underground Railroader as it does in the account of how he saves the two Quakers.

Cornelia Meigs, the author, is one of the best known writers of stories for boys and girls in America. Another story of hers appears later in this volume.

THE BROAD lake at the foot of Mt. Neshobe had been swept by the bitter wind until it was bare of snow, a smooth expanse of blue ice which reached away northward, winding and turning among the rocky spurs of the mountain. For more than an hour Richard Kent could see it spread out below as the sleigh, with its two fast, big, jingling horses, swung down the road cut from the steep hillside. The boy had the feeling, as he looked about him, that the Vermont hills were familiar and friendly and yet totally strange, since, although he had seen them every summer for nearly ten years, he had never before looked at their ridges and sharp summits in the winter, when their abrupt slopes were blanketed with hard-frozen snow instead of being shrouded in the abundant leafy green of the summer forests. The sky was gray behind the mountain tops, for it had snowed yesterday and would, in all probability, snow again before tomorrow. Richard burrowed a little deeper into the warm buffalo robes at the thought of it.

"We are lucky to find the way open," his Uncle Nathan observed, shifting his cold hands to get a new grip on the reins. "One more storm and the whole lake valley will be blocked."

Richard looked up at him, an erect, surprising figure with his tall, bell-crowned hat and close-fitting, caped greatcoat. He seemed curiously out of place, the boy thought vaguely, against that wild landscape of hill and snowdrift. Uncle Nathan Kent was always dressed just as a prosperous lawyer of the 1850's should be garbed, although just now he would have been more comfortable if he had buttoned himself into the old coat which Uncle Hiram Kent had sent along with the sleigh to meet the travelers, a coat which had belonged to a black bear before it had become Uncle Hiram's.

It was strange, also, Richard kept feeling, to be driving this last twenty miles of the accustomed journey without Uncle Hiram's cheerful presence, for it was his delighted face which they always saw first of all when they got down at the coaching station, stiff from the long ride up from Massachusetts. Travel was not easy in those days before the Civil War, but there was no difficulty too great to keep Richard from coming, summer after summer, to spend his vacation on the Vermont farm where his father and his two uncles had all grown up. Nathan and Thomas Kent, Richard's father, had long since made successful places for themselves in a Massachusetts manufacturing town and often wondered aloud how their elder brother could cling so stubbornly to those rocky acres above

Neshobe Lake. Richard had wondered, too — until last summer. It was then that some inkling of an astonishing truth had suddenly burst upon him.

It had been a warm day, hot for Vermont, with brilliant sunshine everywhere, the most complete contrast to the present bleak afternoon. He and Selina had been picking summer apples, Selina being the lively granddaughter of that elderly cousin who kept house for Uncle Hiram. Selina lived the year round on the mountain farm; her cheerful company was always a taken-for-granted part of Richard's vacations. They were both tired on that afternoon, and a little dazzled by the bright sun. Richard, carrying the bushel basket of apples into the kitchen, was moved by a sudden fancy to seek the coolness of the dark cellar. He slipped down the stairs — groping, for he was quite blind in the dimness — and heard, all at once, under the vaulted arch of the farthest recess, the stirring of a big body and a great voice sunk to a thick whisper saying:

"Is you coming to take me out of here, Mars'er Kent? Isn't you going to get me out of this pretty soon?"

He retreated abruptly, but stood for a long minute at the foot of the stairs, his heart hammering in his ears. Everything was still now, but Richard still thought that he could hear, from that far, dusky corner, a faint sound as of some great body trying to keep utterly silent, trying even to breathe as lightly as possible. Should he go forward boldly into the dark and demand who or what was there? Something kept him back, and it was not fear. This was Uncle Hiram's secret, and prying curiosity might bring disaster. He turned about and stumbled up the stairs. Out in the sunny orchard, Selina was still sitting, leaning against a twisted trunk with a yellow apple in her hand. Forbearance had its limits, nor could he have possibly helped putting that breathless question:

"Selina, what's — what's that in the cellar?"

Selina looked at him steadily. She was a year older than he; she had honest blue eyes which could, when she chose, be very determined in the guarding of secrets.

"I'm not to tell you," she answered. She set her lips resolutely, as though she were issuing the order to herself and not to him. "I — I only found out by accident, and Uncle Hiram knows I know, but we don't speak of it. My grandmother has never guessed, but I think Uncle Nathan has, and that he argues with Uncle Hiram about its being wrong."

This baffling statement was far from giving Richard satisfaction, but she told him no more, except to burst out a moment later, "Do you think, when your father and Uncle Nathan have done so much, away from here, that Uncle Hiram has stayed behind for nothing else than to grow hay and potatoes on this stony mountain? Did you ever think that he might be doing something special, too, that the others didn't even dare to think about?"

The time for Richard's departure came so soon after that day that he had little time to push the matter any further. He did slip into the cellar again, but realized from the very feel of the cool shadowy emptiness that there was now no presence there save his own. More than once he looked into Uncle Hiram's kind, sun-browned face and longed to frame a question, but went away without ever having found words for it.

During the next winter there was news that Uncle
Hiram was less well than usual, crippled by rheumatism,
an ancient and stoutly contested enemy. It was on an
evening in early January that Uncle Nathan, immaculate
in blue broadcloth and bright buttons, came to confer
with Richard's father. Although it was still a number
of years before the Civil War, the shadow of that great
upheaval was already on the horizon, and the question
of slavery was drawing closer and closer to the hearts
and souls of all citizens of the United States. It was
not surprising, therefore, that the two Kent brothers
plunged immediately into discussing the new laws which
had to do with runaway slaves. What was odd was that
Uncle Nathan should say suddenly in the midst of the
heated talk, "I'm going up to see Hiram. I can get
there, even through the snow. I worry about him more
every day. I wrote him, and I am starting next week."

A few days later there came, rather surprisingly, a
letter to Richard from Selina. She wrote very seldom
and only when she had something particular to say.
"When Uncle Nathan comes up," she directed now, "ask
to come with him. I believe Uncle Hiram needs you."
She had signed her name with proper messages and then
added: "Do you remember that secret about the cellar?
If ever Uncle Hiram told anyone about it of his own will,
I do believe, Richard, that it would be you."

Richard had never been to the farm in winter, but
there proved to be little difficulty in getting permission
to go. Uncle Nathan was glad to have company on the
stage journey, and it was holiday time from school. So
here were uncle and nephew, driving down the freshly

plowed road, with old Silas, who had brought the sleigh to meet them, tucked up in the back seat. Uncle Nathan, in spite of his elaborate clothes and manners, had not been brought up on a Vermont farm for nothing. He could not bear to drive behind a good pair of horses unless he held the reins himself. It was he who had taught Richard to drive, so that the boy now could appreciate the adroit skill with which his uncle eased the big grays down abrupt drops in the road and around the high-banked curves.

At a narrow place the sound of bells coming toward them made them pull up suddenly. A smaller sleigh drew out to make room for them to pass, and one of the two men in it first hailed Uncle Nathan, and then got down, knee deep in the drifts, to come over to speak to him. Richard had seen the rough-hewn face before, and knew that this was John Halloway, a neighbor of Uncle Hiram's and the sheriff of that county.

"Coming up to see Hiram Kent, be ye?" he asked. When Uncle Nathan answered yes, he went on in a lowered voice: "Just you tell Hiram, from me, that I've had orders to watch him." He jerked his head toward the other man in the smaller sleigh, a stranger with a narrow face sunk deep into the warmth of his big coat. "That fellow there is from down southward, a slave owners' agent, sent up to try to get back runaway property. You see it's my place to show him around, whether I like it or not. It's beyond my duty to say much, but you ask Hiram Kent just to read over the text of the Fugitive Slave Law. That's all."

He turned about hastily, climbed into his sleigh, and

slapped the reins over the horses' backs. Uncle Nathan drove on, looking straight ahead and making no comment upon the message. Richard, after glancing back to observe, as he had expected, that Silas was napping in the rear seat, asked abruptly, "Uncle Nathan, just what is the Fugitive Slave Law?"

"It's a regulation put through Congress by the men who support slavery," his uncle returned. "It says that any person who finds a runaway slave must return him to his master, or help to do so, otherwise he will be liable to arrest and fines. The owners of plantations in the South are complaining loudly over the number of runaways who have been smuggled all the way north as far as Canada."

"Are they free when they get to Canada?" Richard asked.

"They are," answered his uncle and concluded grimly, "The Canadian line, you may remember, is just forty miles from your Uncle Hiram's farm."

"Oh," was all that Richard could say, and was silent for a long time.

It had begun to snow when they drew up at the farm gate, but it was still light enough to see the row of buildings sheltered under the wall of the mountain — the big barns, the square brick smokehouse where the meat was cured for winter use, the long woodshed adjoining the broad, bright-windowed farmhouse itself. Selina was on the step to greet them and bring them in to the blazing fire.

"Uncle Hiram can't come down," she said, "and he wants you to have supper before you come up. You must be starving."

Selina and her grandmother had set forth a real banquet of country fare to which Richard did ample justice, but which seemed scarcely to tempt Uncle Nathan. He hurried through it and got up abruptly, just as Selina was bringing in the pumpkin pie. "I am going up to see my brother," he said. "You finish your supper, Richard, and come later when I call you."

The bountiful meal had long been over and the dishes washed and put away before Richard heard Uncle Nathan's voice summoning him upstairs. Cousin Sarah, Selina's grandmother, had been in the room all the time, so that Selina had said nothing to him in private. But as he mounted the stair the words of her letter were burning within him — "Uncle Hiram needs you. If he ever tells anyone, of his own will, it would be you."

The eldest of the Kent brothers was sitting close to the narrow fireplace which was all that gave warmth to the big, low-ceiled room. Hiram was taller than his brother Nathan, with a broader forehead and deeper, brighter eyes; with a general air of character and command which Nathan Kent, at that moment, seemed to lack. He stood behind his older brother and, in spite of his well-cut coat and his manner of ease and self-confidence, he was, very distinctly, less of a man than this crumpled giant who sat helpless in the great wooden chair. Hiram Kent sat looking at his nephew with twinkling gray eyes, but waited, obviously, for his brother to speak.

"You have surely guessed by now, Richard, what has brought me here — the fact that your Uncle Hiram has been smuggling slaves over the border into Canada, and the need of warning him that he is in danger. Such folly has to be stopped; he is under suspicion already. Even you can add a word. We can save him from his wrong-headed mistakes if we can make him listen to reason."

He walked toward the door, seeming to grow of more consequence the farther he got from that strangely power-ful presence beside the fire. "I have used every argument I can to you," he concluded. "Any sane man can see the danger and what the end will be. I have nothing more to say."

He went out, and Richard came forward to sit on the stool beside the fire. For some minutes the burning wood snapped and crackled and neither of the two spoke.

"Selina sent for you?" Uncle Hiram began at last. "Selina is a wise girl. It is quite true that someone must save me tonight; must save me — and two others. This rheumatism has caught me at a bad moment. I can't leave my chair — and it's forty miles to Canada."

Richard had been sitting with his hands clasped be-tween his knees and his eyes on the floor. He looked up startled; Uncle Hiram gave him the quick flash of a smile and went on, "I can't ask you to involve yourself, Richard. Your Uncle Nathan is sensible and cautious; you will have to stand on his side or mine. You can try to save me from what he calls my folly, or you can save me where I have given my promise that another shall get away to safety. It is our fault, every living Ameri-can's fault, that anything so hideous as slavery exists. It will continue to be our fault until we find some way to be rid of it. Mine is not a good way, Richard, I admit

that; but it is, so far, the best way open. Now think a
little and choose. Don't decide too —"

They were interrupted by a sudden disturbance below,
by voices in the lower hall, and, a moment later, by
Uncle Nathan's bursting into the room. "It's as I told
you," he cried, his voice high with excitement. "John
Holloway gave you one warning; what he could not tell
you was that he was on his way to the village to take out
a search warrant. He's here now with the slave owners'
agent, a fellow named Atkins. They have authority to
search the farm for runaway slaves and they're going to
do it."

"Let them," returned Uncle Hiram easily and quite
unmoved. "Give them the freedom of the place and tell
them to look anywhere they want. But ask Sarah to
give them some hot supper and have Selina light the fire
in the front bedroom. They'll have to stay the night,
with it snowing the way it is. A lot of guests we have
this evening, for a quiet place like Neshobe Mountain
Farm!" As Richard went downstairs to carry the message to the women he heard Hiram Kent chuckling.

As he came into the big kitchen, he saw that John
Holloway was taking a lamp from the table. "We can't
waste any time," Holloway was saying in an undertone
to his companion, Atkins, "especially after what we
heard in the village of what had been seen up here."
He led the way down a dark passage. Richard, unfor-
bidden, came after the two, and Selina followed behind.

They went thoroughly up and down the whole of the
rambling old house, poked their heads into closets, tapped
on walls, flashed the light into dark places behind stairs.

Richard stayed behind when they pushed into Uncle Hiram's room, but he heard cheerful voices and saw that both the men were laughing as they came out. He held his breath as they descended into the cellar. Here were a hundred shadows and hidden places, but search revealed them all as empty. For the first time he saw the big, arched niche from which he had heard that whispered voice the summer before. Nothing was there now save sacks of apples and a row of golden squashes. They all came tramping up the stairs again, with the long shadows trailing behind them.

The men armed themselves with lanterns before they sallied out to examine the barns, Richard and Selina still bringing up the rear. There was little wind, but the snow was coming down in a smooth white curtain, with the air feeling soft and moist. The slave agent shivered and drew his big coat closer about him. "Hideous weather you have in this wilderness," he observed, but he followed stoutly as John Holloway led the way.

It was a long journey all through the great barns, past the stalls where cows were munching comfortably in the dark or where a startled horse, now and again, stamped and rolled a bright eye in the lantern light. In the farthest corner of the loft, where Richard and Selina had played when they were smaller, the expedition came to a brief halt. A ladder reached up to the rafters — a rather tall one which neither of the men seemed anxious to climb.

"Just get up there, Richard," directed Holloway, "and flash the light into that space between the beams."

As the boy hesitated, hoping to exchange glances with Selina and get a signal as to whether he would betray some desperate hiding place, the agent, Atkins, cut in roughly, "What are you waiting for when you have your orders? Don't you know what the law says, that any citizen, anywhere, can be summoned by an officer to help recover a runaway slave? Get up there of yourself or we'll make you."

Sudden, blind fury seized Richard. The man had thrust the lantern into his hand, but he threw it down as he cried hotly, "I won't go. You can't force me to go." He turned about and swung toward the stairs.

"Gently, there, gently, young man," came the sheriff's big voice as he caught up the lantern. "You don't want to burn down Hiram Kent's barn, no matter who is in it. Well, since no one else will, I'll just climb up myself." Glancing over his shoulder, Richard saw the tall man go clambering up the ladder, saw him lift the lantern high to illuminate the dark space and saw, with a gasp of relief, that it was unoccupied. He did not wait, but flung himself down the narrow stair and out of the big door. He breathed deeply of the cold wet air, so different from the warm, hay-perfumed atmosphere within.

There had been some doubt in his mind as he listened to Uncle Nathan and Uncle Hiram — a wonder as to who was right; whether Uncle Hiram was wrong in running his whole household into danger by giving shelter to fugitive slaves. Uncle Nathan was very plausible, but his words no longer carried weight with Richard — not in the face of a law which not only dragged an escaped slave back into captivity, but even haled every free man into taking part in such cruelty. He stood a minute, seeing only faintly the bulk of the buildings about him, knowing that those great familiar mountains were all around — watching him, he almost felt, through the curtain of the dark; watching to see his mettle tried and his courage tested. He would not fail; his mind was made up now; he would help Uncle Hiram to the utmost that was in him.

He turned and saw the lights bobbing toward him from the barn. Selina, wrapped in an old shawl, came to stand beside him while the men strode past through the snow. "Here's one place we haven't looked," Richard heard Atkins say as they passed the brick smokehouse a few yards from the kitchen steps.

The sheriff fumbled at the low oak door, opened it and let out the dull glow of a smoldering fire and the sharp smell of smoke. "No one could abide in that stifling place," he said decisively. "We can be certain there's nothing here, at least."

They went up the steps, opened the kitchen door, showing a stream of ruddy light, and closed it. Even in the shrouding darkness Richard did not dare speak above a whisper, close to Selina. "Whatever has to be done, I am going to do it."

He could just see that she nodded. "You'll have to help. There are two here, and Uncle Hiram can't stir from his chair. I know how to tell you just what to do. But oh, Richard, are you sure?"

"Yes," he answered resolutely. "I'm sure — now." Whatever his Uncle Hiram had dared and accomplished, Richard Kent would do also.

Selina turned about, lifted the latch of the smokehouse door and opened it. She bent her head to the choking smoke within, but pushed forward into the blackness, Richard behind her. An inner door swung open under her hand, through which they stepped and closed quickly behind them. Nobody ever could have guessed that the square smokehouse contained not one room, but a second also, reached through the forbidding interior of the first. There must have been hidden slits at the edge of the roof; for there were no windows in the blank, brick walls, yet it was a comfortable place, spotlessly clean with its own fireplace and burning logs upon the small hearth.

Richard had not known what to expect, but he was completely unprepared for what he saw — a tall, grave-faced man who seemed of the same sort as Uncle Hiram himself, and a neat little lady garbed in gray, whose thin white hands were busy with knitting as she sat beside the fire. They were Quakers from Pennsylvania, they explained to him, friends of Hiram Kent for years, but through correspondence only; for they, at their end, shared in that slave-smuggling traffic which history has called the Underground Railroad. These two, so quiet in their manner, so bold and flagrant in their defiance of injustice, had finally been under such suspicion that they were forced to flee, also, to escape imprisonment and prosecution.

"Thee understands that there was nothing more that we could do for the poor blacks," the little lady said gently, "so it has seemed best for us to go away into Canada while we could. Some day we will come back and begin again in another place. Good friends have seen us thus far on our journey, and it is almost ended."

"Uncle Hiram only just finished building this room

last autumn," Selina told them, "and you are the first to hide in it. He laid the first bricks the day the Fugitive Slave Law was brought up in Congress."

She had slipped out and returned, her arms laden with coats and blankets. She held out to Richard Uncle Hiram's bearskin coat and put his fur cap into her cousin's hands. While the other two were making ready, the boy and girl emerged again into the snow and took their way toward the barn. She was giving rapid and detailed directions as they went.

"You will have to drive on the ice; the road is blocked. Get well out into the middle and then face north. Uncle Hiram has sent you down his compass and says you are to put a lantern under the buffalo robe. That will keep your feet warm, at least."

They came within the cavernous door of the barn. Richard knew at once which sleigh to take and understood now why Uncle Hiram kept that team of swift black horses, too light for farm work. He backed one out of its stall and Selina the other, and the two harnessed quickly as they so often had done in the summer. Selina was continuing those directions which it was not safe to seek at first hand from Hiram Kent. "It's twenty miles you have to go, to Seth Bronson's house, on the shore beyond Goose Neck Point. You remember that we sailed there last summer and the summer before. You must bear in toward shore as you pass the point, and when you get near enough you will see two lights shining from Seth's house for a signal. He will take Uncle Hiram's friends the rest of the way. This is the hardest and most dangerous part of the journey, for it is the one the government men are watching, since they suspect Uncle Hiram."

So many times had they harnessed together that both finished at exactly the same moment. The sleigh runners grated on the board floor, then glided out across the snow. In the recessed door of the smokehouse stood the Quaker pair, muffled to the eyes. The bright windows of the main house showed where the two officials were settling to an evening by the fire, with no intention of leaving shelter again that night.

The little lady murmured a word or two as she got in. "Tell thy uncle — just bless him, that is all."

Richard was in his place with Selina looking up at him through the veil of white flakes. At the last moment misgivings seemed to have seized her. "Are you sure you can find the way?" she asked desperately.

"Yes," he nodded answer. "I will find it." He could see the two big pines which marked the track that led down to the shore. The little black Morgan mare pawed with anxiety to be off, partaking, as horses love to do, in the excitement of the errand. The sleigh slipped between the pines and the house with all its cheerful lights disappeared from view behind the swirling curtain of snow.

A frozen lake makes a magnificent highroad. The horses tugged at the bits as they swung into their course northward. Now and then the two in the rear seat stirred — from this time on, their liberty and even their lives depended on what Richard could do. The team was galloping wildly; now their pace increased and it was almost as though they were running away, only in this vast emptiness there was little sense of speed; no feeling of danger at all. He knew he must hold the horses; that otherwise they would exhaust themselves long before the journey's end. He braced his feet, took an iron grasp of the reins and drew them down to a more reasonable pace, although they still plunged forward the moment his hold relaxed.

They went on for hours; for untold time, it seemed to Richard. Once the snowfall lightened a little and he caught sight of a wooded island just where he had thought it ought to be. The white blanket came down again — still without wind, but with a steady, merciless increase of cold. His feet ached, his hands were numb, his arms up to his elbows were stiff as stone. The smaller of his two passengers had slipped down, completely hidden under the blankets. He heard a despairing voice behind him.

"Are we nearly there? I know thee is doing all thee can, but my poor wife — she can bear little more."

"It's not far now." His lips were so rigid that he could hardly make the words. He looked down at the compass; the needle was just visible. Then the lantern went out; the oil was spent. From that time on he drove blindly, so cold and exhausted that he did not know, and seemed scarcely to care, whether the way was right or not. A dark line of trees rose up before him. This was Goose Neck Point, or else he was hopelessly lost. He bore away to one side, but the line of trees seemed to have no end. He was lost — he wasn't — he was — Suddenly beyond the last tree there was an opening. He rounded into it and saw a pair of twinkling lights, Seth Bronson's signal.

It was the horses, who had been on that errand before, who found their own path up to the house and stopped before a snowdrifted door. It was thrown open as Richard got down, a wooden thing without feeling or joints. He indicated the heap of robes in the back of the sleigh. "Carry her in," he said hoarsely, not knowing his own voice. "I will get the horses into the barn."

They know in Vermont how to revive half-frozen travelers; they have so often had need to do so. Richard, warmed, fed, assured of the well-being of his fellow travelers, slept the day out until late afternoon. The storm had cleared when he came out again, the cold had softened, the black team, sobered to reason, trotted steadily with the sure pull of horses going home. The stars rode high, then began to sink, and the yellow winter dawn was showing behind Neshobe Mountain when he came in sight of Hiram Kent's farm.

The dark gables of the house and the tall bare elms showed plainly against the white hillside. There was a light in one window, growing fainter as the day brightened. Was it Selina's lamp, set there to guide him home? No, this was the upper chamber, where Uncle Hiram sat crippled in his great chair. Suddenly it came to Richard that his part in the work had been small and Hiram Kent's infinitely great. All the responsibility, many times the risk, had been Uncle Hiram's in planning this thing which must be done and done again and again — "until we find some way to be rid of slavery." Instead of excitement and striving and the thrill of triumph to repay him for the danger, he must simply sit and wait in pain and straining anxiety, while his own safety and Richard's and that of the two whom he had promised to save were all thrust into totally inexperienced hands.

It was certain that Uncle Hiram had sat there by the fire through both nights of waiting, watching the lamp, trying to pierce the darkness beyond the window. Richard could see now, even at this distance, that the front door opened and a small figure which must be Selina's stood upon the step. It disappeared instantly and a moment later the light in the window went out. The gold of the sky behind the mountains was so bright now that it was no longer needed; the messenger had come safely home and the task was finished.

Selina came out to him as he was unharnessing the horses in the dusk of the barn. "Uncle Nathan stormed at first, when he found where you had gone," she told him, "but I think finally he was glad. He sat and talked with John Holloway and the other man, and never let them suspect."

The horses were fed and bedded and the two came out together into the white dooryard. Richard knew within himself that he was going to help Hiram Kent not this once, but many times, as long as there was need, until a great evil was brought to its end. The mountains, clear and white against a brilliant sky, were witnesses of how unshakable was his determination to bear his part in all that remained to be done.

QUESTIONS FOR SELF-TESTING

1. How did Richard first learn that his uncle helped run-away slaves to escape?
2. Why would Selina not tell him about the presence in the cellar?
3. How did his uncle answer Richard's question about the Fugitive Slave Law?
4. For what reason did Nathan Kent call Richard upstairs to talk with Hiram?
5. What was it which finally decided Richard to side with Hiram Kent instead of with Nathan?
6. What caused Hiram Kent to lay the first bricks of the hidden room in the smokehouse?
7. What had Hiram Kent been doing during the time Richard was gone?
8. Why did not the sheriff and his companion miss Richard after they went into the house?
9. By what means was Richard, half frozen and exhausted, finally brought to the right door at the end of his drive?

TOPICS FOR THEMES OR DISCUSSION

1. What is the first thing in this story which tells you that it belongs to the pre-Civil War time?
2. How did Richard happen to go to the farm in winter?
3. In some history of the United States or in an encyclopedia, look up the account of the passing of the Fugitive Slave Law and be prepared to tell the class about it.
4. When he was discussing with Richard his way of helping slaves to freedom, Hiram Kent said, "Mine is not a good way, Richard, I admit that." What were his reasons for saying this? Do you think what he said was true?
5. Write a character sketch of Selina.

QUITE SO

By Thomas Bailey Aldrich

Thomas Bailey Aldrich, author of "Quite So," was a man in his thirties at the time of the Civil War. In this story of the war, therefore, he is writing from his own observation of happenings and people. The picture he draws of army life in the 1860's, even more than the fate of Quite So, is what makes his rather old-fashioned writing interesting today.

What he shows us is the gypsy-like, open-air life lived by the Union army in the long intervals between battles, the jokes the soldiers played, the friends they found — and sometimes lost. Among the group of soldiers, Quite So moves silently about, never writing home, never receiving letters, never talking of himself or the life he led before the war, and by his silence gradually rousing the curiosity of all his mates.

Thomas Bailey Aldrich is best known for his Story of a Bad Boy *and for the surprise-ending story, "Marjorie Daw," found in* Marjorie Daw and Other Stories.

Of course that was not his name. Even in the
State of Maine, where it is still a custom to maim a child
for life by christening him Arioch or Shadrach or Ephraim,
nobody would dream of calling a boy "Quite So." It
was merely a nickname which we gave him in camp;
but it stuck to him with such burrlike tenacity, and is
so inseparable from my memory of him, that I do not
think I could write definitely of John Bladburn if I were
to call him anything but "Quite So."

It was one night shortly after the first battle of Bull
Run. The Army of the Potomac, shattered, stunned, and
forlorn, was back in its old quarters behind the earth-
works. The melancholy line of ambulances bearing our
wounded to Washington was not done creeping over Long
Bridge; the blue smocks and the gray still lay in wind-
rows on the field of Manassas; and the gloom that
weighed down our hearts was like the fog that stretched

along the bosom of the Potomac, and infolded the valley of the Shenandoah. A drizzling rain had set in at twilight, and, growing bolder with the darkness, was beating a dismal tattoo on the tent, — the tent of Mess 6, Company A, -th Regiment N. Y. Volunteers. Our mess, consisting originally of eight men, was reduced to four. Little Billy, as one of the boys grimly remarked, had concluded to remain at Manassas; Corporal Steele we had to leave at Fairfax Court House, shot through the hip; Hunter and Suydam we had said good-by to that afternoon. "Tell Johnny Reb," says Hunter, lifting up the leather sidepiece of the ambulance, "that I'll be back again as soon as I get a new leg." But Suydam said nothing; he only unclosed his eyes languidly and smiled farewell to us.

The four of us who were left alive and unhurt that shameful July day sat gloomily smoking our brierwood pipes, thinking our thoughts, and listening to the rain pattering against the canvas. That, and the occasional whine of a hungry cur, foraging on the outskirts of the camp for a stray bone, alone broke the silence, save when a vicious drop of rain detached itself from the ridgepole of the tent, and fell upon the wick of our tallow candle, making it "cuss," as Ned Strong described it. The candle was in the midst of one of its most profane fits when Blakely, knocking the ashes from his pipe and addressing no one in particular, but giving breath, unconsciously as it were, to the result of his cogitations, observed that "it was considerable of a fizzle."

"The 'on to Richmond' business?"

"Yes."

"I wonder what they'll do about it over yonder," said Curtis, pointing over his right shoulder. By "over yonder" he meant the North in general and Massachusetts especially. Curtis was a Boston boy, and his sense of locality was so strong that, during all his wanderings in Virginia, I do not believe there was a moment, day or night, when he could not have made a bee-line for Faneuil Hall.

"Do about it?" cried Strong. "They'll make about two hundred thousand blue flannel trousers and send them along, each pair with a man in it, — all the short men in the long trousers, and all the tall men in the short ones," he added, ruefully contemplating his own leg-gear, which scarcely reached to his ankles.

"That's so," said Blakely. "Just now, when I was tackling the commissary for an extra candle, I saw a crowd of new fellows drawing blankets."

"I say there, drop that!" cried Strong. "All right, sir, didn't know it was you," he added hastily, seeing it was Lieutenant Haines who had thrown back the flap of the tent, and let in a gust of wind and rain that threatened the most serious consequences to our discontented tallow dip.

"You're to bunk in here," said the lieutenant, speaking to someone outside. The someone stepped in, and Haines vanished in the darkness.

When Strong had succeeded in restoring the candle to consciousness, the light fell upon a tall, shy-looking man of about thirty-five, with long, hay-colored beard and mustache, upon which the raindrops stood in clusters, like the night-dew on patches of cobweb in a meadow.

It was an honest face, with unworldly sort of blue eyes, that looked out from under the broad visor of the infantry cap. With a deferential glance towards us, the newcomer unstrapped his knapsack, spread his blanket over it, and sat down unobtrusively.

"Rather damp night out," remarked Blakely, whose strong hand was supposed to be conversation.

"Quite so," replied the stranger, not curtly, but pleasantly, and with an air as if he had said all there was to be said about it.

"Come from the North recently?" inquired Blakely, after a pause.

"Yes."

"From any place in particular?"

"Maine."

"People considerably stirred up down there?" continued Blakely, determined not to give up.

"Quite so."

Blakely threw a puzzled look over the tent, and seeing Ned Strong on the broad grin, frowned severely. Strong instantly assumed an abstracted air, and began humming softly, *"I wish I was in Dixie."*

"The State of Maine," observed Blakely, with a certain defiance of manner not at all necessary in discussing a geographical question, "is a pleasant state."

"In summer," suggested the stranger.

"In summer, I mean," returned Blakely with animation, thinking he had broken the ice. "Cold as blazes in winter, though, — isn't it?"

The new recruit merely nodded.

Blakely eyed the man for a moment, and then, smiling one of those smiles of simulated gaiety which the novelists inform us are more tragic than tears, turned upon him with irony.

"Trust you left the old folks pretty comfortable?"

"Dead."

"The old folks dead!"

"Quite so."

Blakely made a sudden dive for his blanket, tucked it around him with painful precision, and was heard no more.

Just then the bugle sounded "lights out," — bugle answering bugle in far-off camps. When our not elaborate night toilets were complete, Strong threw somebody else's old boot at the candle with infallible aim, and darkness took possession of the tent. Ned, who lay on my left, presently reached over to me, and whispered, "I say, our friend 'quite so' is a garrulous old boy! He'll talk himself to death some of these odd times, if he isn't careful. How he *did* run on!"

The next morning, when I opened my eyes, the new member of Mess 6 was sitting on his knapsack, combing his blond beard with a horn comb. He nodded pleasantly to me, and to each of the boys as they woke up, one by one. Blakely did not appear disposed to renew the animated conversation of the previous night; but while he was gone to make a requisition for what was in pure sarcasm called coffee, Curtis ventured to ask the man his name.

"Bladburn, John," was the reply.

"That's rather an unwieldy name for everyday use,"

put in Strong. "If it wouldn't hurt your feelings, I'd like to call you Quite So, — for short. Don't say no, if you don't like it. Is it agreeable?"

Bladburn gave a little laugh, all to himself seemingly, and was about to say, "Quite so," when he caught at the words, blushed like a girl, and nodded a sunny assent to Strong. From that day until the end, the sobriquet clung to him.

The disaster at Bull Run was followed, as the reader knows, by a long period of masterly inactivity, so far as the Army of the Potomac was concerned. McDowell, a good soldier but unlucky, retired to Arlington Heights, and McClellan, who had distinguished himself in Western Virginia, took command of the forces in front of Washington, and bent his energies to reorganizing the demoralized troops. It was a dreary time to the people of the North, who looked fatuously from week to week for "the fall of Richmond"; and it was a dreary time to the denizens of that vast city of tents and forts which stretched in a semicircle before the beleaguered Capitol — so tedious and soul-wearing a time that the hardships of forced marches and the horrors of battle became desirable things to them.

Roll-call morning and evening, guard duty, dress parades, dominos, wrestling-matches, and such rude games as could be carried on in camp made up the sum of our lives. The arrival of the mail with letters and papers from home was the event of the day. We noticed that Bladburn neither wrote nor received any letters. When the rest of the boys were scribbling away for dear life, with drumheads and knapsacks and cracker boxes for writing desks, he would sit serenely smoking his pipe, but looking out on us through rings of smoke with a face expressive of the tenderest interest.

"Look here, Quite So," Strong would say, "the mail-bag closes in half an hour. Ain't you going to write?"

"I believe not today," Bladburn would reply, as if he had written yesterday, or would write tomorrow: but he never wrote.

He had become a great favorite with us, and with all the officers of the regiment. He talked less than any man I ever knew, but there was nothing sinister or sullen in his reticence. It was sunshine, — warmth and brightness, but no voice. Unassuming and modest to the verge of shyness, he impressed everyone as a man of singular pluck and nerve.

"Do you know," said Curtis to me one day, "that that fellow Quite So is clear grit, and when we come to close quarters with our Palmetto brethren over yonder, he'll do something devilish?"

"What makes you think so?"

"Well, nothing quite explainable; the exasperating coolness of the man as much as anything. This morning the boys were teasing Muffin Fan" (a small mulatto girl who used to bring muffins into camp three times a week, — at the peril of her life!) "and Jemmy Blunt of Company K — you know him — was rather rough on the girl, when Quite So, who had been reading under a tree, shut one finger in his book, walked over to where the boys were skylarking, and with the smile of a juvenile angel on his face lifted Jemmy out of that and set him down gently in front of his own tent. There Blunt sat speechless, staring at Quite So, who was back again under the tree, pegging away at his little Latin grammar."

That Latin grammar! He always had it about him, reading it or turning over its dog's-eared pages at odd intervals and in out-of-the-way places. Half a dozen times a day he would draw it out from the bosom of his blouse, which had taken the shape of the book just over the left breast, look at it as if to assure himself it was all right, and then put the thing back. At night the volume lay beneath his pillow. The first thing in the morning, before he was well awake, his hand would go groping instinctively under his knapsack in search of it.

Curiosity seized upon us boys concerning that Latin grammar, for we had discovered the nature of the book. Strong wanted to steal it one night, but concluded not to. "In the first place," reflected Strong, "I haven't the heart to do it, and in the next place I haven't the moral courage. Quite So would placidly break every bone in my body." And I believe Strong was not far out of the way.

Sometimes I was vexed with myself for allowing this tall, simple-hearted country fellow to puzzle me so much. And yet, was he a simple-hearted country fellow? City bred he certainly was not; but his manner, in spite of his awkwardness, had an indescribable air of refinement. Now and then, too, he dropped a word or a phrase that showed his familiarity with unexpected lines of reading. "The other day," said Curtis, with the slightest elevation of eyebrow, "he had the cheek to correct my Latin for me." In short, Quite So was a daily problem to the members of Mess 6. Whenever he was absent, and Blakely and Curtis and Strong and I got together in the tent, we discussed him, evolving various theories to explain why he never wrote to anybody and why nobody ever wrote him. Had the man committed some terrible crime, and fled to the army to hide his guilt? Blakely suggested that he must have murdered "the old folks." What did he mean by eternally conning that tattered Latin grammar? And was his name Bladburn, anyhow? Even his imperturbable amiability became suspicious. And then his frightful reticence! If he was the victim of any deep grief or crushing calamity, why didn't he seem unhappy? What business had he to be cheerful?

"It's my opinion," said Strong, "that he's a rival Wandering Jew; the original Jacob, you know, was a dark fellow."

Blakely inferred from something Bladburn had said, or something he had not said, — which was more likely, — that he had been a schoolmaster at some period of his life.

"Schoolmaster be hanged!" was Strong's comment. "Can you fancy a schoolmaster going about conjugating baby verbs out of a dratted little spelling-book? No, Quite So has evidently been a — a — Blest if I can imagine *what* he's been!"

Whatever John Bladburn had been, he was a lonely man. Whenever I want a type of perfect human isolation, I shall think of him, as he was in those days, moving remote, self-contained, and alone in the midst of two hundred thousand men.

II

The Indian summer, with its infinite beauty and tenderness, came like a reproach that year to Virginia. The foliage, touched here and there with prismatic tints, drooped motionless in the golden haze. The delicate Virginia creeper was almost minded to put forth its scarlet buds again. No wonder the lovely phantom — this dusky Southern sister of the pale Northern June — lingered not long with us, but, filling the once peaceful glens and valleys with her pathos, stole away rebukefully before the savage enginery of man.

The preparations that had been going on for months in arsenals and foundries at the North were nearly completed. For weeks past the air had been filled with rumors of an advance; but the rumor of today refuted the rumor of yesterday, and the Grand Army did not move. Heintzelman's corps was constantly folding its tents, like the Arabs, and as silently stealing away; but somehow it was always in the same place the next morning. One day, at length, orders came down for our brigade to move.

"We're going to Richmond, boys!" shouted Strong, thrusting his head in at the tent; and we all cheered and waved our caps like mad. You see, Big Bethel and Bull Run and Ball's Bluff (the bloody B's, as we used to call them), hadn't taught us any better sense.

Rising abruptly from the plateau, to the left of our encampment, was a tall hill covered with a stunted growth of red oak, persimmon, and chestnut. The night before we struck tents I climbed up to the crest to take a parting

look at a spectacle which custom had not been able to
rob of its enchantment. There, at my feet, and extending miles and miles away, lay the camps of the Grand
Army, with its campfires reflected against the sky. Thousands of lights were twinkling in every direction, some
nestling in the valley, some like fireflies beating their
wings and palpitating among the trees, and others stretching in parallel lines and curves, like the street-lamps of
a city. Somewhere, far off, a band was playing, at intervals it seemed; and now and then, nearer to, a silvery
strain from a bugle shot sharply up through the night,
and seemed to lose itself like a rocket among the stars
— the patient, untroubled stars. Suddenly a hand was
laid upon my arm.

"I'd like to say a word to you," said Bladburn.

With a little start of surprise, I made room for him on
the fallen tree where I was seated.

"I mayn't get another chance," he said. "You and the
boys have been very kind to me, kinder than I deserve;
but sometimes I've fancied that my not saying anything
about myself had given you the idea that all was not right
in my past. I want to say that I came down to Virginia
with a clean record."

"We never really doubted it, Bladburn."

"If I didn't write home," he continued, "it was because
I hadn't any home, neither kith nor kin. When I said
the old folks were dead, I said it. Am I boring you?
If I thought I was —"

"No, Bladburn. I have often wanted you to talk to me
about yourself, not from idle curiosity, I trust, but because I liked you that rainy night when you came to

camp, and have gone on liking you ever since. This isn't too much to say, when Heaven only knows how soon I may be past saying it or you listening to it."

"That's it," said Bladburn, hurriedly; "that's why I want to talk with you. I've a fancy that I shan't come out of our first battle."

The words gave me a queer start, for I had been trying for several days to throw off a similar presentiment concerning him — a foolish presentiment that grew out of a dream.

"In case anything of that kind turns up," he continued, "I'd like you to have my Latin grammar here — you've seen me reading it. You might stick it away in a bookcase, for the sake of old times. It goes against me to think of it falling into rough hands or being kicked about camp and trampled under foot."

He was drumming softly with his fingers on the volume in the bosom of his blouse.

"I didn't intend to speak of this to a living soul," he went on, motioning me not to answer him; "but something took hold of me tonight and made me follow you up here. Perhaps if I told you all, you would be the more willing to look after the little book in case it goes ill with me. When the war broke out I was teaching school down in Maine, in the same village where my father was schoolmaster before me. The old man when he died left me quite alone. I lived pretty much by myself, having no interests outside of the district school, which seemed in a manner my personal property. Eight years ago last spring a new pupil was brought to the school, a slight slip of a girl, with a sad kind of face and quiet ways. Perhaps it was because she wasn't very strong, and perhaps because she wasn't used over well by those who had charge of her, or perhaps it was because my life was lonely, that my heart warmed to the child. It all seems like a dream now, since that April morning when little Mary stood in front of my desk with her pretty eyes looking down bashfully and her soft hair falling over her face. One day I look up, and six years have gone by — as they go by in dreams — and among the scholars is a tall girl of sixteen, with serious, womanly eyes which I cannot trust myself to look upon. The old life has come to an end. The child has become a woman and can teach the master now. So help me Heaven, I didn't know that I loved her until that day!

"Long after the children had gone home I sat in the schoolroom with my face resting on my hands. There was her desk, the afternoon shadows falling across it. It had never looked empty and cheerless before. I went and stood by the low chair, as I had stood hundreds of times. On the desk was a pile of books, ready to be taken away, and among the rest a small Latin grammar which we had studied together. What little despairs and triumphs and happy hours were associated with it! I took it up curiously, as if it were some gentle dead thing, and turned over the pages, and could hardly see them. Turning the pages, idly so, I came to a leaf on which something was written with ink, in the familiar girlish hand. It was only the words 'Dear John,' through which she had drawn two hasty pencil lines — I wish she hadn't drawn those lines!" added Bladburn, under his breath.

He was silent for a minute or two, looking off towards the camps, where the lights were fading out one by one.

"I had no right to go and love Mary. I was twice her age, an awkward, unsocial man, that would have blighted her youth. I was as wrong as wrong can be. But I never meant to tell her. I locked the grammar in my desk and the secret in my heart for a year. I couldn't bear to meet her in the village, and kept away from every place where she was likely to be. Then she came to me, and sat down at my feet penitently, just as she used to do when she was a child, and asked what she had done to anger me; and then, Heaven forgive me! I told her all, and asked her if she could say with her lips the words she had written, and she nestled in my arms all a trembling like a bird, and said them over and over again.

"When Mary's family heard of our engagement, there was trouble. They looked higher for Mary than a middle-aged schoolmaster. No blame to them. They forbade me the house, her uncles; but we met in the village and at the neighbors' houses, and I was happy, knowing she loved me. Matters were in this state when the war came on. I had a strong call to look after the old flag, and I hung my head that day when the company raised in our village marched by the schoolhouse to the railroad station; but I couldn't tear myself away. About this time the minister's son, who had been away to college, came to the village. He met Mary here and there, and they became great friends. He was a likely fellow, near her own age, and it was natural they should like one another.

Sometimes I winced at seeing him made free of the home from which I was shut out; then I would open the grammar at the leaf where 'Dear John' was written up in the corner, and my trouble was gone. Mary was sorrowful and pale these days, and I think her people were worrying her.

"It was one evening two or three days before we got the news of Bull Run. I had gone down to the burying-ground to trim the spruce hedge set round the old man's lot, and was just stepping into the enclosure, when I heard voices from the opposite side. One was Mary's, and the other I knew to be young Marston's, the minister's son. I didn't mean to listen, but what Mary was saying struck me dumb. *We must never meet again*, she was saying in a wild way. *We must say good-by here, forever — good-by, good-by!* And I could hear her sobbing. Then, presently, she said, hurriedly, *No, no; my hand, not my lips!* Then it seemed he kissed her hands, and the two parted, one going towards the parsonage, and the other out by the gate near where I stood.

"I don't know how long I stood there, but the night-dews had wet me to the bone when I stole out of the grave-yard and across the road to the schoolhouse. I unlocked the door, and took the Latin grammar from the desk and hid it in my bosom. There was not a sound or a light anywhere as I walked out of the village. And now," said Bladburn, rising suddenly from the tree trunk, "if the little book ever falls in your way, won't you see that it comes to no harm, for my sake, and for the sake of the little woman who was true to me and didn't love me? Wherever she is tonight, God bless her!"

As we descended to camp with our arms resting on each other's shoulders, the watch-fires were burning low in the valleys and along the hillsides, and as far as the eye could reach the silent tents lay bleaching in the moon-light.

III

WE imagined that the throwing forward of our brigade was the initial movement of a general advance of the army; but that, as the reader will remember, did not take place until the following March. The Confederates had fallen back to Centreville without firing a shot, and the National troops were in possession of Lewinsville, Vienna, and Fair-fax Court-House. Our new position was nearly identical with that which we had occupied on the night previous to the battle of Bull Run — on the old turnpike road to Manassas, where the enemy was supposed to be in great force. With a field glass we could see the Rebel pickets moving in a belt of woodland on our right, and morning and evening we heard the spiteful roll of their snare drums.

Those pickets soon became a nuisance to us. Hardly a night passed but they fired upon our outposts, so far with no harmful result; but after a while it grew to be a serious matter. The Rebels would crawl out on all fours from the wood into a field covered with underbrush, and lie there in the dark for hours, waiting for a shot. Then our men took to the rifle-pits — pits ten or twelve feet long by four or five deep, with the loose earth banked up a few inches high on the exposed sides. All the pits bore names, more or less felicitous, by which they were known to their transient tenants. One was called "The Pepper-Box," another "Uncle Sam's Well," another "The Reb-

Trap," and another, I am constrained to say, was named after a not to be mentioned tropical locality. Though this rude sort of nomenclature predominated, there was no lack of softer titles, such as "Fortress Matilda" and "Castle Mary," and one had, though unintentionally, a literary flavor to it, "Blair's Grave," which was not popularly considered as reflecting unpleasantly on Nat Blair, who had assisted in making the excavation.

Some of the regiment had discovered a field of late corn in the neighborhood, and used to boil a few ears every day, while it lasted, for the boys detailed on the night picket. The corn-cobs were always scrupulously preserved and mounted on the parapets of the pits. Whenever a Rebel shot carried away one of these guns, there was swearing in that particular trench. Strong, who was very sensitive to this kind of disaster, was complaining bitterly one morning, because he had lost three "pieces" the night before.

"There's Quite So, now," said Strong; "when a Minie-ball comes *ping!* and knocks one of his guns to flinders, he merely smiles, and doesn't at all see the degradation of the thing."

Poor Bladburn! As I watched him day by day going about his duties, in his shy, cheery way, with a smile for everyone and not an extra word for anybody, it was hard to believe he was the same man who, that night before we broke camp by the Potomac, had poured out to me the story of his love and sorrow in words that burned in my memory.

While Strong was speaking, Blakely lifted aside the flap of the tent and looked in on us.

"Boys, Quite So was hurt last night," he said, with a white tremor to his lip.

"What!"

"Shot on picket."

"Why, he was in the pit next to mine," cried Strong.

"Badly hurt?"

"Badly hurt."

I knew he was; I need not have asked the question. He never meant to go back to New England!

Bladburn was lying on the stretcher in the hospital-tent. The surgeon had knelt down by him, and was carefully cutting away the bosom of his blouse. The Latin grammar, stained and torn, slipped, and fell to the floor. Bladburn gave me a quick glance. I picked up the book, and as I placed it in his hand, the icy fingers closed softly over mine. He was sinking fast. In a few minutes the surgeon finished his examination. When he rose to his feet there were tears on the weather-beaten cheeks. He was a rough outside, but a tender heart.

"My poor lad," he blurted out, "it's no use. If you've anything to say, say it now, for you've nearly done with this world."

Then Bladburn lifted his eyes slowly to the surgeon, and the old smile flitted over his face as he murmured,

"Quite so."

UNUSUAL WORDS

cogitations — meditations

fatuously — (the people of the North who looked fatuously for the fall of Richmond) looked for it with foolish conceit *felicitous* — (the pits bore names more or less felicitous) more or less happily suited to them

garrulous — very talkative

imperturbable — (his imperturbable amiability) amiability which nothing could disturb

nomenclature — naming

presentiment — (a foolish presentiment) a feeling that some unfortunate thing was about to happen

prismatic — showing the colors of a prism, rainbow colors

simulated — (of simulated gaiety) of pretended gaiety

soubriquet — nickname or assumed name

QUESTIONS FOR SELF-TESTING

1. When did Quite So first appear to the teller of this story?
2. How did his nickname become fastened on him?
3. Why were Quite So's tent-mates so depressed at the time of his coming?
4. What circumstance made Quite So finally confide his history to the teller of the story?
5. So far as the army was concerned, what immediately followed the battle of Bull Run?
6. How did the men in the army put in their time during this period?
7. What was the chief event of each day?
8. How did Quite So fill his spare minutes?
9. What theories to account for Quite So did his tent-mates develop?
10. What is the significance of the names which the soldiers gave to their rifle-pits?

TOPICS FOR THEMES OR DISCUSSION

1. This is a story distinctly old-fashioned. What seems to you the most old-fashioned element in it?

2. The writer speaks of Quite So's "imperturbable amiability" as one of the things which made his mates suspicious of him. Why should that quality cause suspicion?
3. Using the descriptions of the camp and of camp life given
   in this story, write a letter from any one of the men
   mentioned to one of his family.
4. Mary had promised to marry Quite So. After she fell in
   love with someone else nearer her own age and more like
   her, was she right or wrong in using all her strength and
   courage in trying to keep to her original promise?
5. Since this story is, in some ways, obviously not in the
   present fashion, is it therefore a poor story?

THE RIP VAN WINKLE
MAN–O'–WAR

By H. IRVING HANCOCK

If we could choose to live in whatever period we thought would give us the greatest experience of change, we should probably have a hard time deciding whether to pick the sixteenth century, or the nineteenth, or the opening years of the twentieth. The writer of " The Rip Van Winkle Man-O'-War" shows what a bewildering world people come back to who dropped out in the middle of the nineteenth century and return after the twentieth has opened. Also he brings home to us too how completely inventions and discoveries have altered American life. Just as Indians and wild land were the governing factors of early American living, so now steam and electricity, with the projects they make possible, have become the governing factors of the present. Whether a group of strangers dropped down in present-day America would want to stay or want to hurry back to whatever place they came from is one of the questions the writer poses — and finally answers.

SAIL two points off sta'bu'd bow, sir!" came up to the bridge from the bow watch of the second-class battleship *Tecumseh*, of the United States Navy.

Lieutenant Rowland, officer of the watch, nodded slightly, spyglass at his eyes, for he had made out the stranger at the same moment.

It was morning, just after daylight, on Monday, April 20, 1908. The *Tecumseh*, southbound, and going at slow cruising speed, was in latitude about 30° W., that is to say, about six hundred and fifty miles southeast of Rio Janeiro.

Patches of light-brown, smoky, thick haze that is peculiar to the South Atlantic at this season of the year hung about the trim, bristling, white warcraft. Here and there were open streaks showing deep blue water and unclouded skies overhead.

Out of one of these patches of haze, less than a quarter of a mile away, poked a black bowsprit, topped by a spread of old yellow canvas. This was followed by the looming up of a rusty black hull, high out of water; and then a foremast came into view. But what caused officer and bow watch to start in intense astonishment was the muzzle of a long, old-style, 32-pounder bow gun that, peering out of its canvas jacket, appeared at the stranger's starboard bow.

"The *Flying Dutchman?*" wondered the bow watch.

The men in the wheelhouse and the few other members of the crew on duty forward rubbed their eyes. Whatever he felt within, the calm young officer on the bridge kept his outward composure admirably. The vessel that now came wholly out of the haze proved to be a wooden ship of nearly four thousand tons. Her three masts bore a full spread of much-patched, time-seared canvas, while from a single funnel wood smoke floated indolently. Steam was plainly only auxiliary on this craft. Despite the revolutions of the side paddle-wheels the stranger was making barely six knots an hour northward. A few deck guns were visible, while white-painted, closed ports along the side perhaps concealed others.

It came as a shock to all beholders aboard the *Tecumseh* that this rather ghostly old craft displayed, aft, an old United States flag of many years ago.

"We'll soon know something about this marine ghost, or whatever it is!" said Lieutenant Rowland to himself, as, with a hand on the lever of the mechanical signaling apparatus, he gave the order for the stopping of the battleship's propeller shafts. His verbal command to a marine brought Ensign Waite and Cadet Midshipman Ellis hastily forward.

"Give 'em a blank shot, Mr. Waite!" directed Rowland. "Mr. Ellis, my compliments to the captain and the executive officer, and tell 'em —"

As a puff of white smoke and a sharp report left one of the *Tecumseh's* lighter forward guns, the stranger's colors dipped, while a clump of signal flags was hauled to the old craft's maintop and there broken out.

"I can't make out that bunting gibberish!" muttered Rowland, impatiently, as he studied the flags through his glass. "Any orders, sir?" he asked, from force of habit, as the executive officer reached the bridge just ahead of the captain.

"No," said both. "Wait."

As the old black craft, in slowly stopping headway, turned and came somewhat nearer, the *Tecumseh's* signal flags shook out the challenge, "Who are you?" But the stranger replied only with a single deep-throated blast from her whistle.

"Mr. Thornton," said Captain Loring, turning to an ensign in the group of officers that had hastened close to the bridge, "you're our authority on everything ancient in the navy. Can you place the craft yonder?"

"She carries about an 1856 flag, sir, and looks like one of our old line-of-battle ships before the war. But there's no such craft in commission today, sir."

From davits at the starboard waist of the stranger a cumbersome black rowing cutter was lowered in rather seamanlike manner, though the sailors going stiffly down a side gangway to the cutter appeared to be all old, white-haired men. A feeling almost of awe crept over the hundreds of watchers now on the white battleship's decks.

Though with a stiffness of movement suggestive of something between old age and rheumatism, the men in the cutter got away from their own vessel in good old naval style. Officers and blue-jackets on the *Tecumseh* watched the approaching cutter until Captain Loring roared through a megaphone: "What ship are you from?"

From a white-haired, venerable-faced man of at least seventy years, who sat in the stern sheets of the cutter, and who wore a curious, dingy, old-style blue uniform, even to the ancient "cheese-box" cap of the old navy, came the response:

"We couldn't read your signals, sir, any better than you could make out ours. Our craft is the line-of-battle ship *Neponset*, United States Navy. Sailed from New York November 18, 1858, and frozen in below the Antarctic Circle almost ever since — now free, thank heaven, to return to the United States! Your flag, sir, and your strange, wonderful craft, show us that our country still lives! We —" The ancient officer's speech ended in a huskiness that he could not choke down.

As the cutter came in closer, a side gangway was quickly lowered, while captain and executive officer hurried to receive the wonderful guests.

Only the aged officer who had answered the hail came up the narrow steps. He paused long enough to say to a white-haired brother officer in the cutter:

"Keep all hands in the boat, Midshipman."

"Aye, aye, sir!" came cheerily from that "boy" of past threescore. Then, as this ranking officer, looking as though he had stepped from an old-time print, started to ascend, Ensign Thornton, at a nod from his captain, ran down to give the old man a reverently supporting arm.

"I am Captain Loring, and I welcome you most heartily, sir, on my own behalf and that of my brother officers," said the *Tecumseh's* commander in husky tones, as the pair reached the head of the gangway.

"I tender you my most respectful thanks, sir," came simply, in a now strong, clear voice from the old man. "I am Second Lieutenant Raymond, ranking surviving officer of the old *Neponset*. I have brought our crumbly old ship's papers, sir, for your inspection."

"Come down to my cabin," begged Captain Loring, and led the way.

While the two commanders were below, recovered discipline prevented any curious hails or conversation between the men on the battleship and those in the cutter that rode on the ground swell at a little distance from the ship's side. It was not long ere the *Tecumseh's* executive officer, Mr. Stayton, was sent for. He soon returned to the deck, saying:

"Mr. Rowland, hail the cutter, and ask the men, with Captain Loring's compliments, to come aboard. Mr. Waite, clear away cutters Number Three and Four, placing Mr. Ellis in charge of one. Go aboard the *Neponset* and hand this invitation to Lieutenant Clover. Gentlemen," to the other officers gathered about, "the Captain presents his compliments and invites all not on duty to join our guest and guests-to-come in the wardroom."

As the officers filed below they found the mess servants flying about in the greatest bustle.

"Gentlemen," began Captain Loring, "this strange tale

of the *Neponset* seems proven by the papers that Mr. Raymond brought. You will not be surprised at learning
that I have invited the other officers of the *Neponset* —
only seven survive, I regret to say — to come aboard
and breakfast with us. Until that meal has been met
and vanquished I feel that we shall do well to postpone
asking for the story that I know everyone is waiting in
the utmost suspense to hear."

In a few moments more Midshipman John Dalton,
sixty-five years old, and the youngest survivor of the
Neponset, came below, while his venerable-looking boat's
crew were being received with tremendous cheers by the
Tecumseh's enlisted men overhead. Nor were the two
steam launches long in reaching the old black craft and
in returning with the remaining officers and some thirty
members of the *Neponset's* crew. Undoubtedly the most
disappointed man on the old ship was Boatswain Peterson,
who was obliged to remain in temporary command.

Only greetings and pleasantries of the day followed the
introductions between the officers of the Old Navy and
the New. They seated themselves at the wardroom tables,
old Mr. Raymond at the post of honor.

For nearly an hour, on account of the tension of waiting
for the story to come, the meal proceeded rather solemnly.
Only once did Lieutenant Raymond touch upon the past,
when, looking down at his plate, he sighed: "It seems
good to eat such food again, after half a century."

His words were echoed by a murmur from the other
aged officers of the *Neponset*, yet, being "youngsters" in
point of service rank, they left the remarks mainly to
their commanding officer.

When the meal was being cleared away the first surprise came to the officers of the *Tecumseh*. The waiters brought the choicest cigars of the mess. Looking down into a box held before him, Lieutenant Raymond, with an odd, faraway expression in his eyes, said slowly:

"It is good to see the weed, thank you. We've been nearly fifty years away from tobacco, and so we've lost the habit. But we'd like to try these!"

Then Captain Loring asked:

"Will it be agreeable to you, now, sir, to begin some account of your fifty years in the navy but out of the world?"

"I fear you will be disappointed, there is so little to tell," smiled the old man. "We have about the same story to tell as Rip Van Winkle told when he came back from his long sleep. In fact, sir, of late years I've often thought of the good old *Neponset* as the Rip Van Winkle of the United States Navy.

"I have told you the date when we left New York. Our commanding officer, Captain Howard, was ordered by the Navy Department to go as far south of the Antarctic Circle as possible, for the double purpose of making magnetic observations and geographical discoveries. We were expected to be away for two years, and were provisioned for three. Our only stop was at Rio Janeiro, for fuel.

"Then we plunged boldly southward. On this side of the equator, of course, the summer season is the reverse of that at the north. So we neared the extreme southern seas in what was the height of summer. It was an unusually warm year in the Antarctic, I remember. The sea was so open that we made for the South Orkney Islands without trouble. After stopping there for two days we went somewhat out of our direct course, passing several large tracts of land, but not stopping until we reached Graham Land, which, as you know, is just on the Antarctic Circle. At Graham Land we remained for a week. While some of our officers made volumes of magnetic observations and calculations, Captain Howard kept his eye on the sea conditions.

"Though icebergs dotted the sea in all directions, the water yet remained wonderfully open for the South Polar region. Captain Howard, therefore, decided upon a swift dash southward, even though we ran the risk of becoming icebound until the following year.

"It seemed well worth the trying. I may add, sir and gentlemen, that we made the dash with bold and cheery hearts. Though we had to be content with slow progress past the increasing number of icebergs, yet for days we kept on to the southward. One daybreak found us close to a great wall of ice. That wall, sir, was at least two hundred feet high. Captain Howard decided to skirt that great barrier of ice. Going westward at only about four knots an hour, we followed that wall for over four hundred miles.

"Then, one morning, our eyes were amazed by the sight of great, snow-clad mountain peaks on the further side of the ice wall. Our mathematicians quickly figured that the three visible peaks were from eleven to twelve thousand feet high.   ·

"Within two hours of that time, sir and gentlemen, we found an open passage through the ice wall. We followed that passage through, discovering the ice wall, at that point, to be some two thousand feet thick. But beyond, sir, at the bases of those great mountains, we found the bare black rocks jutting out. The water, too, near this land, was much warmer than any we had encountered in days. By noon we sighted a fourth mountain, a live volcano with smoke issuing from its top.

"As we neared the base of this fourth mountain Captain Howard determined to send several officers and two boats' crews ashore. Almost their first discovery was a rock-lined entrance to a cove beyond. Skirting the cove, hemmed in by the mountains, was a valley of warm, fertile land, comprising some three square miles. Throughout this tract of land geysers of warm water spouted and the creeks formed by their waters kept the land warm and genial in that Antarctic summer. Vegetation grew freely, and at least half of the valley was covered by trees that could not be called stunted in latitude 82° S."

"Eighty-two, sir?" replied Captain Loring, astonished.

"Eighty-two, sir," replied Lieutenant Raymond, gravely.

"Pardon me, sir. I did not mean to interrupt you. But your expedition went further south than any before or since!"

"And stayed there longer!" sighed Mr. Raymond. "For we were fascinated, and reveled in explorations ashore until one morning, a fortnight later, we made the awful discovery that our gap in the ice wall had closed. It has remained closed, ever since, until about a fortnight ago."

A gasp of astonishment — almost of horror — went round the *Tecumseh's* officers.

"Well, sir," continued Lieutenant Raymond, "there is

not much more to be told. We were unable to get out, but we kedged our stanch old *Neponset* into the cove, and later built an especial basin in which we kept her all these years, diverting enough of the flow of the geysers into that basin so that the water about our ship's hull never froze.

"The climate was, of course, cold in winter, but our little three-mile kingdom had as comfortable a climate, winter or summer, as New York can boast. We had plenty of timber for houses and fuel, while the great mountains kept off the iciest Antarctic blasts. Our apothecary had, in a chest, several kinds of vegetable seeds and wheat, from which we harvested a good crop the first summer. There were fish in the waters, a species of seal, and several varieties of birds, so that we fared well enough. We were well stocked with cloth, and made much use also of sealskins and the skins of the larger birds.

"Through it all, sir and gentlemen, we tried never to forget that we belonged to the United States Navy, and that we had one of the nation's vessels and a proud old flag to be returned to the American people. As the years went on I will admit that we often despaired of ever seeing our beloved country again. Our officers fell from eighteen to seven, and our crew from two hundred and eighty-nine to seventy-one. Still we felt that we had enough stout hearts to take the old *Neponset* home. Never once did we grow slack in our duty of fitting in new ship's timbers wherever an old one showed signs of giving out. We actually hoarded our uniform cloths, sir, that we might return home with some of the dignity befitting our country's service.

"Even our paint supply we hoarded, that the good old ship herself might go home shipshape and clean. Our ammunition we could not keep, for, with our best care, it gradually became worthless.

"It was twenty-six years ago that Captain Howard, full of hope and the love of duty to the last, died. His last words were: 'Do not despair, gentlemen. We have all made a brave fight of it. You will yet get back home.'

"Sirs and gentlemen, a fortnight ago we discovered an opening in the wall of ice; and we were ready, as we had been for fifty years. An hour we spent, in reverent homage, at the graves of our beloved comrades in that ice-bound valley. Then, with the boldest hearts possible, we left the place of our ship's long sleep, came safely through the great ice barrier, and — well, the rest of our tale you see before you."

Lieutenant Raymond's fine old eyes gleamed wet as he slipped from his seat at the table for a look through one of the portholes at the not far distant *Neponset*.

"Now," said Captain Loring, speaking very softly, though heard by all, "we younger men understand more of the spirit of the Old Navy. Your ship's company waited a full half-century for your one chance of escape, and then, with true American pluck, took it the first instant that the chance came. Mr. Raymond, may we again shake the hand of each of the *Neponset's* officers? It will make better American sailors of us."

Before the handshaking was finished it rounded off into hearty cheering by these younger men of the New Navy. During the tumult the *Neponset's* aged officers looked actually abashed.

"At the time we — left the world," said Lieutenant Raymond, "war with England was feared in our country. I would like to ask if that has ever come about?"

"No, sir; and England and the United States today, sir, are two of the firmest friends in the world. But," added Captain Loring, very gravely, "within three years after your enforced exile, the Northern and Southern States clashed in the most gigantic war of modern times. Ten years ago we fought Spain. Today, a portion of the United States Navy has just completed a cruise around the world — the most formidable naval fleet that ever made so long a cruise."

"A cruise around the world by a whole fleet!" cried Lieutenant Raymond and some of his brother officers in concert. "And the North and South at war! Tell us about that, I beg you!" pleaded the *Neponset's* commander.

"Mr. Thornton, as our historian aboard, I think you are best qualified for that performance," suggested Captain Loring. "While you are getting ready I will pass the word for such of the *Neponset's* crew as are aboard to come and listen with their officers."

A score and a half of the visiting white-haired enlisted men, all scrupulously neat in their darned and mended, faded blue uniforms, came down, gathering at the far end of the wardroom. They would have stood, but Captain Loring insisted that chairs be placed for these old heroes.

For nearly two hours Thornton described the deeds of the American navy in the Civil War. At first there was deep awe over the story of the great national quarrel.

Later the speaker was often interrupted by hoarse cheers from his enthusiastic listeners. Porter, Farragut, Van Brunt, Mercer, Tatnall, Rodgers, Parker, Morris — these and scores of other names were those of living comrades to the *Neponset's* officers and men, who cheered the valor of their old-time friends to the echo. There were few dry eyes.

Ensign Thornton passed at last to the few but bright glories of the war with Spain. Dewey was a youngster, known to Lieutenant Raymond and two of his brother officers, but Admirals Sampson, Schley, and Evans were names over which they shook their heads even while their eyes brightened.

"You will want books to read on the rest of your homeward cruise, that you may 'pick up' and get into the world again," wound up Mr. Thornton. "I will bring you all that I think will be of use to you."

As he went in search of the books, brother officers excused themselves on the same errand. In a few minutes the old-timers had been supplied with more reading matter than could be digested in a year.

"We shall be as poor in purse as in comprehension of today's world, I imagine," said Mr. Raymond, musingly. "Of course our pay will have been stopped long ago."

"Poor in purse!" Captain Loring exclaimed, bringing a hand down heavily on the table. "I wish I had your prospects of a rich old age. Why, sir, every officer and man of you will be entitled to fifty years of back pay, for you've never been mustered out. And the country will certainly compel Congress to add compound interest at at least four per cent."

"Can that be so?" murmured Mr. Raymond, looking rather uncomfortable.

"Why, it will mount up into millions, altogether!" cried old Midshipman Dalton, after doing some frantic figuring on paper.

"Can that be so?" repeated Mr. Raymond, glancing at his astonished-looking brother officers. "Can the United States stand such a drain?"

"Yes! yes! Of course it can! We are a very rich country now!" laughed Captain Loring. "But, gentlemen of the *Tecumseh*, as our guests must all be mentally tired, I ask you to take them above for a turn in the deck air."

"We can't seem to pick up any craft between here and Rio that has a wireless installation, sir," reported Ensign Waite, approaching his commander. The guests stared so curiously at that that they had to listen, with heads that must have throbbed, to the wonderful story of the wireless telegraph.

Captain Loring arranged with Lieutenant Raymond to have both vessels now shape their course toward Rio Janeiro.

"From there we will cable the Navy Department at Washington," Captain Loring explained, and then remembered that even the submarine cable was new to these men of the Rip Van Winkle man-o'-war.

The guests were now taken to the turrets to inspect the great rifled guns, the wonderful aiming mechanisms, the range finders, and electric firing apparatus. These men of the Old Navy gazed with awe even at the hoisting of massive ammunition from the depths of this steel monster. The torpedo tubes and the great Whitehead messengers of destruction almost made them shudder. The twentieth-century engine room fascinated them. They saw a thousand wonders and new inventions in quick succession, and tried to comprehend each new marvel, yet cried out that they could not.

"We shall suffer collapse if you show us more today," urged Lieutenant Raymond, with a wavering smile. "We have been asleep for fifty years! Now, by the great Paul Jones, it will take us another fifty to wake!"

"We will lunch, then," suggested Captain Loring, and led the way once more to the wardroom. Through the meal the seven guests sat in an almost stunned silence. They were doing their best to recollect what they had heard and seen of naval progress in fifty wonder-filled years.

"With your approval, sir, we shall return to our ship, to think over what has come to us today," proposed Lieutenant Raymond, when luncheon was over. "And to rest," he added, truthfully. "You will understand, sir, when we say that our heads never seemed so near to bursting. But we shall be glad, sir, if as many of you as possible will board us, at dark, and dine with us on the simple fare of which we have an abundance."

That invitation was gladly accepted. Most of the officers and crew of the *Tecumseh* spent a good deal of the afternoon gazing across at the drowsy black hull of the *Neponset*, lumbering along over the ground swell.

Never had any officer of the big white battleship sat at a simpler meal than the guests of the evening partook of aboard the old Rip Van Winkle man-o'-war. The meats were unfamiliar flesh that had been hunted far below the Antarctic Circle, though most of the vegetables were ordinary. There was wheat bread, though of a peculiar flavor.

After dinner it needed but a bare hour for the guests to see the little that was to be seen aboard the old *Neponset*. To modern eyes it was a primitive wooden ship. The furnaces under the boilers would burn either wood or coal. Mr. Raymond explained that they were now burning the former but had coal in reserve. The cannon were of the old smooth-bore type; the few shells in the magazine were worthless from age.

Just as the *Tecumseh's* officers stepped out upon deck, accompanied by their hosts, the great electric searchlight of the white battleship turned its glaring eye on them, flooding the old man-o'-war's decks with an intense glow. A cry of amazement and even fear went up from the white-haired old sailors forward. They turned their faces from this brilliant glare, strangest of all equipment wonders of a modern sea-fighter.

The leave-taking between visiting officers and their hosts was simple but affecting. Then, in a reverent silence the younger, nattier men went over the side into the steam launch.

For some time there was complete silence among the *Tecumseh* group. Finally Mr. Stayton, the executive officer, said: "It was the men, not the machines, that made the Old Navy great!"

The course for the night had been arranged between the respective commanding officers. The vessels were to keep as close together as wisdom in ship-handling permitted. But, as it happened, by six bells, long before midnight, the sky had darkened so as to blot out of sight the stars. A half-hour later a gale suddenly arose that quickly gave the officers of both ships all they wanted to think about. It was like a veritable West Indian hurricane, with a roaring wind and blinding sheets of rain, so that in a jiffy, as it seemed, each vessel lost sight of the other's lights. At first, the old ship's whistle could be heard in answer to the *Tecumseh's* deep-throated notes. Then even the husky old whistle ceased as a sound of near-by presence. No officer on the *Tecumseh* slept that night. The raging winds and waters gave even the modern cruiser a struggle for life, and every man had to be at his post. And the dawn brought no relief, for nothing could be seen even a few ship-lengths away through the solid wall of fiercely driven rain. But, about three hours after daylight, the storm abated, and then the *Tecumseh's* officers swept the sea in vain with their glasses. The *Neponset* had vanished.

Captain Loring searched unceasingly for three days. His officers, well-nigh sleepless, shared the stern vigil with him. The *Neponset* was not seen again, nor was a single piece of wreckage found.

"I cannot bear to think of those grand old fellows going to the bottom!" said Captain Loring, that night, when he dined in the wardroom.

"Do you know, sir," smiled Mr. Thornton, wistfully, "I've just a notion that neither the *Neponset* nor the crew went under the waves?"

"Why, what else can have befallen them, sir?" demanded the captain of his young subordinate.

"Well, sir," went on the ship's historian, slowly, "you remember how awed those fine old men felt over the way the world has gone ahead since their day. Then, too, they didn't have any comprehension of how our country has grown. Why, sir, officers and men alike seemed absolutely scared at thought of coming back into a world and life that were utterly strange to them!"

"So you think —"

"Think?" cried Mr. Thornton, while his brother officers gazed at him with varying emotions. "Why, sir, it looks to me like a nine-to-one chance that the *Neponset* did weather that gale. She was old, but had been admirably kept up. So, sir, what more likely than that the gale gave those splendid old fellows the impulse to put about and make off back to their cove at 82° South?"

The captain rose slowly.

"Any orders, sir?" asked the lieutenant.

"Keep to the course, Mr. Wildman. We will put in at Rio Janeiro and cable the Navy Department. I fear we are going to have a hard time finding people to believe us when the whole story is told. But — for ourselves — we shall always treasure loving thoughts of those fine men of the Old Navy!"

Questions for Self-Testing

1. Without actually telling us, in what way does the author explain that the ship which the men on the *Tecumseh* saw was a very queer old vessel?

2. Where does the author first warn us that he is not telling a true story?

3. What was it in the appearance of the old boat which "came as a shock to all beholders"?
4. How did the officer of the watch on the *Tecumseh* warn the stranger that he wanted her to stop?
5. For what purpose had the *Neponset* been sent on her southern cruise?
6. What tempted her captain to go farther south than he had at first intended?
7. What circumstances compelled the ship and her crew to remain?
8. How long did they remain?
9. Through what circumstances did it come about that the valley which the men from the *Neponset* found was fertile and comparatively warm?
10. Through what fortunate accident were they able to raise wheat?
11. What were some of the more important historical happenings about which the *Neponset's* crew knew nothing?
12. Which of the new inventions impressed them most?
13. What gave the *Neponset* its chance to slip out of sight of the *Tecumseh?*
14. At the end of the story, what two beliefs does the author leave open to us about what had become of the *Neponset?*

Topics for Themes or Discussion

1. In what ways would this story be a good one to pair with *Robinson Crusoe?*
2. The writer speaks of the enlisted men on the *Neponset* as "these old heroes." Since the men had no choice about obeying orders when they sailed south and since, once frozen in, they had to stay, do you think the author is right or wrong in calling them heroes?

3. Why does Captain Raymond look uncomfortable when he learns that he and his comrades will have millions of dollars in back pay?

4. If you had been the commander of the *Neponset*, should you have gone back to the South Pole or on to the United States?

5. If the *Neponset* had come safely to a port in the United States, what astonishing sights would her crew have seen in their first hour ashore?

6. Write the story of the home-coming of one member from the *Neponset's* crew. Decide in advance whether you want readers to find your story amusing or sad.

7. If, instead of escaping from their ice prison in 1908, the men of the *Neponset* had come back in 1937, to what additional marvels would they have had to become accustomed?

THAT SPOT

By JACK LONDON

In 1896, gold was discovered in Alaska. In 1897, Jack London, the author of "That Spot," made his way to the Yukon Valley, partly to hunt gold, and partly to hunt adventure for which he never ceased searching so long as he lived. However little or much gold he found, he found adventure in plenty and recorded it in many stories. "That Spot" tells a little about the difficulties and excitements of his Alaskan life, but especially it is an example of a kind of story which has grown up on every American frontier and of which Americans have always been particularly fond. That is the "tall story." Why "That Spot" is a tall story and what a tall story itself is are evident enough when the next pages have been read.

Of Jack London's other stories some of the most readable are: "All Gold Canyon" (*in* Moonface and Other Stories), "To Build a Fire" (Modern Short Stories), "The God of His Fathers" (McClure's, 1901).

I DON'T think much of Stephen Mackaye any more, though I used to swear by him. I know that in those days I loved him more than my brother. If ever I meet Stephen Mackaye again, I shall not be responsible for my actions. It passes beyond me that a man with whom I shared food and blanket, and with whom I mushed over the Chilkoot Trail, should turn out the way he did. I always sized Steve up as a square man, a kindly comrade, without an iota of anything vindictive or malicious in his nature. I shall never trust my judgment in men again. Why, I nursed that man through typhoid fever; we starved together on the headwaters of the Stewart; and he saved my life on the Little Salmon. And now, after the years we were together, all I can say of Stephen Mackaye is that he is the meanest man I ever knew.

We started for the Klondike in the fall rush of 1897, and we started too late to get over Chilkoot Pass before the freeze-up. We packed our outfit on our backs part way over, when the snow began to fly, and then we had to buy dogs in order to sled it the rest of the way. That was how we came to get that Spot. Dogs were high, and we paid one hundred and ten dollars for him. He looked worth it. I say *looked*, because he was one of the finest-appearing dogs I ever saw. He weighed sixty pounds, and he had all the lines of a good sled animal. We never could make out his breed. He wasn't husky, nor Malemute, nor Hudson Bay; he looked like all of them and he didn't look like any of them; and on top of it all he had some of the white man's dog in him, for on one side, in the thick of the mixed yellow-brown-red-and-dirty-white that was his prevailing color, there was a spot of coal-black as big as a water bucket. That was why we called him Spot.

He was a good looker all right. When he was in condition his muscles stood out in bunches all over him. And he was the strongest-looking brute I ever saw in Alaska, also the most intelligent-looking. To run your eyes over him, you'd think he could outpull three dogs of his own weight. Maybe he could, but I never saw it. His intelligence didn't run that way. He could steal and forage to perfection; he had an instinct that was positively gruesome for divining when work was to be done and for making a sneak accordingly; and for getting lost and not staying lost he was nothing short of inspired. But when it came to work, the way that intelligence dribbled out of him and left him a mere clot of wobbling, stupid jelly would make your heart bleed.

There are times when I think it wasn't stupidity.

Maybe, like some men I know, he was too wise to work. I shouldn't wonder if he put it all over us with that intelligence of his. Maybe he figured it all out and decided that a licking now and again and no work was a whole lot better than work all the time and no licking. He was intelligent enough for such a computation. I tell you, I've sat and looked into that dog's eyes till the shivers ran up and down my spine and the marrow crawled like yeast, such was the intelligence I saw shining out. I can't express myself about that intelligence. It is beyond mere words. I saw it, that's all. At times it was like gazing into a human soul, to look into his eyes; and what I saw there frightened me and started all sorts of ideas in my own mind of reincarnation and all the rest. I tell you I sensed something big in that brute's eyes; there was a message there, but I wasn't big enough myself to catch it. Whatever it was (I know I'm making a fool of myself) — whatever it was, it baffled me. I can't give an inkling of what I saw in that brute's eyes; it wasn't light, it wasn't color; it was something that moved, away back, when the eyes themselves weren't moving. And I guess I didn't see it move, either; I only sensed that it moved. It was an expression, — that's what it was — and I got an impression of it. No; it was different from a mere expression; it was more than that. I don't know what it was, but it gave me a feeling of kinship just the same. Oh, no, not sentimental kinship. It was, rather, a kinship of equality. Those eyes never pleaded like a deer's eyes. They challenged. No, it wasn't defiance. It was just a calm assumption of equality. And I don't mean shine. It didn't shine; it *moved*.

I know I'm talking rot, but if you'd looked into that animal's eyes the way I have, you'd understand. Steve was affected the same way I was. Why, I tried to kill that Spot once — he was no good for anything; and I fell down on it. I led him out into the brush, and he came along slow and unwilling. He knew what was going on. I stopped in a likely place, put my foot on the rope, and pulled my big Colt's. And that dog sat down and looked at me. I tell you he didn't plead. He just looked. And I saw all kinds of incomprehensible things moving, yes, *moving*, in those eyes of his. I didn't really see them move; I thought I saw them, for, as I said before, I guess I only sensed them. And I want to tell you right now that it got beyond me. It was like killing a man, a conscious, brave man who looked calmly into your gun as much as to say, "Who's afraid?" Then, too, the message seemed so near that, instead of pulling the trigger quick, I stopped to see if I could catch the message. There it was, right before me, glimmering all around in those eyes of his. And then it was too late. I got scared. I was trembly all over, and my stomach generated a nervous palpitation that made me seasick. I just sat down and looked at that dog, and he looked at me, till I thought I was going crazy. Do you want to know what I did? I threw down the gun and ran back to camp with the fear of God in my heart. Steve laughed at me. But I noticed that Steve led Spot into the woods, a week later, for the same purpose, and that Steve came back alone, and a little later Spot drifted back, too.

At any rate, Spot wouldn't work. We paid a hundred and ten dollars for him from the bottom of our sack, and he wouldn't work. He wouldn't even tighten the traces. Steve spoke to him the first time we put him in harness, and he sort of shivered, that was all. Not an ounce on the traces. He just stood still and wobbled, like so much jelly. Steve touched him with the whip. He yelped, but not an ounce. Steve touched him again, a bit harder, and he howled — the regular long wolf howl. Then Steve got mad and gave him half a dozen, and I came on the run from the tent.

I told Steve he was brutal with the animal, and we had some words — the first we'd ever had. He threw the whip down in the snow and walked away mad. I picked it up and went to it. That Spot trembled and wobbled and cowered before ever I swung the lash, and with the first bite of it he howled like a lost soul. Next he lay down in the snow. I started the rest of the dogs, and they dragged him along, while I threw the whip into him. He rolled over on his back and bumped along, his four legs waving in the air, himself howling as though he was going through a sausage machine. Steve came back and laughed at me, and I apologized for what I'd said.

There was no getting any work out of that Spot; and to make up for it, he was the biggest pig-glutton of a dog I ever saw. On top of that, he was the cleverest thief. There was no circumventing him. Many a breakfast we went without our bacon because Spot had been there first. And it was because of him that we nearly starved to death up the Stewart. He figured out the way to break into our meat cache, and what he didn't eat, the rest of the team did. But he was impartial. He stole from everybody. He was a restless dog, always very busy snooping around or going somewhere. And there was never a camp within five miles that he didn't raid. The worst of it was that they always came back on us to pay his board bill, which was just, being the law of the land; but it was mighty hard on us, especially that first winter on the Chilkoot, when we were busted, paying for whole hams and sides of bacon that we never ate. He could fight, too, that Spot. He could do everything but work. He never pulled a pound, but he was the boss of the whole team. The way he made those dogs stand around was an education. He bullied them, and there was always one or more of them fresh-marked with his fangs. But he was more than a bully. He wasn't afraid of anything that walked on four legs; and I've seen him march, single-handed, into a strange team, without any provocation whatever, and put the *kibosh* on the whole outfit. Did I say he could eat? I caught him eating the whip once. That's straight. He started in at the lash, and when I caught him he was down to the handle, and still going.

But he was a good looker. At the end of the first week we sold him for seventy-five dollars to the Mounted Police. They had experienced dog drivers, and we knew that by the time he'd covered the six hundred miles to Dawson he'd be a good sled dog. I say we *knew*, for we were just getting acquainted with that Spot. A little later we were not brash enough to know anything where he was concerned. A week later we woke up in the morning to the dangedest dog fight we'd ever heard. It was that Spot come back and knocking the team into shape. We ate a pretty depressing breakfast, I can tell you; but cheered up two hours afterward when we sold him to an official courier, bound in to Dawson with government dispatches. That Spot was only three days in coming back, and, as usual, celebrated his arrival with a rough-house.

We spent the winter and spring, after our own outfit was across the pass, freighting other people's outfits; and we made a fat stake. Also, we made money out of Spot. If we sold him once, we sold him twenty times. He always came back, and no one asked for their money. We didn't want the money. We'd have paid handsomely for any-one to take him off our hands for keeps. We had to get rid of him, and we couldn't give him away, for when we tried everybody became suspicious. But he was such a fine looker that we never had any difficulty in selling him. "Unbroke," we'd say, and they'd pay any old price for him. We sold him as low as twenty-five dollars, and once we got a hundred and fifty for him. That particular party returned him in person, refused to take his money back, and the way he abused us was something awful. He said it was cheap at the price to tell us what he thought of us; and we felt he was so justified that we never talked back. But to this day I've never quite regained all the old self-respect that was mine before that man talked to me.

When the ice cleared out of the lakes and river, we put our outfit in a Lake Bennett boat and started for Dawson. We had a good team of dogs, and of course we piled them on top the outfit. That Spot was along — there was no losing him; and a dozen times, the first day, he knocked one or another of the dogs overboard in the course of fighting with them. It was close quarters, and he didn't like being crowded.

"What that dog needs is space," Steve said the second day. "Let's maroon him."

We did, running the boat in at Caribou Crossing for him to jump ashore. Two of the other dogs, good dogs, followed him; and we lost two whole days trying to find them. We never saw those two dogs again; but the quietness and relief we enjoyed made us decide, like the man who refused his hundred and fifty, that it was cheap at the price. For the first time in months Steve and I laughed and whistled and sang. We were as happy as clams. The dark days were over. The nightmare had been lifted. That Spot was gone.

Three weeks later, one morning, Steve and I were standing on the river bank at Dawson. A small boat was just arriving from Lake Bennett. I saw Steve give a start, and heard him say something that was not nice and that was not under his breath. Then I looked; and there, in the bow of the boat, with ears pricked up, sat Spot. Steve and I sneaked immediately, like beaten curs, like cowards, like absconders from justice. It was this last that the lieutenant of police thought when he saw us sneaking. He surmised that there were law officers in the boat who were after us. He didn't wait to find out, but kept us in sight, and in the M. & M. saloon got us in a corner. We had a merry time explaining, for we refused to go back to the boat and meet Spot; and finally he held us under guard of another policeman while he went to the boat. After we got clear of him, we started for the cabin, and when we arrived, there was that Spot sitting on the stoop waiting for us. Now how did he know we lived there? There were forty thousand people in Dawson that summer, and how did he *savvy* our cabin out of all the cabins? How did he know we were in Dawson, anyway? I leave it to you. But don't forget what I have said about his intelligence and that immortal something I have seen glimmering in his eyes.

There was no getting rid of him any more. There were too many people in Dawson who had bought him up on Chilkoot, and the story got around. Half a dozen times we put him on board steamboats going down the Yukon; but he merely went ashore at the first landing and trotted back up the bank. We couldn't sell him, we couldn't kill him (both Steve and I had tried), and nobody else was able to kill him. He bore a charmed life. I've seen him go down in a dog fight on the main street with fifty dogs on top of him, and when they were separated, he'd appear on all his four legs, unharmed, while two of the dogs that had been on top of him would be lying dead.

I saw him steal a chunk of moose meat from Major Dinwiddie's cache so heavy that he could just keep one jump ahead of Mrs. Dinwiddie's squaw cook, who was after him with an ax. As he went up the hill, after the squaw gave out, Major Dinwiddie himself came out and pumped his Winchester into the landscape. He emptied his magazine twice, and never touched that Spot. Then a policeman came along and arrested him for discharging firearms inside the city limits. Major Dinwiddie paid his fine, and Steve and I paid him for the moose meat at the rate of a dollar a pound, bones and all. That was what he paid for it. Meat was high that year.

I am only telling what I saw with my own eyes. And now I'll tell you something, also. I saw that Spot fall

through a water hole. The ice was three and a half feet
thick, and the current sucked him under like a straw.
Three hundred yards below was the big water hole, used
by the hospital. Spot crawled out of the hospital water
hole, licked off the water, bit out the ice that had formed
between his toes, trotted up the bank, and whipped a big
Newfoundland belonging to the Gold Commissioner.

In the fall of 1898, Steve and I poled up the Yukon on
the last water, bound for Stewart River. We took the
dogs along, all except Spot. We figured we'd been feeding him long enough. He'd cost us more time and trouble
and money and grub than we'd got by selling him on the
Chilkoot — especially grub. So Steve and I tied him down
in the cabin and pulled our freight. We camped that
night at the mouth of Indian River, and Steve and I were
pretty facetious over having shaken him. Steve was a
funny cuss, and I was just sitting up in the blankets and
laughing when a tornado hit camp. The way that Spot
walked into those dogs and gave them what-for was hair-
raising. Now how did he get loose? It's up to you. I
haven't any theory. And how did he get across the
Klondike River? That's another facer. And anyway,
how did he know we had gone up the Yukon? You see,
we went by water, and he couldn't smell our tracks.
Steve and I began to get superstitious about that dog.
He got on our nerves, too; and, between you and me, we
were just a mite afraid of him.

The freeze-up came on when we were at the mouth of
Henderson Creek, and we traded him off for two sacks of
flour to an outfit that was bound up White River after
copper. Now that whole outfit was lost. Never trace

nor hide nor hair of men, dogs, sleds, or anything was ever found. They dropped clean out of sight. It became one of the mysteries of the country. Steve and I plugged away up the Stewart, and six weeks afterward that Spot crawled into camp. He was a perambulating skeleton, and could just drag along; but he got there. And what I want to know is, who told him we were up the Stewart? We could have gone a thousand other places. How did he know? You tell me, and I'll tell you.

No losing him. At the Mayo he started a row with an Indian dog. The buck who owned the dog took a swing at Spot with an ax, missed him, and killed his own dog. Talk about magic and turning bullets aside — I, for one, consider it a blamed sight harder to turn an ax aside with a big buck at the other end of it. And I saw him do it with my own eyes. That buck didn't want to kill his own dog. You've got to show me.

I told you about Spot breaking into our meat cache. It was nearly the death of us. There wasn't any more meat to be killed, and meat was all we had to live on. The moose had gone back several hundred miles and the Indians with them. There we were. Spring was on, and we had to wait for the river to break. We got pretty thin before we decided to eat the dogs, and we decided to eat Spot first. Do you know what that dog did? He sneaked. Now how did he know our minds were made up to eat him? We sat up nights laying for him, but he never came back, and we ate the other dogs. We ate the whole team.

And now for the sequel. You know what it is when

a big river breaks up and a few billion tons of ice go out, jamming and milling and grinding. Just in the thick of it, when the Stewart went out, rumbling and roaring, we sighted Spot out in the middle. He'd got caught as he was trying to cross up above somewhere. Steve and I yelled and shouted and ran up and down the bank, tossing our hats in the air. Sometimes we'd stop and hug each other, we were that boisterous, for we saw Spot's finish. He didn't have a chance in a million. He didn't have any chance at all. After the ice-run, we got into a canoe and paddled down to the Yukon, and down the Yukon to Dawson, stopping to feed up for a week at the cabins at the mouth of Henderson Creek. And as we came in to the bank at Dawson, there sat that Spot, waiting for us, his ears pricked up, his tail wagging, his mouth smiling, extending a hearty welcome to us. Now how did he get out of that ice? How did he know we were coming to Dawson, to the very hour and minute, to be out there on the bank waiting for us?

The more I think of that Spot, the more I am convinced that there are things in this world that go beyond science. On no scientific grounds can that Spot be explained. It's psychic phenomena, or mysticism, or something of that sort, I guess, with a lot of theosophy thrown in. The Klondike is a good country. I might have been there yet, and become a millionaire, if it hadn't been for Spot. He got on my nerves. I stood him for two years altogether, and then I guess my stamina broke. It was the summer of 1899 when I pulled out. I didn't say anything to Steve. I just sneaked. But I fixed it up all right. I wrote Steve a note, and enclosed a package of "rough-on-rats," telling what to do with it. I was worn down to skin and bone by that Spot, and I was that nervous that I'd jump and look around when there wasn't anybody within hailing distance. But it was astonishing the way I recuperated when I got quit of him. I got back twenty pounds before I arrived in San Francisco, and by the time I'd crossed the ferry to Oakland I was my old self again, so that even my wife looked in vain for any change in me.

Steve wrote to me once, and his letter seemed irritated. He took it kind of hard because I'd left him with Spot. Also, he said he'd used the "rough-on-rats," per directions, and that there was nothing doing. A year went by. I was back in the office and prospering in all ways — even getting a bit fat. And then Steve arrived. He didn't look me up. I read his name in the steamer list, and wondered why. But I didn't wonder long. I got up one morning and found that Spot chained to the gatepost and holding up the milkman. Steve went north to Seattle, I learned, that very morning. I didn't put on any more weight. My wife made me buy him a collar and tag, and within an hour he showed his gratitude by killing her pet Persian cat. There is no getting rid of that Spot. He will be with me until I die, for he'll never die. My appetite is not so good since he arrived, and my wife says I am looking peaked. Last night that Spot got into Mr. Harvey's hen house (Harvey is my next door neighbor) and killed nineteen of his fancy-bred chickens. I shall have to pay for them. My neighbors on the other side quarreled with my wife and then moved out. Spot was the cause of it. And that is why I am

disappointed in Stephen Mackaye. I had no idea he was
so mean a man.

Unusual Words

cache — a hiding place for provisions or goods, usually in
the ground

circumventing — (there was no circumventing him) no getting
the better of him by craft or skill

iota — (without an iota of anything vindictive) without the
smallest possible particle of anything vindictive

kibosh — (put the *kibosh* on the whole outfit) made the whole
outfit afraid of him

maroon — to put off a ship and leave behind on an island
or uninhabited coast

mushed — (with whom I mushed over the Chilkoot trail)
with whom I tramped on foot over the Chilkoot trail

perambulating — walking, usually in a wandering, uncertain
fashion

psychic — (a psychic phenomenon) spiritualistic phenomenon

reincarnation — return of the soul, which has left one body,
to a new one

stamina — (my stamina broke) my endurance broke

theosophy — a religious faith which includes a belief in reincarnation

Questions for Self-Testing

1. From what did Spot get his name?
2. What induced the partners to buy him?
3. What did the writer finally decide it was that he saw in
   Spot's eyes?
4. When the teller took Spot out meaning to shoot him,
   why did he fail to do so?

5. Besides being lazy, what other shortcomings did Spot have?
6. How did he usually celebrate his return after being sold?
7. What was the most desperate effort which the partners made to lose Spot?
8. How does the teller explain Spot's finding the cabin of his owners in Dawson?
9. What is one of the evidences that Spot bore a charmed life?
10. What reason does the teller give for leaving Alaska?

TOPICS FOR THEMES OR DISCUSSION

1. What is a "tall story"?
2. Invent or summarize from memory another "tall story."
3. Could this same material be made into a serious story, perhaps a touching or pathetic one? Make some suggestions as to how this could be done.
4. The teller calls Spot intelligent looking. In your opinion, does he prove himself intelligent?
5. Does the teller's explanation of why he did not shoot Spot seem to you convincing?
6. Is the teller justified in his final attitude towards Stephen Mackaye?

THE 'COON AND DOG LOGAN

By JOHN SCHOOLCRAFT

"The 'Coon and Dog Logan" tells how 'coon hunting looks to the 'coon. The men who hunt are doing so partly for excitement and partly to save their chicken yards from losses. The dogs are acting under orders and according to their training. But what the 'coon is doing in the hunt is trying to save its life. From the 'coon's standpoint, therefore, 'coon hunting is a far more exciting business than it can possibly be from the standpoint of either dog or man. Throughout this story we are kept in mind of what the 'coon has at stake, for "The 'Coon and Dog Logan" is one of those unusual narratives in which the wild, pursued animal, not the tame, pursuing one, is the character to which the reader's sympathies go out.

The story appeared first in The American Boy, *to which the author, John Schoolcraft, has been an occasional contributor.*

Tʜʀᴇᴇ hundred days out of the year she slept until full night had come, but this was late afternoon of a cloudy autumn day, and the yelping of the beagle had wakened her. She crawled out of the sycamore branch which held her den and lay there peering down with the cunning, wise expression of some wicked old woman. Below her was a young beagle half covered with dirt, yelling at the top of his musical lungs down a rabbit hole. The puppy was hunting by himself for the first time in his life; he had followed a rabbit trail to the mouth of the burrow and was frantically digging there, while the rabbit, escaped through a back entrance, nibbled clover a half mile farther down the creek. The raccoon settled herself and licked her paws; she almost yawned, for she had whipped dogs three times the size of the beagle — cunning old 'coon dogs, with ears torn to shreds from countless fights with her kind, harked on by bloodthirsty masters.

Once awake, thoughts of food came to her. The creek was running full and muddy from a rain farther back in the hills. There would be good hunting there, for the full mid-stream current drove the fish into the little arms of quiet water. She was no such fisherman as the otter, but she managed to flip many a small bass, chub, or perch. She crawled back to the trunk of the tree and began to come down it, peering over her shoulder now and then, and pausing to lick a forepaw. Above the barking of the hound she heard a rustle in the wet leaves and stopped again to look over her shoulder. A spread-head snake drew his slow length along the ground within a yard of the beagle, intent on hunting the black baby toads brought out by the rain. All wild nature seemed to be flouting the earnest hound.

Within six feet of the ground the 'coon stopped. Above the belling of the beagle, above the rush of the stream, above the sound of the woodsman's ax that ticked like a clock in the still air, came another sound, the muted, muffled bark of a hound. The 'coon hung to the bark of the tree, peering this way and that with her worried, old woman's expression; the spread-head snake lifted a half foot of its body from the ground and the forked tongue played in and out like lightning. The ugly head sought the ground and the serpent glided to the shelter of a protecting oak root. Much faster than she had come down, the 'coon climbed to the hole above, and going within, thrust just the tip of her black muzzle out. The beagle kept up his musical yelling and sprayed the ground about him with a shower of leaf mold as he dug.

A big hound, black except for legs and a curious light

brown marking on the face which gave him the appearance of being spectacled, glided like a shadow between the close trunks of the trees. It was Logan, a big, fierce dog, the best 'coon dog along Deep Run. More than once, the wary animal watching from the hollow limb had heard his deep bay close on her heels, and hearing it had made for water. She might stop to fight with a lesser dog, or take to a tree, but once she had left a hot scent on the ground and the dog had found it, her safety lay in taking to Deep Run. The sharp little muzzle twitched, and she settled herself closer in her den. She was safe, for she had not been on the ground since the rain set in, and the hound, she thought, could not catch her scent from her lair.

Logan was running the same rabbit which had tickled the nose of the little beagle, but he was running "still mouth," except for the single short note that had warned the 'coon. It was his business to run nothing but 'possum and 'coon; in his babyhood he had been beaten for lifting his voice at the smell of rabbit, and he had never forgotten. That did not mean that he never ran rabbit; it meant that he never picked up a scent when there were men about him, and that he ran silently until the fluff of fur was between his jaws. Logan was a surly, mean hound, an inveterate chicken killer in spite of beatings that would have killed an ordinary dog, and unlike most his kind, an inveterate fighter with and killer of other dogs.

He came to a stop at the side of the beagle and nosed the smaller animal. A fierce, smothered bark welled from him, and his lips curled back from his teeth. He was warning the little hound to get away from game that belonged to his betters, but the puppy, thinking his efforts were to be crowned with success now that help had arrived, wagged his tail the harder and stayed in the burrow. His voice came out in a hollow, jubilant peal. Logan caught the puppy by the small of his back; the killing jaws snapped shut on the tender body, and the little dog's joyous yelling changed to a stricken howl. His back had been broken, and he died instantly.

The killer snuffed in the burrow and his keen, experienced nose told him that the game was long since gone. He walked to the side of the puppy and growled, then went to the stream edge and drank.

But when he had satisfied his thirst he did not leave the place as the old 'coon above longed for him to do; and he wandered about under the sycamore tree like an unhappy ghost, sniffing here, scratching there, and sitting down now and then to turn his muzzle to the four points of the compass.

Then he came to the tree trunk, and putting his forepaws on it, stretched his long body as high as it would reach. He began to jump. Each time she heard his scratching, she retreated farther into her den. She licked her paws and rubbed her grizzled head and a faint sound escaped her, like the squalling of a cat. There was a fight looming; she had whipped three dogs at a time, but this would be a struggle to the death.

Suddenly Logan's bark rang out like the deep peal of a bell, and at the sound of it the beating of the woodsman's ax stopped. A faint shrill cry arose. "Hi! Go on, boy!" The Adrians, father and son, were wood cutting — they had listened to the barking of their beagle and chopped on, for it was a little early for rabbit. But Logan's tree bark was as well known as the village fire bell, and it always brought a response, almost as quickly, from any man or boy within hearing. The hound knew that it was his business to keep the quarry off the ground until help arrived, and his voice rose in a ravening yell for blood. The old 'coon quivered, and turning, began to make her way deep into the tree, for even her sturdy heart trembled at the sound of the hound's voice and the long-drawn hunter's cry.

The man and the boy burst through the close growth of birch and stopped in the clearing. The father went at once to the foot of the sycamore and looked up, but the boy, proud owner of the little beagle, saw first the litter of fresh earth, a trail of blood on the ground, and then found his puppy lying where Logan had tossed him. "Look, Dad!" he said. "Tuck's dead!"

His father left the clamoring dog and came to stand beside his son. His eyes narrowed, and his nostrils were pinched and white, for Tuck was the only living son of old Sport, and old Sport had been the best rabbit dog he had ever had. Even in his extreme youth, the beagle had shown that he inherited his father's lovely nose. The old man looked at the scarred and bleeding body and said, "That 'coon done that. Nothing else could tear that-a-way. He must have come down and fit Tuck while he was digging that rabbit. You spell me, boy."

The 'coon hole was in the lowest branch on a big syca-more, the trunk of which was a good three feet in diameter. But when the old man buried his ax in it, the wood rang with a false, hollow note. Under the skillful hands of the old man the white chips and then the brown flew in a damp shower. Six inches of sound wood, after that a half foot of punk, and inside that the ax buried itself in the mold. The son took the ax and worked to the left; at the end of a half hour the great tree tottered, swayed, and fell. Logan was on the stump before the tree had stopped quivering, while the son watched at the hole in the branch above. The dog sniffed, and then, raising his great voice, began to dig in the rotten wood. The two watched him, mystified, for it had been their expectation that the raccoon would come from the hole higher up. Instead, Logan was boring into the stump, and at length the old man caught the hound by the collar and hauled him back, while the son put his head into the hollow stump and searched for sign of the quarry. What he saw made him draw back with an exclamation; he cut a stiff alder pole and went to the creek bank, where he probed beneath the surface of the water.

"He's got clean away, Dad," he said, coming back to his father. "That hole goes through the stump and underground and out into the water. He's got clean away."

Silently the old man shouldered the ax. He patted Logan on the head.

"He's a good dog, that Logan. Is there a moon tonight, son?"

"I reckon not."

"We'll hunt that 'coon. We can get Nellie — she can leave her pups now, and that blue tick dog of Claiburn's and that red dog of Carkle's he's just brought up from Carolina."

"That Tuck was a good dog," said the younger Adrian,

looking down at the white and lemon spotted body of his favorite. "He had a lot of old Sport in him."

"He did and he was the last that had. Son, I want to get that 'coon!"

He walked away through the birches, but the boy lingered. Any other dog he would have left to the buzzards that slanted over the treetops, but Tuck was different. When his father was out of sight, he picked up the beagle and followed. When he got closer to the house he would lay Tuck down, get a shovel, and bury him under the old apple tree.

The old 'coon lived by herself; the single remaining cub of her last litter had left her and set up in a hollow red oak across the creek. Occasionally, he and his mother met, sniffed at each other, and went to hunt together on the creek bank. There they stalked frogs and turned over rocks in search of crickets and beetles. The youngster was quick to learn, but he had not acquired his mother's quickness of foot, and more than once, when the two met, the cub followed to feed from her generosity. It was so on this night — a week after the young beagle had been killed. The cub's eyes glowed green as he crouched beside her and watched her skin a frog which she had scooped out of his marshy bed. It had been a week of terror, for every night the woods had been full of dogs, men, and lanterns, all keen on avenging the death of Tuck. The old 'coon and the young had kept to the trees, feeding on grubs and locusts.

A few quick rubs with her hard paw loosened the skin on the frog's belly and she peeled him as neatly as if he had been a banana. Then she washed him carefully in the water of the creek and laid the cold body on a clean stone between them. They ate, and when the last tender bone had been crunched into nothing, the old 'coon turned and made her way up through the rocks that tumbled down to the creek. It was late; a moon was rising, and she had learned that men come to hunt on dark nights. She was desperately hungry. She knew where, on the hillside, a belated guinea hen had made her nest; she had feasted on the eggs, and it was now in her mind that she and her son might stalk the wary hen herself.

At the top of the hill she skirted an open field from which the lights of the Adrian farmhouse were plainly visible. She kept to the underbrush and, wherever possible, made her way through the thickets of high and low blackberry bushes. She walked steadily with the shambling, rolling gait of an old sailor, but the youngster ran hither and thither, gamboling about his mother as a porpoise gambols about a tramp steamer. Every fox burrow, skunk hole, and rock which looked as though it might shelter crickets had to be investigated. The guinea nest lay in the lee of an old stone fence, a good quarter of a mile from the creek. The farther she got away from water, the more cautious the old 'coon became, for she knew that there lay her real safety. Once she had left a scent on the ground, a tree was no good. The barking of a shepherd dog over the hill made her nervous and apprehensive. Had it not been for an old log shed, the head of which was perhaps an eighth of a mile to her left, she would not have ventured so far away from the creek in times of such danger.

A sudden bell-like note behind her froze her to stone.

Nellie had struck the trail of one of them and had given notice. From the creek bank below came the long-drawn hunter's cry: "Hi! Go on, girl! Work 'em, girl! Hi!" The youngster galloped from the ground hog's den at which he had been sniffing and crouched close to his mother. There was a moment of dreadful silence, and then the bell-like note sounded again — an eager, doubtful sound. Nellie had struck the trail of the cub and its twistings and turnings puzzled her. In the old 'coon's mind there was a map of the country between her and the creek; the patch of open field, blackberry bushes in a long narrow thicket, a long shelf of loose rock under which a small animal could run, open woods, and then the log slide, which pitched as sharply as a barn roof from the top of the creek bank to the water's edge. But before she moved she wanted to hear Nellie again, and she wanted to know where Logan was.

The first dog belled again — three mellow quivering notes, and this time the deep voice of Logan answered her, nearer the creek and far to the right. After Logan's came the voices of the blue tick hound and the red dog from Carolina, all bearing up the hill to the help of Nellie. A treetop shone for a second in the white glare of a flash-light.

The old 'coon began to run, and the youngster ran with her.

She went swiftly; in the deep woods she was a match in speed for any dog, but across the open field Nellie could gain. The hounds were out of the woods and into the open before the quarry had reached the shelter of the first long strip of blackberry bushes. Into it they plunged, and behind them the chorus of tenor and baritone, alto and soprano was punctuated by yelps of pain. The low bush blackberries lay like saw edges in the grass. That strip of barbed torment held for a hundred yards, and once again the 'coons and the hounds were in open field. They sped across a sweet potato patch; Logan was in the lead, and the night air shook with his deep voice.

Water pouring down to the creek from the bare fields had scoured out a channel that ran under slabs of shale. Under it the old 'coon dashed, and after her the cub. He would have stopped, but the old one bore on and out, knowing that while the hounds might not be able to turn them out of their shelter, men could. Behind them the dogs had received a check. The blue tick dog began to dig, so did Nellie; the red dog sat down and scratched, but Logan went over the loose shale, sniffing at the crevices, and at the lower end found the trail again and voiced it. The running was in the deep woods now — territory over which the raccoons could make as much speed as the hounds. The old one even slackened her pace, for the head of the log slide was almost within sight. Once on the slide she could coast to the water, and once in the water she was a match for any dog that lived, more than a match, for she would have there the advantage that a water-polo player would have over a boxer.

Suddenly the old 'coon found that she ran alone. The youngster had lost heart at the yelling behind him, and had gone up a tree. She could see him crouching in the first fork of an ash tree, peering down with frightened, big eyes.

The mother stopped. Her son had left her side more

than a month ago to care for himself, and when they met it was almost as if strangers met. Within another month she would have forgotten him and he would have forgotten her, for by that time each would have mated. But there stirred in her some of the protective instinct that had suckled, reared, and guarded him.

The dogs were so close that she could hear the patter of their feet on the leaves. She ran back to the tree up which the youngster had gone and there crossed his trail slowly and deliberately, so slowly that Nellie and the blue tick hound and the red dog saw her and bore off after her down toward the creek bank. But not the wise Logan — he kept the straight scent that carried him to the foot of the youngster's tree, and there he set up his tree bark. Hearing it, the Adrians, father and son, followed Logan, for they trusted him.

Near the foot of the hill the old 'coon reared with her back against a tree and waited. Logan was the only hound that could drive her to water. Nellie came first, running with her nose down. The sight of the glowing green eyes did not give her a check; she threw herself in and met a raking double stroke of the 'coon's forepaws. Her own jaws clicked harmlessly, while the 'coon's teeth met in the flesh of her shoulder. She rolled back and away, and without the men behind her to urge her on, had no stomach for more. The blue tick dog came next; he threw himself in, standing almost erect with his stiffened forelegs out to ward off the 'coon, but the latter, more agile, closer to the ground, hurled him back with the skin of his belly torn to ribbons. The red dog stopped, wagged his tail, and turned back up the hill.

All the time the steady, baleful barking of Logan and the beat of the ax sounded through the woods. The red dog was joining his voice with Logan's and one by one Nellie and the blue tick dog went up the hill to gain the comforting presence of men. The old 'coon licked her paws, squatted close to the ground, and squalled. The sound of the dogs drowned her outcry; she meant it for a challenge, for an invitation to leave the youngster and follow her. When it was not answered, she moved farther up the hill, so close that she could see the dogs and the legs of the men in the light of the lantern. The cracking of the tree trunk, the shouts of the men, and the baying of the dogs filled her with a consuming rage, and she squalled again. She licked the blood from her lips, but she dared not throw herself among the hunters at the foot of the tree. She sat where she was until the tree crashed, and the growling and worrying and shouting told her that the cub was dead. She squalled again.

Dogs, lanterns, and men moved away from the tree. The younger Adrian carried the cub by his tail. They moved in a direction that carried them toward the log slide, and she followed, bearing in closer as the log slide was nearer. She could see Logan and the red dog running about in the ring of the lantern, sniffing eagerly, aroused by one taste of blood. When the big hound sheared close to her the 'coon squalled again, and he stopped. She could hear him sniffing, then he put his nose to the ground and ran in eager circles. She crouched until his deep voice, scarcely ten yards away, told her he had found her trail, then she scrambled up the log supports at the head of the slide and poised on the edge with her big, phosphorescent eyes turned on the dog. He paused for a moment and then leaped, and the two went down together in a tumbling, worrying mass. The hound had a thick fold of hide in his teeth, but his enemy's claws were raking his belly cruelly, and her teeth were buried in the thick muscles of his throat.

The cold waters of Deep Run received them. They sank far under, but neither released a hold except to take a new one. The brawling current carried them downstream; they bumped on logs and rocks, but clung like burrs until the current swept them into an eddy of quiet, deep water. And all the time the wise old 'coon had been shifting her hold so as to bring her on top of the hound's head. The slow motion of the eddy carried them around and around as they fought. And Logan knew that he was out of his element and tried to get ashore. He was heavy in the water — she was light and her wide feet gave her an advantage. He struggled for a footing, for something on which to stand so that he could slash and grip, but he went under and the water got into his lungs. He let her go and struck out for the shore, but she dragged him back into deep water, swimming only with her hind feet. At last she pulled herself up so that the weight of her chunky body lay on Logan's head. Her teeth and claws were buried in his neck. His tail whipped the water and his big muscles jerked and heaved, but she rode him like an old witch riding a mare to the death. The eddy carried them about in slow, big circles.

A frog, inspired by the late moon, raised his voice. A black wrinkled paw scooped him out of his bed and a single bite at the back of the neck stilled him. The old 'coon carried him to the water's edge, rubbed the thin skin of his belly until it broke loose and then drew him out of his hide with beautiful neatness. Carefully she washed him, and ate. It was almost dawn. From across the creek came the sound of the hunter's horn, calling the dogs home. Nellie heard it, and the blue tick dog, and the red dog from Carolina, but not the fierce Logan, lying inert in the shallow water of the eddy.

UNUSUAL WORDS

beagle — a small, smooth-haired hound

inert — (lying inert in the shallow water) lying without any movement

phosphorescent — (her big, phosphorescent eyes) her eyes shining as if covered with phosphorus

QUESTIONS FOR SELF-TESTING

1. When the raccoon peered down from her tree at the beagle, what does the author say she resembled?
2. Was the raccoon afraid of the beagle?
3. What was the disposition of the dog Logan?
4. What did Logan do first when he found he had treed a 'coon?
5. Why did Logan never bark when he chased rabbits?
6. For what reason do the Adrians so especially want to kill this particular 'coon?
7. When her tree is cut down, how does the raccoon escape?
8. How does the author describe the raccoon's gait when walking?
9. When the old raccoon and the young one are hunting together, what makes the young one's trail the harder to follow?

10. How did the old raccoon try to save her cub?
11. Why was she not successful in saving it?
12. Where does the author make it clear to us that the mother, after her cub was killed, wanted to fight Logan instead of wanting only to escape?

TOPICS FOR THEMES OR DISCUSSION

1. In "The 'Coon and Dog Logan," why is it necessary for the story that the author should make the reader dislike Logan?
2. What, exactly, are the passages which make the reader dislike him?
3. A great many animal stories (for example, the stories in Kipling's *Jungle Books*) tell of animals who are human beings in all but their outside appearance. Does this author anywhere make his animals act like people?
4. The author tells this story from the standpoint of the mother raccoon, so that she is the one in whom the reader is interested. What is another standpoint from which the story might be told?
5. "All wild life ends in tragedy."—Ernest Thompson Seton. Write a page on how "The 'Coon and Dog Logan" illustrates the truth or the untruth of this statement.

BINGISM

By Booth Tarkington

Penrod Schofield is probably the most widely known small boy who has entered American fiction since the time of Huckleberry Finn. Penrod, however, is different in almost every way from Huckleberry Finn. He is younger, he stays in one place, and, worst of all from Penrod's point of view, he belongs to a quite ordinary family, which expects him to be ordinary too.

Penrod's family lives in the everyday fashion of most families except when their way of living is suddenly disturbed by Penrod's experiments and adventures. Those adventures usually have to be manufactured out of happenings which become exciting only after Penrod has been at work on them. Usually, too, as in this story, a very large part of the adventure takes place inside Penrod's own mind.

"Bingism" is taken from the volume of stories called Penrod and Sam. *Booth Tarkington, the author, has written also a volume of stories called* Penrod, *as well as many other stories and novels with grown-up characters.*

Penrod Schofield, having been "kept in" for the unjust period of twenty minutes after school, emerged to a deserted street. That is, the street was deserted so far as Penrod was concerned. Here and there people were to be seen upon the sidewalks, but they were adults, and they and the shade trees had about the same quality of significance in Penrod's consciousness. Usually he saw grown people in the mass, which is to say, they were virtually invisible to him, though exceptions must be taken in favor of policemen, firemen, streetcar conductors, motormen, and all other men in any sort of uniform or regalia. But this afternoon none of these met the roving eye, and Penrod set out upon his homeward way wholly dependent upon his own resources.

To one of Penrod's inner texture, a mere unadorned walk from one point to another was intolerable, and he had not gone a block without achieving some slight remedy for the tameness of life. An electric-light pole at the corner, invested with powers of observation, might have been surprised to find itself suddenly enacting a rôle of dubious honor in improvised melodrama. Penrod, approaching, gave the pole a look of sharp suspicion, then one of conviction; slapped it lightly and contemptuously with his open hand; passed on a few paces, but turned abruptly, and, pointing his right forefinger, uttered the symbolic word, "Bing!"

The plot was somewhat indefinite; yet nothing is more certain than that the electric-light pole had first attempted something against him, then growing bitter when slapped, and stealing after him to take him treacherously in the back, had got itself shot through and through by one too old in such warfare to be caught off his guard.

Leaving the body to lie where it was, he placed the smoking pistol in a holster at his saddlebow — he had decided that he was mounted — and proceeded up the street. At intervals he indulged himself in other encounters, reining in at first suspicion of ambush with a muttered, "Whoa, Charlie!" or "Whoa, Mike!" or even "Whoa, Washington!" for preoccupation with the enemy outweighed attention to the details of theatrical consistency, though the steed's varying names were at least harmoniously masculine, since a boy, in these creative moments, never rides a mare. And having brought Charlie or Mike or Washington to a standstill, Penrod would draw the sure weapon from its holster and — "Bing! Bing! Bing!" — let them have it.

It is not to be understood that this was a noisy performance, or even an obvious one. It attracted no attention from any pedestrian, and it was to be perceived only that a boy was proceeding up the street at a somewhat irregular gait. Three or four years earlier, when Penrod was seven or eight, he would have shouted "Bing!" at the top of his voice; he would have galloped openly; all the world might have seen that he bestrode a charger. But a change had come upon him with advancing years. Although the grown people in sight were indeed to him as walking trees, his dramas were accomplished principally by suggestion and symbol. His "Whoas" and "Bings" were delivered in a husky whisper, and his equestrianism was established by action mostly of the mind, the accompanying artistry of the feet being unintelligible to the passerby.

And yet, though he concealed from observation the stirring little scenes he thus enacted, a love of realism was increasing within him. Early childhood is not fastidious about the accessories of its drama — a cane is vividly a gun which may instantly, as vividly, become a horse; but at Penrod's time of life the lath sword is no longer satisfactory. Indeed, he now had a vague sense that weapons of wood were unworthy to the point of being contemptible and ridiculous, and he employed them only when he was alone and unseen. For months a yearning had grown more and more poignant in his vitals, and this yearning was symbolized by one of his most profound secrets. In the inner pocket of his jacket he carried a bit of wood whittled into the distant likeness of a pistol, but not even Sam Williams had seen it. The wooden pistol never knew the light of day, save when Penrod was in solitude; and yet it never left his side except at night, when it was placed under his pillow. Still, it did not satisfy; it was but the token of his yearning and his dream. With all his might and main Penrod longed for one thing beyond all others. He wanted a Real Pistol!

That was natural. Pictures of real pistols being used to magnificently romantic effect were upon almost all the billboards in town, the year round; and as for the "movie" shows, they could not have lived an hour unpistoled. In the drugstore, where Penrod bought his candy and soda when he was in funds, he would linger to turn the pages of periodicals whose illustrations were fascinatingly pistolic. Some of the magazines upon the very library table at home were sprinkled with pictures of people (usually in evening clothes) pointing pistols at other people. Nay, the Library Board of the town had emitted a "Selected List of Fifteen Books for Boys," and Penrod had read fourteen of them with pleasure, but as the fifteenth contained no weapons in the earlier chapters and held forth little prospect of any shooting at all, he abandoned it halfway, and read the most sanguinary of the other fourteen over again. So, the daily food of his imagination being gun, what wonder that he thirsted for the Real!

He passed from the sidewalk into his own yard, with a subdued "Bing!" inflicted upon the stolid person of a gatepost, and, entering the house through the kitchen, ceased to bing for a time. However, driven back from the fore part of the house by a dismal sound of callers, he returned to the kitchen and sat down.

"Della," he said to the cook, "do you know what I'd do if you was a crook and I had my orromatic with me?"

Della was industrious and preoccupied. "If I was a cook!" she repeated ignorantly, and with no cordiality. "Well, I *am* a cook. I'm a-cookin' right now. Either g'wan in the house where y'b'long, or git out in th' yard!"

Penrod chose the latter, and betook himself slowly to the back fence, where he was greeted in a boisterous manner by his wistful little old dog, Duke, returning from some affair of his own in the alley.

"Get down!" said Penrod coldly, and bestowed a spiritless "Bing!" upon him.

At this moment a shout was heard from the alley, "Yay, Penrod!" and the sandy head of comrade Sam Williams appeared above the fence.

"Come on over," said Penrod.

As Sam obediently climbed the fence, the little old dog Duke moved slowly away, but presently, glancing back over his shoulder and seeing the two boys standing together, he broke into a trot and disappeared round a corner of the house. He was a dog of long and enlightening experience; and he made it clear that the conjunction of Penrod and Sam portended events which, from his point of view, might be unfortunate. Duke had a forgiving disposition, but he also possessed a melancholy wisdom. In the company of either Penrod or Sam, alone, affection often caused him to linger, albeit with a little pessimism, but when he saw them together, he invariably withdrew in as unobtrusive a manner as haste would allow.

"What you doin'?" Sam asked.

"Nothin'. What you?"

"I'll show you if you'll come over to our house," said

Sam, who was wearing an important and secretive expression.

"What for?" Penrod showed little interest.

"Well, I said I'd show you if you came on over, didn't I?"

"But you haven't got anything I haven't got," said Penrod indifferently. "I know everything that's in your yard and in your stable, and there isn't a thing —"

"I didn't say it was in the yard or in the stable, did I?"

"Well, there ain't anything in your house," returned Penrod frankly, "that I'd walk two feet to look at — not a thing!"

"Oh, no!" Sam assumed mockery. "Oh, no, you wouldn't! You know what it is, don't you? Yes, you do!"

Penrod's curiosity stirred somewhat.

"Well, all right," he said, "I got nothin' to do. I just as soon go. What is it?"

"You wait and see," said Sam, as they climbed the fence. "I bet *your* ole eyes'll open pretty far in about a minute or so!"

"I bet they don't. It takes a good deal to get me excited, unless it's sumpthing mighty —"

"You'll see!" Sam promised.

He opened an alley gate and stepped into his own yard in a manner signaling caution — though the exploit, thus far, certainly required none — and Penrod began to be impressed and hopeful. They entered the house, silently, encountering no one, and Sam led the way upstairs, tiptoeing, implying unusual and increasing peril. Turning, in the upper hall, they went into Sam's father's bedroom, and Sam closed the door with a caution so genuine that already Penrod's eyes began to fulfil his host's prediction. Adventures in another boy's house are trying to the nerves; and another boy's father's bedroom, when invaded, has a violated sanctity that is almost appalling. Penrod felt that something was about to happen — something much more important than he had anticipated.

Sam tiptoed across the room to a chest of drawers, and, kneeling, carefully pulled out the lowest drawer until the surface of its contents — Mr. Williams' winter underwear — lay exposed. Then he fumbled beneath the garments and drew forth a large object, displaying it triumphantly to the satisfactorily dumfounded Penrod.

It was a blue-steel Colt's revolver, of the heaviest pattern made in the Seventies. Mr. Williams had inherited it from Sam's grandfather (a small man, a deacon, a dyspeptic) and it was larger and more horrible than any revolver either of the boys had ever seen in any picture, moving or stationary. Moreover, greenish bullets of great size were to be seen in the chambers of the cylinder, suggesting massacre rather than mere murder. This revolver was Real and it was Loaded!

Both boys lived breathlessly through a magnificent moment.

"Leave me have it!" gasped Penrod. "Leave me have hold of it!"

"You wait a minute!" Sam protested, in a whisper. "I want to show you how I do."

"No; you let me show you how *I* do!" Penrod insisted; and they scuffled for possession.

"Look out!" Sam whispered warningly. "It might go off."

"Then you better leave me have it!" And Penrod, victorious and flushed, stepped back, the weapon in his grasp. "Here," he said, "this is the way I do: You be a crook; and suppose you got a dagger, and I —"

"I don't want any dagger," Sam protested, advancing. "I want that revolaver. It's my father's revolaver, ain't it?"

"Well, *wait* a minute, can't you? I got a right to show you the way I *do*, first, haven't I?" Penrod began an improvisation on the spot. "Say I'm comin' along after dark like this — look, Sam! And say you try to make a jump at me —"

"I won't!" Sam declined this rôle impatiently. "I guess it ain't *your* father's revolaver, is it?"

"Well, it may be your father's but it ain't yours," Penrod argued, becoming logical. "It ain't either's of us revolaver, so I got as much right —"

"You haven't either. It's my fath —"

"*Watch*, can't you — just a minute!" Penrod urged vehemently. "I'm not goin' to keep it, am I? You can have it when I get through, can't you? Here's how *I* do: I'm comin' along after dark, just walkin' along this way — like this — look, Sam!"

Penrod, suiting the action to the word, walked to the other end of the room, swinging the revolver at his side with affected carelessness.

"I'm just walkin' along like this, and first I don't see you," continued the actor. "Then I kind of get a notion sumpthing wrong's liable to happen, so I — No!" He interrupted himself abruptly. "No; that isn't it. You wouldn't notice that I had my good ole revolaver

with me. You wouldn't think I had one, because it'd be
under my coat like this, and you wouldn't see it." Penrod stuck the muzzle of the pistol into the waistband of
his knickerbockers at the left side and, buttoning his
jacket, sustained the weapon in concealment by pressure
of his elbow. "So you think I haven't got any; you think
I'm just a man comin' along, and so you —"

Sam advanced. "Well, you've had your turn," he said.
"Now, it's mine. I'm goin' to show you how I —"

"*Watch* me, can't you?" Penrod wailed. "I haven't
showed you how *I* do, have I? My goodness! Can't
you watch me a minute?"

"I *have* been! You said yourself it'd be my turn soon
as you —"

"My goodness! Let me have a *chance*, can't you?"
Penrod retreated to the wall, turning his right side toward
Sam and keeping the revolver still protected under his
coat. "I got to have my turn first, haven't I?"

"Well, yours is over long ago."

"It isn't either! I —"

"Anyway," said Sam decidedly, clutching him by the
right shoulder and endeavoring to reach his left side —
"anyway, I'm goin' to have it now."

"You said I could have my turn out!" Penrod, carried
away by indignation, raised his voice.

"I did not!" Sam, likewise lost to caution, asserted
his denial loudly.

"You did, too."

"You said —"

"I never said anything!"

"You said — Quit that!"

"Boys!" Mrs. Williams, Sam's mother, opened the door of the room and stood upon the threshold. The scuffling of Sam and Penrod ceased instantly, and they stood hushed and stricken, while fear fell upon them. "Boys, you weren't quarreling, were you?"

"Ma'am?" said Sam.

"Were you quarreling with Penrod?"

"No, ma'am," answered Sam in a small voice.

"It sounded like it. What was the matter?"

Both boys returned her curious glance with meekness. They were summoning their faculties — which were needed. Indeed, these are the crises which prepare a boy for the business difficulties of his later life. Penrod, with the huge weapon beneath his jacket, insecurely supported by an elbow and by a waistband which he instantly began to distrust, experienced distressful sensations similar to those of the owner of too heavily insured property carrying a gasoline can under his overcoat and detained for conversation by a policeman. And if, in the coming years, it was to be Penrod's lot to find himself in that precise situation, no doubt he would be the better prepared for it on account of this present afternoon's experience under the scalding eye of Mrs. Williams. It should be added that Mrs. Williams' eye was awful to the imagination only. It was a gentle eye and but mildly curious, having no remote suspicion of the dreadful truth, for Sam had backed upon the chest of drawers and closed the damnatory open one with the calves of his legs.

Sam, not bearing the fatal evidence upon his person, was in a better state than Penrod, though when boys fall

into the stillness now assumed by these two, it should
be understood that they are suffering. Penrod, in fact,
was the prey to apprehension so keen that the actual
pit of his stomach was cold.

Being the actual custodian of the crime, he understood
that his case was several degrees more serious than that
of Sam, who, in the event of detection, would be convicted
as only an accessory. It was a lesson, and Penrod already
repented his selfishness in not allowing Sam to show how
he did, first.

"You're sure you weren't quarreling, Sam?" said Mrs.
Williams.

"No, ma'am; we were just talking."

Still she seemed dimly uneasy, and her eye swung to
Penrod.

"What were you and Sam talking about, Penrod?"

"Ma'am?"

"What were you talking about?"

Penrod gulped invisibly.

"Well," he murmured, "it wasn't much. Different
things."

"What things?"

"Oh, just sumpthing. Different things."

"I'm glad you weren't quarreling," said Mrs. Williams,
reassured by this reply, which, though somewhat baffling,
was thoroughly familiar to her ear. "Now, if you'll come
downstairs, I'll give you each one cookie and no more, so
your appetites won't be spoiled for your dinners."

She stood, evidently expecting them to precede her.
To linger might renew vague suspicion, causing it to become more definite; and boys preserve themselves from

moment to moment, not often attempting to secure the future. Consequently, the apprehensive Sam and the unfortunate Penrod (with the monstrous implement bulking against his ribs) walked out of the room and down the stairs, their countenances indicating an interior condition of solemnity. And a curious shade of behavior might have here interested a criminologist. Penrod endeavored to keep as close to Sam as possible, like a lonely person seeking company, while, on the other hand, Sam kept moving away from Penrod, seeming to desire an appearance of aloofness.

"Go into the library, boys," said Mrs. Williams, as the three reached the foot of the stairs. "I'll bring you your cookies. Papa's in there."

Under her eye the two entered the library, to find Mr. Williams reading his evening paper. He looked up pleasantly, but it seemed to Penrod that he had an ominous and penetrating expression.

"What have you been up to, you boys?" inquired this enemy.

"Nothing," said Sam. "Different things."

"What like?"

"Oh — just different things."

Mr. Williams nodded; then his glance rested casually upon Penrod.

"What's the matter with your arm, Penrod?"

Penrod became paler, and Sam withdrew from him almost conspicuously.

"Sir?"

"I said, What's the matter with your arm?"

"Which one?" Penrod quavered.

"Your left. You seem to be holding it in an unnatural position. Have you hurt it?"

Penrod swallowed. "Yes, sir. A boy bit me — I mean a dog — a dog bit me."

Mr. Williams murmured sympathetically: "That's too bad! Where did he bite you?"

"On the — right on the elbow."

"Good gracious! Perhaps you ought to have it cauterized."

"Sir?"

"Did you have a doctor look at it?"

"No, sir. My mother put some stuff from the drugstore on it."

"Oh, I see. Probably it's all right, then."

"Yes, sir." Penrod drew breath more freely, and accepted the warm cookie Mrs. Williams brought him. He ate it without relish.

"You can have only one apiece," she said. "It's too near dinner-time. You needn't beg for any more, because you can't have 'em."

They were good about that; they were in no frame of digestion for cookies.

"Was it your own dog that bit you?" Mr. Williams inquired.

"Sir? No, sir. It wasn't Duke."

"Penrod!" Mrs. Williams exclaimed. "When did it happen?"

"I don't remember just when," he answered feebly. "I guess it was day before yesterday."

"Gracious! How did it —"

"He — he just came up and bit me."

"Why, that's terrible! It might be dangerous for other children," said Mrs. Williams, with a solicitous glance at Sam. "Don't you know whom he belongs to?"

"No'm. It was just a dog."

"You poor boy! Your mother must have been dreadfully frightened when you came home and she saw —"

She was interrupted by the entrance of a middle-aged colored woman. "Miz Williams," she began, and then, as she caught sight of Penrod, she addressed him directly, "You' ma telefoam if you here, to send you home right away, 'cause they waitin' dinner on you."

"Run along, then," said Mrs. Williams, patting the visitor lightly upon his shoulder; and she accompanied him to the front door. "Tell your mother I'm so sorry about your getting bitten, and you must take good care of it, Penrod."

"Yes'm."

Penrod lingered helplessly outside the doorway, looking at Sam, who stood partially obscured in the hall, behind Mrs. Williams. Penrod's eyes, with a veiled anguish, conveyed a pleading for help as well as a horror of the position in which he found himself. Sam, however, pale and determined, seemed to have assumed a stony attitude of detachment, as if it were well understood between them that his own comparative innocence was established, and that whatever catastrophe ensued, Penrod had brought it on and must bear the brunt of it alone.

"Well, you'd better run along, since they're waiting for you at home," said Mrs. Williams, closing the door. "Good-night, Penrod."

. . . Ten minutes later Penrod took his place at his

own dinner table, somewhat breathless but with an expression of perfect composure.

"Can't you *ever* come home without being telephoned for?" demanded his father.

"Yes, sir." And Penrod added reproachfully, placing the blame upon members of Mr. Schofield's own class, "Sam's mother and father kept me, or I'd been home long ago. They would keep on talkin', and I guess I had to be *polite*, didn't I?"

His left arm was as free as his right; there was no dreadful bulk beneath his jacket, and at Penrod's age the future is too far away to be worried about. The difference between temporary security and permanent security is left for grown people. To Penrod, security was security, and before his dinner was half eaten his spirit had become fairly serene.

Nevertheless, when he entered the empty carriage house of the stable, on his return from school the next afternoon, his expression was not altogether without apprehension, and he stood in the doorway looking well about him before he lifted a loosened plank in the flooring and took from beneath it the grand old weapon of the Williams family. Nor did his eye lighten with any pleasurable excitement as he sat himself down in a shadowy corner and began some sketchy experiments with the mechanism. The allure of first sight was gone. In Mr. Williams' bedchamber, with Sam clamoring for possession, it had seemed to Penrod that nothing in the world was so desirable as to have that revolver in his own hands — it was his dream come true. But, for reasons not definitely known to him, the charm had departed; he turned the

cylinder gingerly, almost with distaste; and slowly there
stole over him a feeling that there was something repellent
and threatening in the heavy blue steel.

Thus does the long-dreamed Real misbehave — not only
for Penrod!

More out of a sense of duty to bingism in general than
for any other reason, he pointed the revolver at the
lawn-mower, and gloomily murmured, "Bing!"

Simultaneously, a low and cautious voice sounded from
the yard outside, "Yay, Penrod!" and Sam Williams
darkened the doorway, his eye falling instantly upon the
weapon in his friend's hand. Sam seemed relieved to see
it.

"You didn't get caught with it, did you?" he said
hastily.

Penrod shook his head, rising.

"I guess not! I guess I got *some* brains around me,"
he added, inspired by Sam's presence to assume a slight
swagger. "They'd have to get up pretty early to find
any good ole revolaver, once I got *my* hands on it!"

"I guess we can keep it, all right," Sam said confi-
dentially. "Because this morning papa was putting on
his winter underclothes and he found it wasn't there,
and they looked all over and everywhere, and he was
pretty mad, and said he knew it was those cheap plumbers
stole it that mamma got instead of the regular plumbers
he always used to have, and he said there wasn't any
chance ever gettin' it back, because you couldn't tell which
one took it, and they'd all swear it wasn't them. So it
looks like we could keep it for our revolaver, Penrod,
don't it? I'll give you half of it."

Penrod affected some enthusiasm. "Sam, we'll keep it out here in the stable."

"Yes, and we'll go huntin' with it. We'll do lots of things with it!" But Sam made no effort to take it, and neither boy seemed to feel yesterday's necessity to show the other how he did. "Wait till next Fourth o' July!" Sam continued. "Oh, oh! Look out!"

This incited a genuine spark from Penrod.

"Fourth o' July! I guess she'll be a little better than any firecrackers! Just a little 'Bing! Bing! Bing!' she'll be goin'. 'Bing! Bing! Bing!'"

The suggestion of noise stirred his comrade. "I'll bet she'll go off louder'n that time the gas-works blew up! I wouldn't be afraid to shoot her off *any* time."

"I bet you would," said Penrod. "You aren't used to revolavers the way I —"

"You aren't, either!" Sam exclaimed promptly. "I wouldn't be any more afraid to shoot her off than you would."

"You would, too!"

"I would not!"

"Well, let's see you then; you talk so much!" And Penrod handed the weapon scornfully to Sam, who at once became less self-assertive.

"I'd shoot her off in a minute," Sam said, "only it might break sumpthing if it hit it."

"Hold her up in the air, then. It can't hurt the roof, can it?"

Sam, with a desperate expression, lifted the revolver at arm's length. Both boys turned away their heads, and Penrod put his fingers in his ears — but nothing

happened. "What's the matter?" he demanded. "Why
don't you go on if you're goin' to?"

Sam lowered his arm. "I guess I didn't have her
cocked," he said apologetically, whereupon Penrod loudly
jeered.

"Tryin' to shoot a revolaver and didn't know enough
to cock her! If I didn't know any more about revolavers
than that, I'd —"

"There!" Sam exclaimed, managing to draw back the
hammer until two chilling clicks warranted his opinion
that the pistol was now ready to perform its office. "I
guess she'll do all right to suit you *this* time!"

"Well, why'n't you go ahead, then; you know so
much!" And as Sam raised his arm, Penrod again turned
away his head and placed his forefingers in his ears.

A pause followed.

"Why'n't you go ahead?"

Penrod, after waiting in keen suspense, turned to be-
hold his friend standing with his right arm above his head,
his left hand over his left ear, and both eyes closed.

"I can't pull the trigger," said Sam indistinctly, his
face convulsed as in sympathy with the great muscular
efforts of other parts of his body. "She won't pull!"

"She won't?" Penrod remarked with scorn. "I'll bet *I*
could pull her."

Sam promptly opened his eyes and handed the weapon
to Penrod.

"All right," he said, with surprising and unusual mildness. "You try her, then."

Inwardly discomfited to a disagreeable extent, Penrod
attempted to talk his own misgivings out of countenance.

"Poor 'ittle baby!" he said, swinging the pistol at his side with a fair pretense of careless ease. "Ain't even strong enough to pull a trigger! Poor 'ittle baby! Well, if you can't even do that much, you better watch me while I —"

"Well," said Sam reasonably, "why don't you go on and do it then?"

"Well, I *am* goin' to, ain't I?"

"Well, then, why don't you?"

"Oh, I'll do it fast enough to suit *you*, I guess," Penrod retorted, swinging the big revolver up a little higher than his shoulder and pointing it in the direction of the double doors, which opened upon the alley. "You better run, Sam," he jeered. "You'll be pretty scared when I shoot her off, I guess."

"Well, why don't you *see* if I will? I bet you're afraid yourself."

"Oh, I am, am I?" said Penrod, in a reckless voice — and his finger touched the trigger. It seemed to him that his finger no more than touched it; perhaps he had been reassured by Sam's assertion that the trigger was difficult. His intentions must remain in doubt, and probably Penrod himself was not certain of them; but one thing comes to the surface as entirely definite — that trigger was not so hard to pull as Sam said it was.

Bang! Wh-a-a-ack! A shattering report split the air of the stable, and there was an orifice of remarkable diameter in the alley door. With these phenomena, three yells, expressing excitement of different kinds, were almost simultaneous — two from within the stable and the third from a point in the alley about eleven inches lower than the orifice just constructed in the planking of the door. This third point, roughly speaking, was the open mouth of a gayly dressed young colored man whose attention, as he strolled, had been thus violently distracted from some mental computations he was making in numbers, including, particularly, those symbols of ecstasy or woe, as the case might be, seven and eleven. His eye at once perceived the orifice on a line enervatingly little above the top of his head; and, although he had not supposed himself so well known in this neighborhood, he was aware that he did, here and there, possess acquaintances of whom some such uncomplimentary action might be expected as natural and characteristic. His immediate procedure was to prostrate himself flat upon the ground, against the stable doors.

In so doing, his shoulders came brusquely in contact with one of them, which happened to be unfastened, and it swung open, revealing to his gaze two stark-white boys, one of them holding an enormous pistol and both staring at him in a stupor of ultimate horror. For, to the glassy eyes of Penrod and Sam, the stratagem of the young colored man, thus dropping to earth, disclosed, with awful certainty, a slaughtered body.

This dreadful thing raised itself upon its elbows and looked at them, and there followed a motionless moment — a tableau of brief duration, for both boys turned and would have fled, shrieking, but the body spoke:

"'At's a nice business!" it said reproachfully. "Nice business! Tryin' blow a man's head off!"

Penrod was unable to speak, but Sam managed to summon the tremulous semblance of a voice.

"Where — where did it hit you?" he gasped.

"Nemmine anything 'bout where it *hit* me," the young colored man returned, dusting his breast and knees as he rose. "I want to know what kine o' white boys you think you is — man can't walk 'long street 'thout you blowin' his head off!" He entered the stable and, with an indignation surely justified, took the pistol from the limp, cold hand of Penrod. "Whose gun you playin' with? Where you git 'at gun?"

"It's ours," quavered Sam. "It belongs to us."

"Then you' pa ought to be 'rested," said the young colored man. "Lettin' boys play with gun!" He examined the revolver with an interest in which there began to appear symptoms of a pleasurable appreciation. "My goo'ness! Gun like 'iss blow a team o' steers thew a brick house! *Look* at 'at gun!" With his right hand he twirled it in a manner most dexterous and surprising; then suddenly he became severe. "You white boy, listen me!" he said. "Ef I went an' did what I *ought* to did, I'd march straight out 'iss stable, git a policeman, an' tell him 'rest you an' take you off to jail. 'At's what you need — blowin' man's head off! Listen me: I'm goin' take 'iss gun an' th'ow her away where you can't do no mo' harm with her. I'm goin' take her way off in the woods an' th'ow her away where can't nobody fine her an' go blowin' man's head off with her. 'At's what I'm goin' do!" And placing the revolver inside his coat as inconspicuously as possible, he proceeded to the open door and into the alley, where he turned for a final word. "I let you off 'iss one time," he said, "but listen me — you listen, white boy: you bet' not tell you' pa. *I* ain'

goin' tell him, an' *you* ain' goin' tell him. He want know
where gun gone, you tell him you los' her."

He disappeared rapidly.

Sam Williams, swallowing continuously, presently
walked to the alley door, and remarked in a weak voice,
"I'm sick at my stummick." He paused, then added
more decidedly: "I'm goin' home. I guess I've stood
about enough around here for one day!" And bestowing
a last glance upon his friend, who was now sitting dumbly
upon the floor in the exact spot where he had stood to
fire the dreadful shot, Sam moved slowly away.

The early shades of autumn evening were falling when
Penrod emerged from the stable; and a better light might
have disclosed to a shrewd eye some indications that here
was a boy who had been extremely, if temporarily, ill.
He went to the cistern, and, after a cautious glance
round the reassuring horizon, lifted the iron cover. Then
he took from the inner pocket of his jacket an object
which he dropped listlessly into the water: it was a bit
of wood, whittled to the likeness of a pistol. And though
his lips moved not, nor any sound issued from his vocal
organs, yet were words formed. They were so deep in
the person of Penrod they came almost from the slowly
convalescing profundities of his stomach. These words
concerned firearms, and they were:

"Wish I'd never seen one! Never want to see one
again!"

Of course Penrod had no way of knowing that, as re-
gards bingism in general, several of the most distinguished
old gentlemen in Europe were at that very moment in
exactly the same state of mind.

UNUSUAL WORDS

brusquely — (his shoulder came brusquely in contact) his shoulder came abruptly in contact

cauterized — burned with a hot iron to prevent danger from the bite of a dog which might be mad

conjunction — (the conjunction of Penrod and Sam) the joining of Penrod and Sam

enervatingly — (on a line enervatingly little above the top of his head) weakeningly little above the top of his head

fastidious — (early childhood is not fastidious) not over-particular nor hard to please

improvisation — (Penrod began an improvisation on the spot) began to make up something on the spot

orifice — hole

poignant — (a yearning had grown more and more poignant) more and more piercing and sharp

profundities — depths

sanguinary — bloody

solicitous — worried; desirous of helping

QUESTIONS FOR SELF-TESTING

1. How did Duke, Penrod's dog, express himself when he saw Penrod and Sam together?
2. When Penrod came out after school to a street which was "deserted so far as Penrod was concerned," what was really on that street?
3. What were some of the influences which made Penrod mightily desire a pistol?
4. Before Penrod saw the pistol, what had already worked him up to excitement?
5. What brought Mrs. Williams on the scene?

6. When Mrs. Williams interrupted the two boys, why did Penrod feel far more guilty than Sam?

7. By what thoughtful action did Sam prevent his mother from suspecting that he had been displaying the pistol?

8. How did Sam act towards Penrod when they went downstairs?

9. How did Penrod shift the responsibility when his father blamed him for being late for dinner?

10. When Sam explained to Penrod that they could safely keep the pistol, was Penrod really pleased?

11. When Penrod finally did pull the trigger of the revolver, what "phenomena" did the author say followed his action?

12. When one of the stable doors swung open following Penrod's shot, what horrifying sight did the two boys think they saw outside it?

13. How did the young colored man succeed in getting the gun?

14. How did the writer tell us at the end that Penrod was through with pistols — at least for a while?

TOPICS FOR THEMES OR DISCUSSION

1. Leaving the last paragraph out of account, is there any one sentence elsewhere in the story which seems to you to express its general idea?

2. Ever since they were written, the Penrod stories have been widely popular both with boys and girls and with grown-ups. Judging from this story, what do you consider some of the reasons for their being so much liked?

3. Taking the last paragraph of this story as your text, write an explanation or an illustration of it.

4. Write the dialogue in which the young colored man tells

one of his doubting friends how he came into possession
of the revolver. (Truth need not limit you here any
further than you think it limited him.)

5. This story is amusing because of what it tells, but it is
also amusing because of the way it is told. Select four
passages in which the way of telling adds particularly to
the fun of the story.

6. Rewrite one scene in the story in such a way as to make
it pathetic instead of amusing.

7. Contrast Penrod with some small boy whom you have
come across in your reading or whom you have seen presented in the movies.

SNAPSHOT OF A DOG

By JAMES THURBER

If you have ever owned a dog and loved him, then "Snap-shot of a Dog" is the kind of story you would probably write about him if you could. In his owners' eyes, Rex, the hero of this story, has all the virtues and not a vice of any kind. Even though he is a famous fighter, the fighting is never his fault but always the fault of some dog which attacked him. And his faithfulness and courage and devotion to his owners are precisely the qualities which one's own dog always has, however blind outsiders may be to their existence.

James Thurber, the author, has written many stories, some of which are listed in the Magazine Index. *He contributes frequently to* The New Yorker, *in which magazine this story made its first appearance.*

I RAN across a dim photograph of him the other day,
going through some old things. He's been dead twenty-
five years. His name was Rex (my two brothers and I
named him when we were in our early 'teens) and he
was a bull terrier. "An American bull terrier," we used
to say proudly; none of your English bulls. He had one
brindle eye that sometimes made him look like a clown
and sometimes reminded you of a politician with derby
hat and cigar. The rest of him was white except for a
brindle saddle that always seemed to be slipping off and
a brindle stocking on a hind leg. Nevertheless, there was
a nobility about him. He was big and muscular and
beautifully made. He never lost his dignity even when
trying to accomplish the extravagant tasks my brothers
and myself used to set for him. One of these was the
bringing of a ten-foot wooden rail into the yard through

the back gate. We would throw it out into the alley and tell him to go get it. Rex was as powerful as a wrestler, and there were not many things that he couldn't manage somehow to get hold of with his great jaws and lift or drag to wherever he wanted to put them, or wherever we wanted them put. He would catch the rail at the balance and lift it clear of the ground and trot with great confidence toward the gate. Of course, since the gate was only four feet wide or so, he couldn't bring the rail in broadside. He found that out when he got a few terrific jolts, but he wouldn't give up. He finally figured out how to do it, by dragging the rail, holding on to one end, growling. He got a great wagging satisfaction out of his work. We used to bet kids who had never seen Rex in action that he could catch a baseball thrown as high as they could throw it. He almost never let us down. Rex could hold a baseball with ease in his mouth, in one cheek, as if it were a chew of tobacco.

He was a tremendous fighter, but he never started fights. I don't believe he liked to get into them, despite the fact that he came from a line of fighters. He never went for another dog's throat but for one of its ears (that teaches a dog a lesson), and he would get his grip, close his eyes, and hold on. He could hold on for hours. His longest fight lasted from dusk until almost pitch dark, one Sunday. It was fought in East Main Street in Columbus with a large, snarly nondescript that belonged to a big colored man. When Rex finally got his ear grip, the brief whirlwind of snarling turned to screeching. It was frightening to watch and to listen to. The Negro boldly picked the dogs up somehow and began swinging them around his head, and finally let them fly like a hammer in a hammer throw, but although they landed ten feet away with a great plump, Rex still held on.

The two dogs eventually worked their way to the middle of the car tracks, and after a while two or three streetcars were held up by the fight. A motorman tried to pry Rex's jaws open with a switch rod; somebody started a fire and made a torch of a stick and held that to Rex's tail, but he paid no attention. In the end, all the residents and storekeepers in the neighborhood were on hand, shouting this, suggesting that. Rex's joy of battle, when battle was joined, was almost tranquil. He had a kind of pleasant expression during fights, not a vicious one, his eyes closed in what would have seemed to be sleep had it not been for the turmoil of the struggle. The Oak Street Fire Department finally had to be sent for — I don't know why nobody thought of it sooner. Five or six pieces of apparatus arrived, followed by a battalion chief. A hose was attached and a powerful stream of water was turned on the dogs. Rex held on for several moments more while the torrent buffeted him about like a log in a freshet. He was a hundred yards away from where the fight started when he finally let go.

The story of that Homeric fight got all around town, and some of our relatives looked upon the incident as a blot on the family name. They insisted that we get rid of Rex, but we were very happy with him, and nobody could have made us give him up. We would have left town with him first, along any road there was to go. It would have been different, perhaps, if he had ever started fights or looked for trouble. But he had a gentle disposition. He never bit a person in the ten strenuous years that he lived, nor ever growled at anyone except prowlers. He killed cats, that is true, but quickly and neatly and without especial malice, the way men kill certain animals. It was the only thing he did that we could never cure him of doing. He never killed, nor even chased, a squirrel. I don't know why. He had his own philosophy about such things. He never ran barking after wagons or automobiles. He didn't seem to see the idea of pursuing something you couldn't catch, or something you couldn't do anything with even if you did catch it. A wagon was one of the things he couldn't tug along with his mighty jaws, and he knew it. Wagons, therefore, were not a part of his world.

Swimming was his favorite recreation. The first time he ever saw a body of water (Alum Creek), he trotted nervously along the steep bank for a while, fell to barking wildly, and finally plunged in from a height of eight feet or more. I shall always remember that shining, virgin dive. Then he swam upstream and back just for the pleasure of it, like a man. It was fun to see him battle upstream against a stiff current, struggling and growling every foot of the way. He had as much fun in the water as any person I have known. You didn't have to throw a stick in the water to get him to go in. Of course he would bring back a stick to you if you did throw one in. He would even have brought back a piano if you had thrown one in.

That reminds me of the night, way after midnight, when he went a-roving in the light of the moon and brought back a small chest of drawers that he found somewhere — how far from the house nobody ever knew; since it was Rex, it could easily have been half a mile. There were no drawers in the chest when he got it home, and it wasn't a good one — he hadn't taken it out of anybody's house; it was just an old, cheap piece that somebody had abandoned on a trash heap. Still, it was something he wanted, probably because it presented a nice problem in transportation. It tested his mettle. We first knew about his achievement when, deep in the night, we heard him trying to get the chest up onto the porch. It sounded as if two or three people were trying to tear the house down. We came downstairs and turned on the porch light. Rex was on the top step trying to pull the thing up, but it had caught somehow and he was just holding his own. I suppose he would have held his own till dawn if we hadn't helped him. The next day we carted the chest miles away and threw it out. If we had thrown it out in a near-by alley, he would have brought it home again, as a small token of his integrity in such matters. After all, he had been taught to carry heavy wooden objects about, and he was proud of his prowess.

I am glad Rex never saw a trained police dog jump. He was just an amateur jumper himself, but the most daring and tenacious I have ever seen. He would take on any fence we pointed out to him. Six feet was easy for him, and he could do eight by making a tremendous leap and hauling himself over finally by his paws, grunting and straining; but he lived and died without knowing that twelve- and sixteen-foot walls were too much for him. Frequently, after letting him try to go over one for a while, we would have to carry him home. He would never have given up trying.

There was in his world no such thing as the impossible. Even death couldn't beat him down. He died, it is true, but only, as one of his admirers said, after "straight-arming the death angel" for more than an hour. Late one afternoon he wandered home, too slowly and too uncertainly to be the Rex that had trotted briskly homeward up our avenue for nearly ten years. I think we all knew when he came through the gate that he was dying. He had apparently taken a terrible beating, probably from the owner of some dog that he had got into a fight with. His head and body were scarred. His heavy collar with the teeth marks of many a battle on it was awry; some of the big brass studs in it were sprung loose from the leather. He licked at our hands and, staggering, fell, but got up again. We could see that he was looking for some-one. One of his three masters was not home. He did not get home for an hour. During that hour the bull terrier fought against death as he had fought against the cold, strong current of Alum Creek, as he had fought to climb twelve-foot walls. When the person he was waiting for did come through the gate, whistling, ceasing to whistle, Rex walked a few wabbly paces toward him, touched his hand with his muzzle, and fell down again. This time he didn't get up.

QUESTIONS FOR SELF-TESTING

1. What has reminded the writer to tell this story?
2. What was Rex's strong point as a fighter?

3. Did he enjoy fighting?
4. When Rex fought with the Negro's dog, how did the relatives of his owners feel about the fight?
5. What kind of disposition does the writer say Rex had?
6. What was the only thing they could never teach Rex not to do?
7. What were the limits of Rex's jumping power?
8. How many masters did Rex have?
9. About how long did his masters own him?
10. What did Rex look like?

TOPICS FOR THEMES OR DISCUSSION

1. Tell the story of Rex's great fight from the standpoint of an onlooker who was not one of his owners.
2. Write a dialogue between the motorman on one of the delayed streetcars and a very impatient passenger.
3. Write a monologue in which one of Rex's owners tells the story of the fight to his two brothers.
4. Pick out three sentences which seem to you to show especially the owners' pride in Rex.
5. Write a story or an anecdote about a dog you have owned.

SEMAPHORE

By JOSEPH HUSBAND

Probably the most important thing which has happened in the last thousand years has been the discovery of how to harness steam and make it useful. Except for that discovery, Americans would still be crowded along the coasts and waterways of North America, with weeks of time required for a journey from one area of settlement to another. It is steam which has brought San Francisco and New York and New Orleans and El Paso and St. Paul all close enough together so that the people in any one of those cities can know of, and have dealings with, the people in all the others.

"Semaphore" is taken from America at Work, *a volume of narratives concerning American industry and means of communication. In the narrative included here, the author writes of the power of steam and the terrifying beauty of the great engine rushing through the night. But in spite of the important place that steam and its instruments are given, the story is really about something even more necessary in life than either engines or steam.*

Every night, at exactly eight minutes past nine, the limited roars through the village. I can see it coming several miles away, its powerful headlight fingering rails and telegraph wires with a shimmer of light. Silently and slowly it seems to draw nearer; then suddenly, it is almost above me. A wild roar of steam and driving wheels, the wail of its hoarse whistle at the crossing, and then, looming black against the night sky, it smashes past, and in the swing of drivers and connecting rods I think of a greyhound, or a racehorse thundering the final stretch. High in the cab window a motionless figure peers ahead into the night; suddenly he is blackly silhouetted by the glare of the opened fire door, and in the orange light I can see the fireman swing back and forth as he feeds his fire. The light burns against the flying steam and smoke above; then blackness — and now the white windows of the Pullmans flicker past, and through

the swirl of dust and smoke I watch the two red lights
sink down the track.

Every time I see that black figure in the cab I wonder
how far he can peer ahead into the night, and I wonder
at the perfect faith that is his: faith in silent men who
keep the semaphores lighted and true, and in those humble
servants whose constant watchfulness guards him from
broken rail and loosened fishplate. Last night I sat
beside him.

It was not my limited that I boarded, but a faster,
greater engine that helps to rush half across the continent
a train before which all others wait and all tracks are
cleared. I stood with the division superintendent on the
platform of the little station where it must pause for
water. Beyond the yardlights its song rose clear and
vibrant. With a flare of lofty headlight and the grind
of brakes it was beside us, steel lungs panting heavily,
a reek of oil sweating from heated sides.

The engineer, a torch in his hand, swung down, and
we shook hands before I climbed the iron rungs to the
cab. From the high windows I watched him oil and
stroke the sinews of his monster. Behind, on the top of
the tender, the fireman was filling the tanks with a torrent of water. Then they joined me, and in the torchlight
I saw the black studded end of the boiler, like a giant
cask-head, a tangle of pipes across its face; water gauge
and steam dial dimly illumined by shaded bull's-eyes.
The engineer blew out the torch and climbed into his
seat. Opposite him, I settled into mine, the fireman behind me.

There was the thin piping of a whistle in the cab and the

engineer slowly opened the throttle. We were off. Rumbling and swaying, we passed the upper windows of the station. Telegraphers in shirtsleeves were fingering their instruments beneath shaded lights. The chill of the frosty night air penetrated the cab, and I buttoned my coat about me and looked ahead into the darkness. We were gathering headway. A string of freight cars on a siding swept behind us; already the lights of the village were far behind. Ahead of the long body of the locomotive, extending incredibly beyond the small front windows of the cab, the track, hardly visible in the ray of the headlight, terminated suddenly in the darkness. The roar of drivers and machinery was deafening. From side to side the engine rocked like a plunging derelict. The crashing roar grew louder, loud beyond belief, and the rocking and trembling almost threw me from the seat.

The fireman slid open the jaws of the firebox, flooding the cab with light and heat. Within, the flame, white to pale daffodil in its intensity, twisted like streams of fluid in the draught. Behind the cab the black end of the tender rose high above my line of vision, rocking and swaying in contrary motion to the engine, like a bulldog twisting on a stick. Balancing on the smooth steel floor, the fireman stoked his grate-bars, his shovel feeding spots where the coal was thinnest. Then darkness as he closed the doors with his foot. Only the two dim lights on gauge and indicator; and on each side, and above, the stars racing evenly beside us. I looked down at the roadbed: it was flooding past us like a torrent.

"Green." I caught the word above the tumult.

"Green," echoed the fireman.

Far ahead, four colored lights gleamed like gems against the sky. Two rubies below; above, another ruby and beside it the pale green of an emerald. The green light was in the upper right-hand corner of the square.

"Seventy-five to eighty." The fireman shouted in my ear.

"Block's clear. That green light gives us a clear track."

Already the block semaphores were behind us. Blinded by the rush of air I tried to see the track ahead. Like a dark avalanche the world seemed pouring under our pilot, and beneath I felt the roadbed, at last in motion, shivering and swirling like a mill-race. From under the engine puffs of steam shredded into fog-rift, white in the light from the round holes beneath the grate-bars. And through the two great circles of light projected by them, as from a stereopticon, flickered embankments, telegraph poles, hills and houses, like a reeling cinematograph.

"Green."

"Green," came the confirmation.

The fixed green star shone for a minute and flashed past.

Faintly I heard the fireman at my ear.

"Almost ninety."

Long ago the headlight had become useless except as a warning of our approach; we were past the farthest range of its illumination before the eye could discern what lay before us. Blind and helpless we tore on. Broken rail, a train on the crossing, or open switch, — we would never see it. But "green" shone the light, and wholly trusting in the silent men who flashed to us their word of safety we never faltered. I thought of a stalled train that might lie sleeping on our rails. But "green" was the light — their thin cry through the long night watches.

The engineer, silent, his hand fingering throttle and air brake, sat huddled high on his seat. Through his goggles he watched the blackness ahead. A brief second's time to set his brakes was all he asked. Far off in the great city the chief dispatcher was following our flight mile by mile, block to block. Over the wires his voice and the voices of his helpers told the rapid story of our progress. In the lonely tower at the next curve someone would flash the green beacon to our straining eyes, and report us on our way. To him others were now reporting, giving him the certain knowledge that our way was safe. Keepers of the safety of our path; how perfectly we trusted them; how great and unrewarded is their perfect service.

I looked back. Behind, the Pullmans cast steady squares of light on the racing cut. Here was our freight. Sons of Mary: even more blindly they trusted, "Peacefully sleeping and unaware."

Sons of Martha; they were beside me.

"Green," they chorused.

Out of the night came the instant crash of the westbound express. With a blast of air and a slamming roar it seemed to brush us. It was gone.

Through a sleeping village we tore on with a wild hoarse cry. Darkened windows flashed reflected light. A station platform whipped past our heels; huddled groups of people pressed back against the building.

"Green!"

Like brilliant stars from a rocket gleamed a constellation at a double crossing. Ruby drops of fire; but the pale green light shone steadily above. The wheels hammered on the crossing.

Thicker and thicker, like colored fireflies, the switch-lights tangled in a maze. We were entering the city. There was the constant rattle of switch points, and I felt the growing murmur of the streets. On either side buildings piled up in shapeless walls like a canyon; there were sudden glimpses of interrupted streets, waiting streetcars, and the glare of arc lights. We were slowing down.

Cleveland. The station echoed with the iron coughing of engines. Men and women surged between waiting trains; their voices mingled in the uproar. The departing, the returning; men staggering with bags and suitcases, women with little children in their arms. In the green star they trusted.

TOPICS FOR THEMES OR DISCUSSION

1. Write a description of a passenger bus or a loaded truck coming down the highway at night, and contrast its approach and passing with that of the train here described.
2. Why is the story called "Semaphore"?
3. Note the phrases in which the writer speaks of the engine as though it were human.
4. If you were writing a story such as this about an airplane, at what time point should you begin it — when the plane was passing overhead, when it was in the act of landing, when it was preparing to start, when it was rising from the ground at the beginning of its flight? Give reasons for your choice.

5. Select three phrases used by the author which seem to you to bring color particularly clearly before your eyes.

6. Look up in Luke, Chapter X, verses 38–42 (the King James version) the Biblical reference to Mary and Martha. In what way is the reference appropriate here?

7. Select a passage in which the way that the writer shapes or breaks up his sentences is what gives to the reader his appreciation of how fast the train moved.

8. Write a passage dealing with the speed (or slowness) of some means of transportation, making the way that you form and arrange your sentences as well as the words you use convey to the reader a sense of speed or slowness.

9. In your opinion, what advantage does the author gain by telling his story in the first person?

OCEAN GOLD

By John D. Morse

"Ocean Gold" deals with one of the remote and fascinating parts of the United States — one where the warm and brilliant ocean (which in this story changes suddenly into the dangerous ocean) has a part in everybody's life. Native Hawaiians are usually almost as much at home in the water as on the land, and swimming is as easy and customary an exercise for them as is walking. Not many people, though, Hawaiians or others, swim for as large prizes or against as great dangers as do the boys in this story. Not many people, either, have to make such quick decisions or to carry them out with lives and fortunes depending on the decisions' having been right.

John D. Morse, the author, has published a number of other exciting stories about brown-skinned Americans. Two of them are "Kai" (St. Nicholas, June, 1933) and "The Dynamiters" (St. Nicholas, February, 1935).

Ambergris!'' The tall Hawaiian's exultant cry rose above the pounding of the white surf. Leaving his brother standing amazed on the rock from which they had been sighting fish, Kolani Pai leaped into the sea and, with powerful brown arms flashing, swam toward a gray mass that eddied around the coral ledge a few yards from shore.

One arm encircled the floating lump, and, with a glance out to sea to be sure there were no big waves coming in, Kolani breast-stroked his way cautiously back to shore. As he waded dripping out of the surf and up the steep sand slope of the beach, his brother left the rock and ran forward.

"Here's your college education, Jimmy," the older Hawaiian cried, gingerly setting the gray lump down on a brown palm frond that had fallen from one of the coconut trees lining the shore.

Jimmy looked doubtful. Then he held his nose.

"Whatever that stuff is, I don't like its smell," he said, still holding his nose and stepping back in mock disdain. Then his curiosity overcame him.

"What is it, Kolani? I know it must be worth something or you wouldn't have swum out to the reef in a sea like this. But what's it got to do with my college education?"

"You do need to go to school, young fellow. Haven't you ever heard of ambergris, the stuff they find in sperm whales?"

"My ignorance, Professor Pai, is the family scandal. Enlighten me." Jimmy bowed a black, curly head.

Kolani grinned and let a handful of sand trickle into his brother's hair.

"Ambergris," he proclaimed in a professorial manner, "is the fatty substance found in the stomachs of diseased sperm whales. It is believed to be the indigestible part of squid on which the whales feed. When first vomited up by the whale it has an offensive odor, as you know, but after it has floated about in the sea for a time the ambergris smells less violently."

Jimmy looked quickly out to sea.

"Then the whale who owns this can't be far off," he remarked.

"To continue, and to come rapidly to the point," went on Kolani, "ambergris is used in the manufacture of perfume and is so rare that it is actually worth more than its weight in gold."

Jimmy's bantering mood dropped like a swift shadow.

"But this lump must weigh ten pounds, Kolani," he

cried excitedly, seizing it in both hands, unmindful of the smell. "That means — how much is gold worth, anyway?"

"Wait a minute, Jimmy," replied Kolani. "Gold is worth about twenty dollars an ounce, but we're not sure of this stuff. The only ambergris I've ever seen was a small piece at the Bishop Museum in Honolulu, and it looked different from this. I read up on it once, though. The highest price ever paid was over twenty dollars an ounce; lots of it isn't worth that much. But the sure test for all ambergris is to see if it dissolves in hot alcohol. Have we any back on the boat?"

"I think there's some of that left in the bottle we used to pickle the queer fish for Professor Spencer."

"Good! Let's beat it back to the boat. But hold on —" The excitement in Kolani's black eyes gave way to a serious, troubled look. "How about the people who own this beach? Don't they get a share of the find?"

"Ai-a!" exclaimed Jimmy, lapsing for a second into his native Hawaiian. "I forgot about David."

The two brothers had left the *Ehukai*, their sixty-five foot fishing sampan, anchored in the next inlet in charge of its four-man crew. They had climbed over one of the high, green ridges that separate the deep valleys of the Molokai coast, and in addition to finding good fishing water for the throw net, had found an old Hawaiian couple living all alone in a shack set well back from the shore.

David Kopiko (he had told them his name) urged them to try his fishing grounds, and had even pointed out the best places. He was waiting now on the flower-covered veranda of his shack to see what luck they had had. And it is Hawaiian custom to divide the catch. The two young Hawaiians looked at each other. Jimmy was silently calculating how much money their find would bring them. For 160 ounces at twenty dollars an ounce — $3200! Enough to start his medical education in California — the education that had been postponed when they had had to mortgage the sampan to replace a torn set of nets. But if they divided the money with David . . .

"Well," Kolani thought aloud, "it seems to me there's nothing to do but split the ambergris with these people — that's Hawaiian custom. It won't leave much to start you in the medical school you're set on. If you were only satisfied to go to the University of Hawaii as I did, we could swing it all right. But we've gone over that before, and I guess you're right. Anyway, let's not count our fish before they're caught. This stuff may be worthless for all we know."

"We've got to tell David about it, though," said Jimmy. "It will be hard to convince him that a lump of fat smelling like a dead fish is worth anything. And then if we find out it's not really ambergris he won't believe us afterward. He'll think we've kept the whole wad."

"That's right," reflected Kolani. "Maybe we'd better just give David half these fish we caught and not mention the ambergris till we find out for sure. Then we'll offer to divide the money with him fifty-fifty. Let's do that."

"All right," said Jimmy, rising to his feet. "I'll wrap it up in the net; you carry the fish."

Kolani picked up the dozen fine moi they had caught, and the boys started up the path leading to David's house.

"Aloha," the old man greeted them in Hawaiian. "Any luck?"

"Only few we catch, David," said Kolani. "Here, these six moi for you. Sorry no more."

"No, you keep all. I can catch plenty myself. Ah, thank you, thank you," as Kolani dropped the fish on the porch.

"What have you in the net?" the old Hawaiian continued, his sharp eyes taking in the bulge under the folds of the net Jimmy was carrying. He peered out from under his bushy, white eyebrows, and then looked questioningly at Kolani.

"Only some funny kind of fat we found," replied Kolani casually. "I'm taking it to Honolulu to show a friend of mine at the University. I think maybe he never see this kind before."

The old man seemed still curious, but Jimmy stopped the conversation.

"We'd better be getting back to the boat, Kolani," he said. "Thank you, David, for letting us fish here. Fine place you got."

"Sure, you're welcome. Come again any time. Thanks for the fish."

As the brothers began the climb up over the ridge David called out again the word that means both hello and good-by in Hawaiian.

"Aloha."

They turned and waved to him, both feeling guilty over the deception they had practised on him.

Down again in their own valley they signaled to the sampan anchored out in the bay, and at once one of the crew put out in the outrigger canoe used as a dinghy.

"Is that Tony coming for us?" Kolani squinted out across the water.

"Yes, I guess the others are asleep. Let's not say anything about the ambergris, Kolani. Somehow I don't trust Tony. He's a nice kid, and I don't know what it is about him. But I wish you'd let him go after Tom comes back."

"I'll feel better myself, Jimmy, when Tom's leg is healed, and we don't need Tony."

The object of their conversation paddled diligently toward the steep ledge on which they waited, looking over his shoulder now and then at the sea in order not to be surprised by a sudden wave.

The waves were running along the steep sides of the little U-shaped bay, and were breaking near the shore. It would have been impossible to take a canoe through those breakers and beach it, so Kolani and Jimmy waited on a ledge some distance from the shallow water where the waves broke to rush roaring and swirling at the beach. Where they stood the water surged up and down against the rock wall, but the movement was regular, and could be timed for landing a canoe.

Tony ran the long canoe in close to the ledge and held it there, its fragile bow lifting up and down with the surge of the water, almost grazing the sharp rock. Lightly both Hawaiians jumped into the boat, Jimmy in the middle, facing Tony.

"Back! Quick!" cried Jimmy suddenly.

A great wave was on its swift way in from the sea. It

was one of those seventh waves that rise suddenly out of the ocean, topping all the rest like a peak in a mountain range.

Tony looked quickly over his shoulder and turned terrified toward Kolani. His face went white. His muscles seemed frozen. He was paralyzed by fear.

The wave was almost upon them. Unless the canoe were a good six feet from the ledge its bow would be smashed to kindling against the rock. With one continuous movement Kolani rose to his feet in the bow and sprang to the ledge, at the same time shoving the canoe clear. Jimmy seized the useless paddle from Tony, and after easing the boat out away from the rock while the next few waves swept past, ran in again to take on Kolani.

Nothing was said. Tony changed places with Jimmy, and the two brothers with Kolani in the bow seat turned the canoe around to paddle her back to the sampan.

When the three had climbed aboard the sampan and secured the canoe Jimmy went forward with the ambergris still wrapped in the throw net. Kolani turned over to Pete the fish they had caught. A fire was already burning in the tin-lined box on the canvas-covered shelter deck. Supper was under way.

While Jimmy was unwrapping the ambergris on the narrow table between the two bunks of the brothers' cabin, Kolani found the alcohol and went out to heat it at the cooking fire. Jimmy's eyes shone with excitement. If the evil-smelling stuff dissolved in alcohol, it meant that in two months he would be on his way to the mainland.

"How do you work the test, Kolani?" he cried as his brother returned to the tiny room.

For answer Kolani with his knife sliced off a flake of

the waxy lump and dropped it into the bottle. It sank slowly through the hot alcohol and disappeared.

"It dissolved!" shouted Jimmy. He tried to hug his brother across the table, but succeeded only in upsetting the alcohol. He leaned over the ambergris as though he were inhaling the fragrance of a rose garden, and then turned to Kolani with an expression that showed anything but appreciation.

"Honestly, Kolani, do they use that stuff to make perfume?"

"They do," grinned Kolani. "If I remember right, it's because ambergris has the rare property of holding a scent in solution. I'll tell you more about it after you go get us some food. Don't say anything about this bouquet to the boys, though."

The brothers ate the same food provided for the crew — poi from the red barrel filled up in Honolulu before each trip, fish cooked every meal by Pete, fruit foraged from the different deserted shores where they touched — but they ate alone in the forward cabin instead of with the four men who squatted comfortably beneath the canvas of the shelter deck. As Jimmy went aft to bring food, Kolani slipped on a warm sweat shirt, and slid the ambergris under his bunk.

Over their fish and poi the boys talked about Jimmy's future and about his medical schooling at last made possible. His excitement over the prospect of his first trip to the mainland made him gush with ideas, and it was dark before they realized it.

"Well," said Kolani at last, "let's leave some of the plans for tomorrow. I'm going aft to see if Moki thinks we can fish tomorrow with the long net. We ought to take some fish as well as treasure back to Honolulu."

He found the old head fisherman puffing away at his pipe and holding forth in voluble Hawaiian under the canvas.

"Moki, you think we can take out the long net to-morrow?" he asked.

The old Hawaiian looked out at the sky, felt the wind, and appeared doubtful.

"I think get more rough tonight. Afraid too much white water this place tomorrow. Maybe we try that place you went today. Did you see David Kopiko?"

"Yes," Kolani replied. "He told us all right to fish anywhere and come back again. Fine place he has."

"He love his home very much." Moki liked to talk. "One time he find that kind stuff that comes from the whale. Take to Honolulu and sell for five thousand dollars. Stay there a little while. Then he get tired of noise. Say all time no good to move fast. Quick come home. Stay home ever since."

Kolani started.

"You mean ambergris, Moki?"

Moki nodded emphatically.

"That's it — five thousand dollars he get for a little piece three times big as my head."

The old man was eager to go on with the story, but Kolani cut him off gently.

"By 'n' by you tell me more, Moki. Now I want talk with Jimmy."

Kolani threw open the door of the cabin to find Jimmy aglow with joy.

"If this test is genuine," he cried, "we've got more

than three thousand dollars' worth of ambergris here. I've just weighed it with the small scales. Eleven and a quarter pounds, 180 ounces at twenty dollars an ounce — that's $3600!"

"Not so loud, Jimmy," cautioned Kolani. "It'll do no good to let the men know about this yet; we're not sure of all of them. And now I've got some news for you.

"David Kopiko himself found some ambergris in that bay. A long time ago he picked up a five-thousand-dollar piece, sold it in Honolulu, and then came back here because he tired of city life. You remember how he looked closely at the net today. I'll bet anything he knew exactly what we had in it, and that now he's thinking we're a couple of sneaks."

"Golly! That's right, Kolani. I feel almost like going over tonight with his half. What he must think of us! We can explain it in the morning, though, and surely he'll understand. Anyway, the news that he's got $1800 coming to him out of a clear sky — or sea — ought to put any man in a forgiving mood."

"Just the same," returned Kolani, "I'm not going to enjoy my customary honest rest tonight, I'm afraid. I feel like a thief."

"Tomorrow morning you can feel like an angel then, when you break the news to David. That ought to make up for it.

"And in the meantime," Jimmy continued, "even if this stuff is worth its weight in gold, I don't fancy sleeping all night with a rotten fish in this dinky cabin. Suppose we put it in the bag and hang it just outside the door in the alleyway. All right?"

"Sure," Kolani returned. "What's a paltry thirty-six hundred dollars to us? Throw it anywhere you like and douse that lamp. I need some sleep."

II

An insistent, recurring "thump, thump" — the wind was rising, sure enough. Rain drummed on the cabin roof, and something loose on deck was rolling around with the pitching boat — a true sailor's nightmare. With a groan of annoyance Kolani shoved his feet out of the bunk, and reached for his oilskins.

A second after he had stepped out of the cabin, Kolani was back inside, shaking Jimmy by the shoulder.

"Where did you put that ambergris?" he almost shouted in his brother's ear.

Jimmy was instantly awake.

"Right outside the door, on the hook that holds it against the wall when it's open. Why? Is it gone?"

Not waiting for an answer, Jimmy was on his feet and outside as he finished the question.

"Gone!" he cried. "Where's the flashlight? Let's look along the deck."

But a quick search in the narrow alleyway and about the deck revealed nothing. Excitedly Jimmy flashed the light back and forth in increasing circles over the pitching boat — there was nothing but the wet planks and the sparkling of the rain as it cut across the beam of the flash.

By this time the crew had emerged from their sleeping quarters beneath the afterdeck, and Kolani quickly interrogated Moki.

"Where's Tony?" he shouted above the pounding surf.

Moki ducked back into the low forecastle, and was out again in a second.

"Gone," he reported, "and most of his clothes."

Without wasting words Kolani began giving orders.

"Tony has stolen plenty money from me," he announced. "We try and catch him. Sam, start the engine and stop down below ready to move. Pete, get all rope you find up forward, big kind, little kind. Moki, you stop here. Jimmy, me, we get searchlight."

But Jimmy, anticipating his brother's command, had already returned with the big searchlight which was always clamped to a bracket on the stubby mast when the *Ehukai* maneuvered at night. Quickly he had it in place, and Kolani plugged in the cable. Instantly a glare of light flashed over the stern of the rocking sampan into the wet night.

"There!" Moki's keen eyes had spotted their quarry, and he pointed straight astern where the waves were booming white against the sugar-loaf rock. "Ah," cried the old Hawaiian, "Tony is evil, and the Wakini stone has caught him for us."

In the bright beam of the powerful light the three men saw Tony, crouched on the high rock fifty yards astern, the waves reaching hungrily up for him. In his arms he clutched the bag containing the ambergris, and beside him was the splintered canoe. Kolani guessed what had happened.

Tony had overheard Jimmy's elated report of the weight of the ambergris, and after all hands were asleep had tried to escape with it in the canoe — an enterprise which only a foolhardy boy would have attempted in that rising sea.

He had misjudged the Wakini stone, and a bigger than ordinary wave had lifted him, canoe and all, square on top of the huge rock, stranding him and smashing the boat. And now he sat, paralyzed with fear, just as in the afternoon he had remained frozen in the stern of the canoe while the prow grazed the ledge.

Jimmy groaned.

"There goes my college education," he said. "Just a question of time till that fool realizes his only chance is swimming ashore. If he does, he'll probably get battered up in the surf, but in this valley he could hide out with the stuff and keep alive till he was able to make a getaway. And even if he was glued to that rock we couldn't get him off in this sea."

A terrific wave crashed high up on the rock, drenching Tony and confirming Jimmy's fears. The sampan was pitching fearfully, and the foaming breakers thundered into the little bay, booming a wild accompaniment to a wilder scene.

"No," said Kolani, "I think Tony will stay on that rock till the sea picks up enough to knock him off. He's scared stiff — can't move a muscle — but that doesn't do us much good unless —" He turned suddenly to the fisherman.

"Moki, does that rock come up straight from the bottom on this side?"

"Ai!" replied the Hawaiian, "too much deep this side Wakini stone."

Kolani Pai started brain and muscles into action.

"I'll try it," he said. "We can pay out the anchor ropes of the sampan, and the wind will take her straight toward the rock. Jimmy, stand at the wheel and keep her backed straight, using the engine if you have to. Go tell Pete to splice another length on both ropes."

"But Kolani," cried Jimmy, "the sampan is already mortgaged. If she cracks up on the rock we've lost everything."

"She won't crack up if you watch your ropes, Jimmy. It's our only chance. We've got to get that ambergris!"

"Moki," Kolani continued rapidly, "we tie rope under my arms. You hang on to this end. When I get close to rock you wait till big water come. Then let go, and wave will take me up on rock beside Tony. Next big wave I jump in this side, and you pull like everything. Can do?"

Moki shook his grizzled head.

"Ai-a! No good. Suppose wave take you against that rock — break, break, any place." He struck his arms, legs, and head significantly. "Man not strong enough for the sea. More better we leave that boy where he is. By 'n' by he get ashore all right. Suppose anchor ropes break — no more sampan. More better we lift anchor, move out."

Kolani knew the old man was right. Moki had known the sea for seventy-odd years, and he feared it. But he was a better swimmer than Moki.

"But Moki," he cried. "Tony steal ambergris we find today. Half belong to David. We've got to get it back. I try anyway."

He seized one of the ropes Pete had brought from the bow and tied it securely around his chest, just under the arms. Already the sampan was approaching the rock as Jimmy and Pete paid out the two anchors. When she was within twenty yards of the rock, leaping up and down like a mad whale, they made her fast, and Jimmy came back to take the wheel.

Kolani slipped on trousers and shirt to protect his skin from the razor-cutting shells that cover the shore rocks, and after repeating his instructions to the doubtful Moki, plunged into the sea.

At once he realized more clearly the hazard of his undertaking. It was the roughest water he had ever been in. Swimming was futile, like trying to walk a straight line in a hurricane. He needed all his swimmer's strength and skill merely to keep above the foaming, twisting surface of the water.

Moki began paying out the rope, and slowly Kolani's body was swept nearer and nearer the rock. And now a new difficulty arose. The current divided to pass on either side of the rock, sweeping Kolani first to one side and then to the other as Moki drew back the rope and paid it out again. Then the old Hawaiian's knowledge of the sea, combined with Kolani's swimming ability, saved them.

Moki knew that soon a big wave would break just before it got to the rock instead of slightly beyond it as most of them were doing. So he was going to let Kolani ride the top of it up to the rock, as surf riders travel shoreward on the crest of breakers. It would take luck, daring, and considerable skill to carry through such a stunt, but it was their only chance.

He drew back the rope till the swimmer was about five yards from the rock. Tensely he waited till the sampan's stern rose higher than ever above the level of the rock, and he knew that a big wave was bearing down on Kolani. Then, as the strain on the rope increased, he suddenly let it slack, trusting that Kolani would act.

Kolani felt the pull of the rope, then its sudden slacking, and knew that a big wave was over him. In a flash he saw Moki's intention and began churning the water. The wave was about to break just this side of the rock, and he must be on its crest, going as fast as possible to keep from being carried under by the boiling water. Swiftly he was carried up, and in a smother of foam felt the rock beneath him. Dropping his feet he stood upright to present less resistance to the surging water, and found himself standing beside a pale and terrified Tony.

There was no time to lose. Any fisherman would have known that one big wave follows another, so Kolani seized the helpless boy under the arms, grasping the bag in one hand, and turned just in time to leap full into another wave as high as the one that had carried him onto the rock.

A million hands clutched at his clothes, and a million more seized the body of Tony to tear it out of his grasp. Under his arms a burning band cut deep into his chest. A ton of sand fell suddenly on his head, carrying him down, down — out of reach of the clutching, tearing hands, but smothering him with its weight.

Half conscious, Kolani was pulled aboard the *Ehukai*, and while Moki attended to the stricken Tony, Jimmy with a quick slash cut the rope from his brother's chest and stretched him out on the deck. He jerked off his own sweat shirt, rolled it into a pillow, and then began

rubbing Kolani's arms and legs. So tight was his grip
on the bag that Jimmy left it unloosened for the moment.

"It wasn't worth it, Kolani. You should never have
gone," he said over and over as he frantically rubbed
the blood into circulation.

Kolani opened his eyes.

"Did I get back with him?" he asked.

"Him?" echoed his brother. "Oh, you mean that
whelp. Sure, he's okay. It's you I'm thinking about;
how do you feel?"

"How about — it?" Kolani turned his face to look
about the deck.

Jimmy lifted his brother's head and focused his eyes
on the hand that still clutched the neck of the bag.

"I don't think Mr. Sperm Whale himself could get
that away from you," he grinned. "At least I couldn't.
Think you can make it to the cabin?"

III

Next morning Moki's prediction of rough water was
verified. The head fisherman himself had a close moment
with the sampan's small extra rowboat when he landed
Jimmy and Kolani on the ledge. They started to climb
the ridge that divided their valley from David's.

"What shall we do with Tony?" asked Jimmy as he
dug his toes into the steep trail behind his brother.

"Fire him as soon as we get back to Honolulu," returned
Kolani. "We were going to do that anyway, and this'll
make it easier. He's had his lesson. He'll probably go
straight from now on, but nothing will ever put backbone

in him. That's what he needs. There's David waiting for us."

"Aloha." The old Hawaiian seemed to be expecting them.

Kolani plunged at once into his story, speaking Hawaiian. He told the old man about their find of the day before, and how they had decided not to let him know till they were sure it was really ambergris.

"We think it will bring maybe $3600 — half for you and half for us," he concluded.

David's deep eyes twinkled under his bushy brows, and he leaned forward to speak.

"I believe you. Yesterday I don' know what to think when I saw what you had in the net. Now I understand. If you had told me then what you found I would save you trouble. I know the stuff that comes from the whale, and I know that money brings me only worry.

"Here I need nothing that comes from the store. I am happy to live in old Hawaiian style, so you keep all the money."

"But —" Kolani began.

"No, I am an old man, and I know what I want. Here, try these bananas I brought this morning from up in the valley."

The two boys looked at one another. Then Jimmy grinned the grin with which he met all situations, and reached for a banana.

QUESTIONS FOR SELF-TESTING

1. What reason was there for David Kopiko's having a share in the ambergris the boys found?

2. Why did the boys decide not to tell David at once about their find?

3. How did Tony learn that the lump of fat the boys brought back to the boat was valuable?

4. Before the theft of the ambergris, had the author given us any reason for liking or disliking Tony?

5. What is it which Kolani said Tony lacked and always would lack, even if he stayed honest from that time on?

6. How did Kolani test the lump of fat to find out whether or not it was ambergris?

7. Why was it so very important to the boys to get possession just at this time of a large sum of money?

8. How did Kolani discover that David had once before found ambergris in his bay?

9. How did this discovery that David knew about ambergris make the boys feel?

10. After Tony had stolen the ambergris, how did he happen to get caught on the rock?

11. Which brother did most of the planning and acting?

12. Why did David refuse his half of the ambergris?

TOPICS FOR THEMES OR DISCUSSION

1. Were the brothers right in deciding not to punish Tony?

2. If Kolani had tested the fat and it had proved not to be ambergris, who would have been the more disappointed?

3. In what ways, if any, do these two Hawaiian boys seem to you different from boys brought up in the United States?

4. Write the story of what went on in Tony's mind while crouched on the rock and waiting for Kolani to rescue him from his dangerous place.

5. Leaving out ambergris and gold, place two boys in a situation which will enable them to come by chance upon some natural substance of great value.

THE WHITE DOGS OF ARRAN

By CORNELIA MEIGS

Even after Indians were no longer hostile and railroads had found their way across what was once called the Great American Desert, there were spaces enough left in the United States where absence of neighbors and presence of wild life combined to make existence dangerous. Automobiles and paved and graveled roads and telephones have brought many of these remote spots closer to neighbors, but they have by no means done away with them. "The White Dogs of Arran" tells the story of the dangers of one such lonely place and of the strange yet natural way in which help came to it.

"The White Dogs of Arran" *is taken from* The Pool of Stars, *one of the many books of stories which Cornelia Meigs has written.* Rain on the Roof, Windy Hill, *and* As the Crow Flies *are some of her others, and her short stories appear often in* St. Nicholas.

F OR A long hour, on that November afternoon, Ted had been standing at the gate below the ranch house, waiting and waiting, while the twilight filled the round hollow of the valley as water slowly fills a cup. At last the figure of a rider, silhouetted against the rose-colored sky, came into view along the crest of the rocky ridge. The little cow pony was loping as swiftly as the rough trail would permit, but to Ted's impatient eyes it seemed to crawl as slowly as a fly on a window pane. Although the horseman looked like a cowpuncher, at that distance, with his slouch hat and big saddle, the eager boy knew that it was the district doctor making his far rounds over the range. A swift epidemic had been sweeping over Montana, passing from one ranch to another and leaving much illness and suffering behind. Ted's uncle and the cousin who was his own age had both been stricken two days before and it seemed that the doctor would never come.

"I'm glad you are here," he said as the doctor's pony,

covered with foam and quivering with fatigue, passed
through the open gate. "We have two patients for you."
The man nodded.

"Fever, I suppose," he commented, "and aching bones,
and don't know what to make of themselves because
they have never been sick before? I have seen a hundred
such cases in the last few days. It is bad at all the ranches,
but the sheep herders, off in their cabins by themselves,
are hit particularly hard."

He slipped from the saddle and strode into the house,
leaving Ted to take the tired pony around to the stables.
It was very dark now and growing cold, but he felt
warmed and comforted, somehow, since the doctor had
come. He heard running feet behind him and felt a
dog's nose, cold and wet, thrust into his hand. It was
Pedro, the giant, six months' old wolfhound puppy, long-
legged and shaggy-haired, the pride of Ted's life and
the best beloved of all his possessions. The big dog followed his master into the stable and sat down, blinking
solemnly in the circle of lantern light, while the boy was
caring for the doctor's horse and bedding it down.

Ted's thoughts were very busy, now with his anxieties
about his uncle, now racing out over the range to wonder
how those in the stricken ranch houses and lonely cabins
might be faring. There was the ranch on Arran Creek —
people there were numerous enough to care for each other.
It might be worse at Thompson's Crossing, and oh, how
would it be with those shepherds who lived in tiny
cottages here and there along the Big Basin, so far from
neighbors that often for months they saw no other faces
than the woolly vacant ones of their thousands of sheep?

There was one, a big, grizzled Irishman, whom Ted had seen only a few times. Nevertheless, he was one of his closest friends. They had met on a night when the boy was hunting, and he could remember still how they had lain together by the tiny camp fire, with the coyotes yelping in the distance, with the great plain stretching out into the dark, with the slender curl of smoke rising straight upward, and the big stars seeming almost within reach of his hand in the thin air. The lonely Irishman had opened his heart to his new friend and had told him much of his own country, so unlike this big bare one, a dear green land where the tumbledown cottages and little fields were crowded together in such comforting comradeship.

"You could open your window of a summer night and give a call to the neighbors," he sighed, "and you needn't to have the voice of the giant Finn McCoul to make them hear. In this place a man could fall sick and die alone and no one be the wiser."

His reminiscences had wandered farther and farther until he began to tell the tales and legends familiar in his own countryside, stories of the "Little People" and of Ireland in ancient times. Of them all Ted remembered most clearly the story of the white greyhounds of the King of Connemara, upon which his friend had dwelt long, showing that in spite of its being a thousand years old, it was his favorite tale.

"Like those dogs on Arran Creek, they were perhaps," the Irishman said, "only sleeker of coat and swifter of foot, I'm thinking."

"But they couldn't be faster," Ted had objected.

"The Arran dogs can catch coyotes and jackrabbits, and people have called those the quickest animals that run."

"Ah," returned the other with true Irish logic, "those Arran dogs are Russian, they tell me, and these I speak of were of Connemara, and what comes out of Ireland, you may be sure, is faster and fairer than anything else on earth."

Against such reasoning Ted had judged it impossible to argue and had dropped into silence and finally into sleep with the voices of the coyotes and the legend of the lean, white Irish greyhounds still running like swift water through his dreams.

After that he had visited the lonely shepherd whenever he could find time to travel so far. Together they had hunted deer and trapped beaver in the foothills above the Big Basin or, when the sheep had to be moved to new pasture, had spent hours in earnest talk, plodding patiently in the dust after the slow-moving flock. The long habit of silence had taken deep hold upon the Irishman, but with Ted alone he seemed willing to speak freely. It was on one of these occasions that he had given the boy the image of Saint Christopher, "For," he said, "you are like to be a great roamer and a great traveler from the way you talk, and those who carry the good Saint Christopher with them always travel safely."

Now, as Ted thought of illness and pestilence spreading across the thinly settled state, his first and keenest apprehension was for the safety of his friend. His work done, he went quickly back to the house where the doctor was already standing on the doorstep again.

"They are not bad cases, either of them," he was saying

to Ted's aunt. "If they have good care there is no danger, but if they don't — then Heaven help them, I can't."

Ted came close and pulled his sleeve.

"Tell me," he questioned quickly, "Michael Martin isn't sick, is he?"

"Michael Martin?" repeated the doctor. "A big Irishman in the cabin at the upper edge of Big Basin? Yes, he's down, sick as can be, poor fellow, with no one but a gray old collie dog, about the age of himself, I should think, to keep him company."

He turned back to give a few last directions.

"I suppose you are master of the house with your uncle laid up," he said to Ted again, "and I will have to apply to you to lend me a fresh horse so that I can go on."

"You're never going on tonight?" exclaimed Ted. "Why, you have been riding for all you were worth, all day!"

"Yes, and all the night before," returned the doctor cheerfully, "but this is no time to spare horses or doctors. Good gracious, boy, what's that?"

For Pedro, tall and white in the dark, standing on his hind legs to insert an inquisitive puppy nose between the doctor's collar and his neck, was an unexpected and startling apparition.

"That's my dog," Ted explained proudly; "Jim McKenzie, over on Arran Creek, gave him to me; he has a lot of them, you know. Pedro is only half grown now; he is going to be a lot bigger when he is a year old. Yes, I'll bring you a horse right away; yours couldn't go another mile."

When, a few minutes later, the sound of hoofs came clattering up from the stables it seemed certain that there were more than four of them.

"What's this?" the doctor inquired, seeing a second horse with saddlebags and blanket roll strapped in place and observing Ted's boots and riding coat.

"My aunt and the girls will take care of Uncle," the boy replied, "so I am going out to see Michael Martin. You can tell me what to do for him as we ride up to the trail."

They could feel the sharp wind almost before they began climbing the ridge. So far, summer had lingered into November, but the weather was plainly changing now and there had been reports of heavy snowfalls in the mountains. The stars shone dimly, as though through a veil of mist.

"You had better push on as fast as you can," advised the doctor as they came to the parting of their ways. "When a man is as sick as Michael, whatever is to happen, comes quickly." His horse jumped and snorted. "There's that white puppy of yours again. What a ghost he is! He is rather big to take with you to a sick man's cabin."

Pedro had come dashing up the trail behind them, in spite of his having been ordered sternly to stay at home. At six months old the sense of obedience is not quite so great as it should be, and the love of going on an expedition is irresistible.

"It would take me forever to drive him home now," Ted admitted; "I will take him along to Jim McKenzie's and leave him there with his brothers. I can make Arran Creek by breakfast time and ought to get to Michael's not long after noon. Well, so long!"

The stars grew more dim and the wind keener as he rode on through the night. His pony cantered steadily with the easy rocking-horse motion that came near to lulling him to sleep. Pedro padded alongside, his long legs covering the miles with untiring energy. They stopped at midnight to drink from the stream they were crossing, to rest a little and to eat some lunch from the saddlebags. Then they pressed on once more, on and on, until gray and crimson began to show behind the mountains to the eastward, and the big white house of Arran at last came into sight.

Jim McKenzie's place was bigger than the ordinary ranch house, for there were gabled roofs showing through the group of trees, there were tall barns and a wide fenced paddock where lived the white Russian wolfhounds for which the Arran ranch was famous. A deep-voiced chorus of welcome was going up as Ted and Pedro came down the trail. The puppy responded joyfully and went bounding headlong to the foot of the slope to greet his brothers. It was a beautiful sight to see the band of great dogs, their coats like silver in the early morning light, romping together like a dozen kittens, pursuing each other in circles, checking, wheeling, rolling one another over, leaping back and forth over the low fences that divided the paddock, with the grace and free agility of deer. Early as it was, Jim McKenzie was walking down to the stables and stopped to greet Ted as, weary and dusty, he rode through the gate.

"Sure, we'll keep Pedro," he said when he had heard the boy's errand. "Yes, we've a good many sick here; I'd have sent out on the range myself but there was nobody to spare. They tell me the herds of sheep are in terrible confusion, and most of the herders are down. Poor old Michael Martin! I hope you get there in time to help him. Turn your horse into the corral; we'll give you another to go on with. Now come in to breakfast."

Ted snatched a hurried meal, threw his saddle upon a fresh pony, and set off again. For a long distance he could hear the lamentations of Pedro protesting loudly at the paddock gate. The way, after he passed Arran Creek, led out into the flat country of the Big Basin with the sagebrush-dotted plain stretching far ahead. It seemed that he rode endlessly and arrived nowhere, so long was the way and so unchanging the landscape. Once, as he crossed a stream, a deer rose, stamping and snorting among the low bushes, and fled away toward the hills, seeming scarcely to touch the ground as it went. Later, something quick and silent and looking like a reddish-brown collie, leaped from the sagebrush and scudded across the trail almost under his horse's feet.

"A coyote, out in the open in daylight," he reflected, somewhat startled. "It must have been cold up in the mountains to make them so bold. That looks bad for the sheep."

It was disturbing also to see how many scattered sheep he was beginning to pass, little bands, solitary ewes with half-grown lambs trotting at their heels, adventurous yearlings straying farther and farther from their comrades. Once or twice he tried to drive them together, but owing to his haste and his inexperience with their preposterous ways, he had very little success.

"There is going to be bad weather, too," he observed

as he saw the blue sky disappear beneath an overcast of gray. "I had better get on to Michael's as fast as I can."

He saw the little mud and log cabin at last, tucked away among some stunted trees near the shoulder of a low ridge. It looked deceivingly near, yet he rode and rode and could not reach it. White flakes were flying now, fitfully at first, then thicker and thicker until he could scarcely see. His growing misgivings gave place to greater and greater anxiety concerning his friend, while there ran through his mind again and again the doctor's words, "Whatever is to happen, comes quickly."

It was past noon and had begun to seem as though he had been riding forever when he breasted the final slope at last, jumped from his horse, and thundered at the cabin door. The whine of a dog answered him within, and a faint voice, broken but still audible, told him that Michael was alive.

The cabin, so it seemed to him as he entered, was a good ten degrees colder than it was outside. Poor Michael, helpless and shivering on the bunk in the corner, looked like the shrunken ghost of the giant Irishman he had known before. Ted rekindled the fire, emptied his saddlebags, piled his extra blankets upon the bed and, with a skill bred of long practice in camp cookery, set about preparing a meal. Michael was so hoarse as to be almost unable to speak and so weak that his mind wandered in the midst of a sentence, yet all of his thoughts were on the care of his sheep.

"When I felt the sickness coming on me I tried to drive them in," he whispered, "but they broke and scattered and I fell beside the trail — they must get in — snow coming —"

In an hour his fever rose again; he tossed and muttered with only fleeting intervals of consciousness. Ted had found food and shelter for his horse in the sheep shed, and had settled down to his task of anxious watching. The snow fell faster and faster so that darkness came on by mid-afternoon. He had tried to drive the old collie dog out to herd in the sheep, but the poor creature would not leave its master and, even when pushed outside, remained whining beside the door.

"He couldn't do much anyway," sighed Ted as he let him in again. "How those coyotes yelp! I wish, after all, that I had brought Pedro."

Michael had heard the coyotes too and was striving feebly to rise from his bed.

"I must go out to them, my poor creatures," he gasped. "Those devil beasts will have them driven over the whole country before morning."

But he fell back, too weak to move farther, and was silent a long time. When he did speak it was almost aloud.

"With the cold and the snow, I'm thinking there will be worse things abroad this night than just the coyotes."

He lay very still while Ted sat beside him, beginning to feel sleepy and blinking at the firelight. Eleven o'clock, twelve, one, the slow hands of his watch pointed to the crawling hours. Michael was not asleep but he said nothing; he was listening too intently. It was after one and the boy might have been dozing, when the old man spoke again.

"Hark," he said.

For a moment Ted could hear nothing save the pat-pat of the snow against the window, but the collie dog bristled and growled as he lay upon the hearth and pricked his ears sharply. Then the boy heard it too, a faint cry and far off, not the sharp yelping of the coyotes, though that was ominous enough, but the long, hungry howl of a timber wolf.

Tears of weakness and terror were running down the Irishman's face.

"My poor sheep, I must save them!" he cried. "What's the value of a man's life alongside of the creatures that's trusted to him! Those murderers will have every one of them killed for me."

Ted jumped up quickly and bundled on his coat.

"Where's your rifle, Michael?" he asked. "I don't know much about sheep, but I will do what I can."

"The rifle?" returned Michael doubtfully. "Now, I had it on my shoulder the day I went out with the sickness on me, and it is in my mind that I did not bring it home again. But there is the little gun hanging on the nail; there's no more shells for it but there's two shots still left in the chamber."

The boy took down the rusty revolver and spun the cylinder with a practiced finger.

"Two shots is right," he said, "and you have no more shells? Well, two shots may scare a wolf."

If Michael had been in his proper senses, Ted very well knew, he would never have permitted without protest such an expedition as the boy was planning. As it was, however, he lay back in his bunk again, his mind wandering off once more into feverish dreams.

"If it was in the Old Country," he muttered, "the very Little People themselves would rise up to help a man in such a plight. You could be feeling the rush of their wings in the air and could hear the cry of the fairy hounds across the hills. America is a good country, but ah — it's not the same!"

Hoping to quiet him, Ted took the little Saint Christopher from his pocket and laid it in the sick man's hand. Then he finished strapping his big boots, opened the door and slipped out quietly. Michael scarcely noticed his going.

The snow had fallen without drifting much, nor was it yet very deep. He hurried down the slope, not quite knowing what he was to do, thinking that at least he would gather as many sheep as he could and drive them homeward. But there were no sheep to be found. Where so many had been scattered that afternoon there was now not one. The whole of the Big Basin seemed suddenly to have emptied of them. Presently, however, he found a broad trail of trampled snow which he followed, where it led along a tiny stream at the foot of the ridge. As he turned, he heard again that long, terrifying howl coming down the wind. The sheep, perverse enough to scatter to the four winds when their master sought to drive them in, had now, it seemed, gathered of their own will when so great a danger threatened. Ted came upon them at last, huddled together in a little ravine where the sparse undergrowth gave some shelter from the snow. He could just see them in the dim light, their gray compact bodies crowded close, their foolish black faces seeming to look up piteously to him for help. They were very quiet, although now and then they would shift a little, stamp, and move closer. The cry of the wolf was stilled at last, but not because the fierce marauder was not drawing nearer.

Yes, as he stood watching, there slipped a swift dark shape over the opposite edge of the hollow and flung itself upon a straggling ewe on the outskirts of the flock. It was followed by a second silent shadow, and a third. The poor sheep gave only one frantic bleat, then all was still again save for the sound of a hideous snapping and tearing, of a furious struggle muffled in the soft depths of the snow. Ted raised the revolver and took careful aim; he pulled the trigger, but no explosion followed. Michael's improvidence in letting his stock dwindle to only two cartridges might be counted upon also to have let those two be damp. Helplessly the boy spun the cylinder and snapped the hammer again and again, but to no purpose.

The sheep was down now with one of the savage hunters standing over it, another tearing at its throat while the third was slipping along the edge of the flock selecting a fresh victim. Ted's weapon was useless, yet he must do something; he could not stand and see the whole herd destroyed before his eyes. Perhaps he could frighten them away as one could coyotes: he was so angry at this sense-less, brutal slaughter that he lost all sense of prudence. He waved his arms up and down and shouted at the top of his lungs. He saw the creatures drop their prey and turn to look up at him. He ran along the slope, still shouting, then, of a sudden, stepped into an unexpected hollow, lost his balance, and fell headlong. One of the wolves left the flock and came creeping swiftly toward him, its belly dragging in the snow.

His cry must have carried far in the quiet of the night, for it was answered from a great way off. A deep voice broke the stillness and another, the call of coursing hounds who have winded their quarry but have not yet found its trail. And mingled with the barking chorus there rose high the joyful yelp of a puppy who seeks his beloved master.

Ted, slipping in the snow, struggled to his knees and called again and again. The stealthy, approaching shadow crept a yard nearer, then paused to lift a gray muzzle and sniff the air. The second wolf, with slobbering bloody jaws, turned to listen, the flock of sheep snorted and stamped in the snow. A minute passed, then another. The boy managed to get to his feet. Then across the edge of the hollow, white against the dark underbrush, he saw the dogs coming, a line of swift, leaping forms, huge, shaggy and beautiful, their great voices all giving tongue together. Down the slope they came like an avalanche, one only separating himself from the others for a moment to fling himself upon Ted, to lick his face in ecstatic greeting and to rub a cold nose against his cheek. That nimble puppy nose it was that had lifted the latch of a gate not too securely fastened, and so set the whole pack free. Then Pedro ran to join his brothers who were sweeping on to battle. Wolfhounds are taught to catch, not to kill their quarry, but the thirst for blood was in the hearts of the dogs of Arran that night. There was only a moment of struggle, a few choking cries, and the fight was over.

Day broke next morning, clear and bright, with the chinook blowing, the big warm wind that melts the snows and lays the white hills bare almost in an hour. Michael Martin, fallen into a proper sleep at last, woke suddenly and sat up in his bunk. He startled Ted, who, rather stiff and sore from his night's adventures, was kneeling by the fire preparing breakfast. The boy came quickly to his patient's side to inquire how he did.

"It's better I am in body," the Irishman answered; "indeed I begin to feel almost like a whole man again. But —" he shook his head sadly, "my poor wits, they're gone away entirely."

"What can you mean?" Ted demanded.

Michael sighed deeply.

"After you were gone last night," he answered, "even my wandering senses had an inkling of what a dangerous errand it was, and I got up from my bed and stumbled to the window to call you back. Yes, the sickness has made me daft entirely, for as sure as I live, I saw the white greyhounds of Connemara go over the hill. But daft or no —" he sniffed at the odor of frying bacon that rose from the hearth, "I am going to relish my breakfast this day. Eh, glory me, if there isn't another of the creatures now!"

For Pedro, once more applying a knowing muzzle to the clumsy latch, had pushed open the door and stood upon the step, wagging and apologetic, the morning sun shining behind him. Long-legged and awkward, he stepped over the threshold and came to the bedside to sniff inquisitively at the little silver image that lay on the blanket. Michael could never be persuaded to be-

lieve otherwise than that Saint Christopher had brought
him.

Questions for Self-Testing

1. Where is the scene of this story laid?
2. What was the immediate effect on Ted of the doctor's coming?
3. Besides worrying about his uncle, what else had Ted to worry about?
4. Which of Michael's stories did Ted remember most clearly?
5. What evidences of his being in almost uninhabited country did Ted meet as he rode from Jim McKenzie's ranch towards Michael's cabin?
6. Why was Pedro more willing to stay behind at the McKenzie ranch than he had been at Ted's home?
7. What conclusion did Ted draw from seeing a coyote out in the open by daylight?
8. What was Michael's chief anxiety in his illness?
9. What did Ted expect to do when he went out from Michael's cabin?
10. When the wolves appeared, why did Ted not frighten them off by a revolver shot?
11. What saved Ted after he slipped and fell in the snow?
12. How had the hounds succeeded in getting free?

Topics for Themes or Discussion

1. Is there anything in the first sentence of this story which shows you that the author is a gifted and experienced writer?
2. Note the specific pieces of information which are found in the first paragraph.

3. What was there about Michael which made Ted so warmly fond of him?
4. Write a brief character sketch of the doctor, based on hints given about him in the story.
5. What seems to you the finest piece of description in this story?
6. In the early part of this story (before Ted goes out with the revolver), note any sentences in which the writer prepares for what is to happen, so that the reader will be unconsciously made ready for it.

TAMERLANE

By BIGELOW NEAL

It is not often in fiction that a bull has been made either the hero of the story or an animal friendly to men. In "Tamerlane," however, the handsome, cherry-red bull is a hero from the time we see him walking unwillingly towards the challenger in his first fight to the moment when his last fight is ended. And in telling us the life story of the red bull Tamerlane, the author tells us too a good deal of the story of the country in which Tamerlane grew up — the thinly settled stretches of the Rocky Mountains, with their scattered ranches, their great unfenced ranges and grazing herds.

Bigelow Neal, the author, lives in North Dakota. He has written many stories dealing with Western life — especially animal life. His short stories appear frequently in The American Boy. *One of his longer animal stories,* The Last of the Thundering Herd, *was the 1933 selection of the Junior Literary Guild.*

On a patch of blue and white alkali where the sun
glared down in merciless fury, Tamerlane had taken his
stand. There, showing neither anger nor fear, he awaited
the charge of his larger opponent.

The fight was not of the young Hereford's seeking.
He had come on the range with nothing but friendliness
in his heart, and after a long, fifteen-mile walk in the
wake of Bill Dailey's saddle horse, he asked nothing but
a chance to drink from the bubbling waters of the little
stream and, perhaps, to stand belly-deep in its cool
current. But this was not to be. Released a mile or so
from the stream, he had wandered among the herd until,
as he neared the water hole, he had caught a scent that
reminded him of the great, gentle, white-faced cow that
had been his mother. Tamerlane was three years old,
but his memory was good; so, raising his head, he had
sent a plaintive note from the repertoire of his calf days

up toward the rocky knoll above the creek, whence the scent came.

Half a mile away, the great shorthorn, master of the herd, had heard the sound, and his answer had been a low, pitiless roar. And now he was coming; coming with a threat of mortal combat; coming with the lust to kill that his leadership might not be questioned.

Tamerlane stopped. He wanted to go on to the water. But he must wait for the shorthorn. He felt no hatred for the oncoming monster. Neither did he feel fear; to run was impossible, anyhow, for already the herd was gathering. A vast oval of curious cows was forming about the alkali, and there remained no way but to await the inevitable.

The shorthorn was coming slowly, but there was something in his very slowness that spoke of the inexorable. Twenty-four hundred pounds he weighed, more than a ton of hitherto irresistible bone and muscle. White foam dripped and floated from his mouth and nostrils. Fires of rage glowed dully in his bloodshot eyes. He carried his head low, and the sunlight sparkled on the saberlike points of his curving horns.

Tamerlane carried six hundred pounds less weight, but some of the difference was to his advantage. Where the shorthorn bore great waves of fat, Tamerlane was sleek and smooth and the muscles rippled beneath the cherry red of his skin like undulating velvet. His eyes were not bloodshot; instead they were mild and clear. The curly hair on his forehead hung well below his brows and the snowy white of his neck and head suggested something of beauty rather than a fighting machine. And yet there

was that in the corded thickness of his neck, in the breadth
of his chest, and in the muscle-knotted sweep of his
shoulders which spelled strength, and now as he dropped
his head and watched the approach of his enemy, the
mildness of his eyes hardened to confidence. He raked
one forefoot across the alkali to throw up a jet of snowlike
dust above his back.

The shorthorn, having come to the point where action
and not bluff must decide the fortunes of the day, stopped
a hundred yards away. And he, too, threw up clouds of
dust while he sent another roar of rage reverberating
among the hills.

The living wall of cows closed in, rank after rank, and
the center space became a vast arena. Dropping his
head and arching his great back, the shorthorn moved
forward. A walk, a trot, a few short jumps, and then
came the final charge. Nor was the mild-eyed white-
face found wanting. He, too, dropped his white crest
and lunged forward. Two columns of chalk-white dust
rose from the alkali, hanging for a moment above the
milling herd. Then they met and from under them came
a wild bone-splintering crash. A gentle breeze moved
the column of dust aside. Neither of the great warriors
had lost an inch. Both knelt where they had met, and
now the fury in the eyes of the shorthorn was equaled
by the fury in the eyes of the white-face.

While yet half dazed from the shock of the impact,
both gladiators got to their feet. Head to head, eye to
eye, and nose to nose, they stood, and beneath them
the dust swirled and eddied from the spurts of their
laboring breath. And now began the battle that was to

become epic among the cowmen in the valley of Clear Creek. Back and forth across the alkali and clay, Tamerlane and the shorthorn charged and countercharged. Around them, a choking cloud of dust; above them, the blazing sun.

From the hills around and from the cluster of tents far up the valley, foaming horses brought man after man to stem the tide. Rope after rope shot into the surging mass, to hold a moment and then to crack like the report of a pistol. Once Bill Dailey forced his horse between the combatants. That he lived was a miracle. No power on earth short of a bullet could stop those engines of destruction.

Toward the last it seemed that the curving weapons of the shorthorn must surely win. Once they cut a long gash over the ribs of the white-face, and again they plowed a crimson furrow across his throat. Now the dripping foam was flecked with red, and the alkali was splashed with roses where the dust gathered on a purple background.

Tamerlane was sorely hurt. The strength of the gallant white-face was oozing away through scores of wounds. The shorthorn was almost unscarred, for the horns of his lighter antagonist, set squarely at right angles to the sides of his head, could not be brought into play. At last, however, the heat began to tell. Tamerlane was breathing heavily, but the breath of the shorthorn came in choking sobs.

And then, the end.

Once more and for the last time those hate-charged tons of bone and muscle came together. Perhaps it was due to exhaustion, perhaps to blindness, but whatever the reason the shorthorn held his head too high and Tamerlane's ironlike crest caught him below the bridge of the nose. The shorthorn's head buckled under and the white-face drove through to the breast. Slowly, very slowly, the head and shoulders of the shorthorn rose skyward. A moment he stood erect, his blood-reddened horns like banners above the dust cloud; then, like a column pushed from its base, he fell. Making a great effort, he got to his knees only to crash down and over as a living battering ram caught him full in the side. Again he tried, and once more the white-face leaped ahead. His third and last effort was made on the very bank of the creek. Tamerlane put every ounce of his strength into this last assault.

Then, a few minutes later, a weakened and chastened shorthorn climbed the farther shore and turned wearily away, while Tamerlane stood belly-deep in the cold water, panting, trembling, but victorious.

Toward evening, when the sun had lost its heat, Bill Dailey rode into the water beside Tamerlane and slipped a noose over the Hereford's horns. Obeying a gentle tug from the cowman's saddlehorn, the white-faced warrior followed his master from the water and along the valley to a cluster of tents marking the camp of the cowmen. There, tied to a feed rack and munching ground oats the while, Tamerlane submitted to the surgery of Dailey and Chuck McArthur, foreman of the cowherd.

For several days Tamerlane stayed by the feed rack. Each morning his wounds were dressed with turpentine, and the big fellow made no complaint, for ground oats had become a part of the ritual. At last, with a final dressing of tar to keep the flies away, he was at liberty to join the herd. But the oats had become a habit. Morning and night he returned to the camp, nor was he ever disappointed. In the beginning the foreman fed him oats to build up his strength; in the end, because Tamerlane had become a great pet; and in time he came to associate both Dailey and the foreman with oats, and then, too, in the evening when flies and mosquitoes settled thickly on his sensitive skin he found the foreman always willing to rub his back and shoulders.

When fall came and the herd moved in to the corrals, Tamerlane was given a special stall in the horse barn. There, behind thick log walls, he spent the winter listening to the roar of blizzards and eating more oats but passing a good deal of his time in sleep. Twice a day he followed a procession of his mates down to the creek for water, followed because Chuck McArthur sat astride his cherry expanse of satin back and used him for a cow pony.

As the years came and went, the friendship between the two cowmen and the great Hereford grew. Men who live out of doors in the land of cattle are much alone. In the absence of human companions, they turn often to the animals in their care. The dog becomes half owner of the shelter tent; the horse is a full partner in everything; and sometimes, as in Tamerlane's case, a member of the herd is admitted to this society of friends. But there is a law of the prairie that is founded neither upon justice nor upon sentiment. Even the gratitude that is due to long and faithful service gives way before it. It is an inexorable rule of the cattlemen that the useless must go.

So one day in the early fall an order went forth from 4X headquarters, and the next day Tamerlane was driven across miles of prairie to another camp.

It meant the beginning of the end. It meant that the old Hereford was no longer of value. It meant that his sole remaining mission was to put on fat and prepare himself for a long trip toward the east and the slaughterhouse.

Then came another day when the herds of the 4X closed in toward the ranch and the air rang with the plaintive calls of mothers separated from their young while, later, the nights were made hideous by the ceaseless bellowing of deserted and lonely calves.

Then came the night when Tamerlane lay down for the last rest at home. Knowing nothing of the cruel fate in store, in perfect faith in the future and the men who were his friends, he passed the night in quiet and sleep.

At daybreak came the clattering of bars, and he watched his corral mates streaming in a heavy column through the gate. He watched in a detached and impersonal sort of way as he had done, times without number, in the past. That this was the beginning of their last trek he did not realize, and when a cowpuncher urged him to his feet, he stretched his great frame in lazy enjoyment and swung in behind his herd.

All day they moved slowly eastward. There was no hurry. Grazing, step by step, as it went, the herd moved across the old familiar range. At nightfall they reached the water and Tamerlane stood on a bluff above the creek and gazed steadily into the west, for back there somewhere was home and the cords of home love were growing taut. When they moved on, once more, slowly, through the

twilight, Tamerlane was on a range that was new to him.
Again he turned his head toward home, and now a low,
mournful bellow trembled deep within his chest.

With the coming of darkness they stopped and the herd
began to bed down. The moon rose, and its yellow light
glistened on the tents of the camp. A fire crackled before
the cook tent, and men moved rapidly from camp to picket
lines and back again. For a while Tamerlane stood by the
tents, but Bill Dailey was not there. Neither had he been
at the corrals in the morning. Perhaps Bill Dailey, too,
felt, and therefore avoided, the parting.

With a quiet night, a moon, and a tired herd, only one
man was needed on night herding, and it was Tamerlane's
other friend, Chuck McArthur, who took the first shift.
Hour after hour the cowman sat his horse beside the
resting cattle. With arms folded and head hung low, he
appeared to be asleep. Suddenly the great Hereford arose
from his place among the sleeping herd and threaded his
way through the reclining bodies of his mates. The broad
brim of the night herder's hat lifted and became hori-
zontal. Now Tamerlane was at the edge of the herd and
moving toward the open prairie. But Chuck McArthur
apparently heard nothing and saw nothing, for once again
the hat brim lowered until the watchman's chin was
against his breast. Tamerlane was trotting steadily into
the west.

The first tinge of dawn glowed faintly along the eastern
horizon, and in the corral of the 4X no sound broke the
stillness save the occasional squeaking of the upper door of
the calf pen. Ordinarily that would have been closed and
silent, but a careless ranch hand had failed to catch the

latch. Within, scattered through the darkness of the shed,
lay the cream of Bill Dailey's pure-bred calves, and their
value ran to many thousands.

And now, moving silently as the night itself, there
appeared on the timbers above the gate a long tawny form
— the lion of the bad lands. Presently she dropped to the
ground within the corral and began moving slowly toward
the swinging door. Every step or two she paused to listen
and peer with yellowish-green eyes ahead and into the
gloom of the shed. A sluggish movement of air swung
the door open and brought to the lion's nostrils the scent
of the calves inside. Now she crouched close to the ground
and her tail took up a waving motion from flank to flank.
Followed another long period of listening, and then she
sprang up and over the closed lower half of the door. Once
again the corral was given over to the night.

The light in the east grew brighter. From the branches
of a thorn apple that swept the fence, a kingbird uttered a
single note. From somewhere out on the prairie came the
clicking of hoofs and the ponderous tread of some heavy
animal. Then, from the calf shed, a cry of agony, half
moan, half shriek, that ended in a gurgle. And, as though
in answer, a deep rumbling roar swelled on the night air.
The sound of clicking hoofs changed to the thunderous
tread of running feet. Now the crash of splintering wood.
The heavy poles that formed the gate bent under the impact and flew into a shower of splinters. Tamerlane had
returned.

Another crash, another shower of matchwood, and the
door to the calf shed was no more. In the opening stood
the white-faced old emperor of the prairies. Head low,

nostrils dilated, eyes flashing, he paused. A flash of moonlight struck fire from his burnished horns. A cloud of dust burst from under his raking feet, and then, as he saw the flickering orbs of light ahead, he charged.

Bill Dailey will show you today where a cottonwood timber, nearly the size of a man's body, snapped like a pipe stem under the impact of Tamerlane's first assault. He will show you where the outer wall, built to withstand the surging of cattle and the crushing power of blizzard and tornado, was swept from its foundations and driven outward to the point of bursting. Then, too, along the walls where Tamerlane followed the retreating, hissing, spitting cat, he will show you deep gouges where the great Hereford's horns plowed through cottonwood and pine as though the heavy timbers were made of cork.

Tamerlane had learned much since the day he had fought the shorthorn war lord on the alkali. And so, failing in his first and direct attack, he changed his tactics. Now he followed his lightning-quick opponent with short, savage, quartering jabs. Back and forth across the shed, over the body of the dead calf, through scattering groups of the fear-stricken living, the battle raged.

Cornered between feed rack and wall, the lion took the offensive. Charging, she leaped to the Hereford's shoulders, raking his neck and sides with claws that cut and ripped until the blood ran in streams. Cornered again, she buried her teeth in the great beast's neck, at the same time striking out with her terrible hind feet, to score his sides from shoulder to flank. Once more she leaped and struck, but Tamerlane had learned his lesson. With a sudden lunge he darted through the low-framed door, knocking the lion to the ground, and before she could recover her balance he had wheeled and thrown his entire weight behind a downward thrust. And the men who came running through the night heard a blood-curdling roar of triumph, for Tamerlane had felt the yielding flesh and crunching bone.

For an instant the Hereford held his adversary pinned to the frosty ground, but even then she was ripping his face to shreds. Nearly blinded by blood and almost wild with the stinging pain, he withdrew his horns for another strike, whereupon with a single leap the lion reached the fence — but weak and trembling, she hesitated halfway between the ground and the upper rail.

Tamerlane seemed to see his chance. With a roar of blood-urged hate, he summoned the last of his waning strength and lunged forward. Two thousand four hundred pounds on vengeance bent. For the last time a high-pitched scream of anguish rent the air. A section of fence swayed, buckled, and collapsed. On through the wreckage drove Tamerlane, carrying the crushed body of the lion on his horns. Belly-deep in broken poles and posts, he stopped. For a moment he stood swaying from side to side, then sagged slowly forward and down.

An hour later, extricated from the tangle of splintered wood, his wounds dressed, back in his own stall at the horse barn, Tamerlane lay at ease. Beside him stood Bill Dailey and the ranch hand who had acted as assistant surgeon. The Hereford's tongue was scraping the bottom of a pail that once had contained ground oats. Now the oats were gone and he withdrew his head. Slowly it swung on the ponderous neck until the curly white face rested against the cherry of his flank. With a last sigh of content, the eyelids dropped and Tamerlane was asleep.

The ranch hand, leaning across the reclining body of the great beast, whispered to his boss, "Is he goin' to die?"

Bill Dailey stooped and ran his hand across the curly head of the Hereford. "Sure he'll die, some day — they all do. But when Tamerlane dies, the coroner is goin' to have to report either old age or an overdose of ground oats."

Unusual Words

inexorable — not to be changed by pity or by the pleading of others

repertoire — (a plaintive note from the repertoire of his calf days) usually the list of musical numbers, plays, or recitations which a person or a company of persons can perform

reverberating — resounding, echoing

ritual — usually refers to part of the order of service in a church

taut — (the cords of home love were growing taut) were being drawn tight

undulating — (like undulating velvet) like velvet stirred by a wavelike motion

Questions for Self-Testing

1. What did Tamerlane look like?
2. In what kind of country does the reader first find him?
3. For what reason did Tamerlane announce his presence when he drew near the water hole?
4. The author says that the great shorthorn was coming towards Tamerlane "with a threat of mortal combat." What was it that the shorthorn was fighting to defend?

5. How did the men from the ranch try to stop the combat?
6. What attitude towards the fight did the cows take?
7. Just before the end of the battle, why does it seem that the shorthorn must win?
8. How did Tamerlane finally win?
9. Did Tamerlane kill his enemy?
10. How did Tamerlane become a pet on the ranch?
11. In winter, what use was made of him?
12. Since Tamerlane was a pet, how does the author explain his not being kept at the ranch when the other animals were sent for slaughter?
13. How does the author let us know that Chuck McArthur was not really asleep at the time Tamerlane left the herd and started home?
14. What accident at the ranch left the pure-bred calves at the mercy of the mountain lion?
15. When the ranch men reached the corral after the fight with the lion, what evidences of Tamerlane's enormous strength did they find?

TOPICS FOR THEMES OR DISCUSSION

1. In what ways does the author make sure that the reader's sympathy will be with Tamerlane in his great battle against the shorthorn?
2. Write an opening to the story which will make the reader want the shorthorn to win.
3. How does it happen that Tamerlane became friendly with men instead of savage towards them?
4. At how many points in the story does the fact that he was friendly with them affect his fate?
5. Using as many of the phrases out of the story as you wish, write a description of the country in which Tamerlane ranged when he was not kept at the ranch.

6. Select one of the descriptions, either of scenery or of action, in "Tamerlane" which seems to you especially effective and explain what makes it so.

Questions on
"THE WHITE DOGS OF ARRAN"
and "TAMERLANE"

1. Pedro wins our affections because he is a dog and beautiful and faithful, and because we are accustomed to like dogs. We are not in the habit of liking bulls. What means does the writer take for causing us to like the bull Tamerlane?

2. In "Tamerlane," we are given a full description of the fight with the mountain lion. In "The White Dogs of Arran," we are told only the outcome of the dogs' fight with the wolves. What reasons do you find for this difference in treatment in the two stories?

3. Both of these stories are placed in thinly settled country. Why does the country in which Pedro grows up seem so much more desolate and dangerous than that in which Tamerlane is placed?

4. Do we get in "Tamerlane" any suggestions of kinds of danger existing in the cattle country which are not shown in the Montana sheep country?

MR. BROWNLEE'S ROSES

By ELSIE SINGMASTER

The last months of the last year in high school find thousands of boys and girls thinking of the thing which fills the mind of the heroine of this story. That is, how to get what Jennie Swenson calls "a yob." Why Jennie is so eager to get a job, what she fears will keep her from getting one, and what the qualities are which finally get her exactly the kind she can enjoy and do well are explained in this story of a Pennsylvania mining town.

The author, Elsie Singmaster, lives in Pennsylvania. She has written many stories about her home state. Among the most widely known are her stories of Gettysburg at and soon after the time of the famous three days' battle, and her stories of the Pennsylvania Dutch. Some interesting ones in either group are: "Mary Bowman of Gettysburg" (Harper's Magazine, *January, 1912*), *"The Man Who Was Nice and Common"* (Harper's Magazine, *November, 1911*), *and "A Courier of the T-Zar"* (Saturday Evening Post, *June 7, 1924*).

As JENNIE SWENSON closed the outer door of her
mother's kitchen, pulling with all her strength against
the wind, she heard far up the street a man's loud singing.

> "I took my girl to a ball one night,
>> It was a fancy hop;
> We danced until the lights went out,
>> And the music it did stop."

Stanislaus Sobieski, usually called Stan Sobski, night
fireman at Mr. Brownlee's greenhouse, was going to his
work. His song was old; new songs, he said, did not
fit his voice. He was apparently not disturbed by the
fact that work began at six o'clock and it was now seven.

To Jennie, Mr. Brownlee's greenhouse was paradise;
she did not understand how anyone could be late for work
there. All else in the mining town was black and grim;
there was no money for paint, and there was no time for
cultivating gardens. At each end of Main Street towered

a frame structure called a breaker, to whose lofty summit ran cars filled with coal. Beside each breaker rose a mountain of black refuse, separated from the coal as it descended in long chutes.

There had been a third mine along the hillside, and its owner, Mr. Brownlee's father, had built a small greenhouse for his own pleasure. As the mine grew lean, he began to sell flowers. Presently he was shipping a thousand American Beauties each night to New York. The present Mr. Brownlee was shipping three thousand before he went to war. Now he and his sister were once more sending roses, five thousand in a night — not American Beauties, but newer and more fashionable varieties, Premier and Columbia and Radiance, in various shades of rose and pink; Talisman, a blending of pink and apricot and gold; double white Killarneys and long, yellow buds of Souvenir de Claudius Pernet.

Jennie did not know their names or even their distinct and lovely odors; she knew only their colors, seen when she walked slowly by, looking eagerly for panes of glass on which the white paint was worn away. She often watched Mr. Brownlee and his sister. He was tall and a little lame, and his hair was slightly gray; Miss Brownlee was short and broad, but not stout. She had clear blue eyes, wavy hair, and a broad white forehead. Her brother could do no strenuous work, but she worked from morning till night, directing the laborers, inspecting rows of plants, and superintending the packing of roses.

At the same instant that Jennie heard Stan singing, she wound her scarf more tightly around her neck, locked the door, and hung the key behind a shutter. For hours a light snow had been falling, and now an east wind was beginning to blow. Stan had now reached the middle of his song.

> "And this is what she ate:
> A dozen raw, a plate of slaw,
> A chicken and a roast,
> Some oyster-stew and ice-cream too,
> And several quail on toast."

In the moment while she waited for Stan to pass, Jennie was tempted to turn back to the kitchen and study. There was a good light and perfect quiet — for Mrs. Swenson, a nurse, was on a case, and Jennie's sisters, Anna and Gertrude, lived in Wilkes-Barre.

But what Jennie required for study was not quiet — it was company. There were incomprehensible passages in her Latin lesson; insoluble problems in her algebra. If she did not graduate in June she could not get a position. Better the storm and the long walk to Hilda Yonson's kitchen, where there were no less than eight younger children, than peace and quiet and blankness of mind.

Gertrude and Anna were astonished at her dullness. She could not be a stenographer because she was too slow; she could not teach because she was too dull; she could not be a nurse because she was too timid. The teachers gave aptitude tests, but she showed no aptitude for anything. When she was excited or embarrassed her Swedish tongue refused to say "*j*"; it refused now.

"I must get a yob!" wailed Jennie aloud to the storm.

She stepped from the boardwalk, already swept bare, into a drift up to her knees. Instantly she laughed and shook the tears out of her eyes. She was a true Swede, tall and broad and strong. She started briskly down the street. The lights in the neighbors' houses were dimmed by whirling snow, but far above them hung a light at the top of the breaker.

She heard a shrill bell which heralded the rising of the elevator from the mine. In a moment a line of tired men would pass the corner. Five years ago there had been an evening when the loud whistle blew and everyone went running and crying to the pithead. Mrs. Swenson had been the first to get there and first to know that she was widowed.

At the third corner Jennie halted. There were two ways to the Yonson house, one down Main Street, the other through side streets, past Mr. Brownlee's greenhouse. Jennie took a step in that direction, then laughing at herself, ran on down Main Street, then up a sharp hill.

From the Yonson's porch the whole of the Wyoming Valley was visible in daylight — cities and towns and roads, churches and schools and factories; and in every town and village a towering breaker. A part of the valley had a strange and solemn name, "The Shades of Death," a memorial of Colonial war and massacre.

Tim Yonson sat before the stove, in a coal-blackened rocker reserved for his use. His face and hands were clean, but they were not white. He smoked a long pipe and talked to Mrs. Yonson, who was washing dishes. There was a child on each side of the table, each pair of eyes on a book.

"Good efening, Yennie," said Tim.

"Good efening," said Mrs. Yonson.

Hilda looked up. "Hello! Thought you weren't coming."

As Jennie unwound her scarf, Mrs. Yonson set a large plate of Swedish cookies on the table to lighten the evening's labors, and it was not until half-past nine that Jennie rose to leave. Mr. Yonson had gone to bed and so had five or six children.

"I certainly am grateful," sighed Jennie.

Mrs. Yonson had difficulty with many English letters. "Come efery night till you are old, and Hilda will not yet pay what your moder done for us."

Jennie had expected to have the wind in her face, but it blew from every direction in turn. Regardless of the stinging snow, she turned down the dark street which led to Mr. Brownlee's greenhouse. A new section had been added and the low, dimly lighted buildings occupied a solid block.

She walked slowly past. There they were, the pinks, the yellows, the shades of rose! She stood still, though the wind seemed to blow through her. The snow hissed against the glass — how could this thin protection keep the roses safe?

The office was furnished with two broad desks, a half-dozen chairs, a bookcase, and many files. Neither of the Brownlees was in sight, but Mr. Brownlee's gray overcoat hung on a hook, his soft gray hat above it, and a crumpled newspaper lay on the floor beside his chair. At the back of the room a door opened on a stairway leading to the boiler-room. The door was ajar; perhaps he was down there with Stan. Probably he would stay in the greenhouse all night. She would, in his place!

In ten minutes she was at home. The house rocked a little in the wind. She shook down the fire, put on fresh coal, and while it caught, undressed near the stove.

Though she was warm in bed she could not sleep. She shut her eyes, determined not to open them again; then, startled by a sound, she sat up. "Mother?" she called.

There was no answer. The sound came from outside and grew each moment louder.

"I took my girl to a ball one night!" shouted Stan Sobieski at the gate. "To a ball! Fifty cents!"

Jennie was terrified. But Stan was an honest fellow — he would not break into a house! That is, when he was sober! She sprang out of bed and went to the window. She could not see him, but she could hear him. "I took my girl to a social hop!"

He was not going toward the greenhouse, he was going in the opposite direction!

"And this is what she ate! And this is what she ate —" he yelled, from far away. "She ate —"

It was not until Jennie had one knee on her bed and was about to creep back that she was really awake. It was a bitter night, and Mr. Brownlee's roses were in the midst of their most profitable bloom. Suppose the fires should go out? But Mr. Brownlee was there! But suppose Mr. Brownlee had gone home?

Foolish though it seemed, she put on her slippers and went downstairs. In the pale glow from the fire she could see her clothes spread on the chair; they seemed to say: "Put us on! Put us on!"

"How silly!" said Jennie. "I'm going back to bed."

Instantly she had another delusion; she saw thousands

of roses standing with drooping heads. No, as plants froze they got stiffer and stiffer, and held their heads straight. It was only after the sun came out that they got limp and black.

"I don't care if I am crazy," she said, and began to dress.

As she opened the door the wind seemed to drag her out, rather than drive her back. It blew with a roaring sound, far above her head. She heard a loud crash, as though the roof of a house had been blown off. She could see the breaker light when the clouds of snow blew away, but no other.

She laughed hysterically and ran. Stan had another old song — "I don't know where I'm going, but I'm on my way."

"That's me!" said Jennie.

The great area of dim light was as it had been. She slowed her step: there were the roses, beautiful and unchanged. The office was brightly lighted and still empty of human beings, but Mr. Brownlee's coat hung on its hook, and the door to the boiler-room was open.

"It's all right!" thought Jennie.

Above Mr. Brownlee's desk hung a clock with a large face. "Look at me, Jennie!" it seemed to say. It was half past one! At the same instant she saw that Mr. Brownlee's crumpled newspaper lay exactly where it had been at half past nine.

Jennie went up the step and opened the door. How warm it was, how sweet, how like paradise!

"Mr. Brownlee!" she called faintly.

There was no answer.

"Mr. Brownlee!" Alarm sharpened her voice.

"Who is there?" Undoubtedly it was Mr. Brownlee, speaking from the boiler-room.

"Jennie Swenson." She could not help giggling — what did "Jennie Swenson" mean to Mr. Brownlee?

"In the name of mercy, Jennie Swenson, come down here!"

The words were pitiful, yet there was an undertone of amusement. Trembling, Jennie went down the steps. The room was low and paved with brick. At one end was a huge boiler; along one side were coal-bins and piles of wood, and along the other shelves filled with cans and bottles of insecticides and sprays. Before the boiler stood an old couch, and on it lay Mr. Brownlee.

"Open that fire-box door quick, will you, and pile in wood."

Jennie picked up a chunk as she dashed to the furnace.

"Finer pieces, plenty of them! Pretty low, isn't it?"

"Not so very bad," said Jennie.

"What are you crying for?"

"Will they die?"

"Humph!" said Mr. Brownlee. "Go to my desk and take the flashlight you'll find there; then go to the farthest corner of every greenhouse and read the thermometers. And you might pray as you go!"

"Did Stan tie you?" asked Jennie, running up the stairs swiftly.

"Lumbago tied me."

Jennie came running back. The wood in the fire box was burning briskly. Mr. Brownlee's eyes shone like points of fire.

"Forty-eight degrees is the lowest."

Mr. Brownlee threw up his arm. It covered his eyes and mouth. "What did you say your name is?"

"Jennie Swenson."

"Where do you come from?"

"Up the street."

"You come from Heaven!" Mr. Brownlee still kept his eyes covered. "Can you put coal on the fire?"

"Sure!"

"Have you no father who may be out looking for you? No mother who is anxious? Are you real?"

"My father was killed in Shaft Eighteen. I guess you remember that time."

"Remember!" exclaimed Mr. Brownlee.

"My mother's a nurse, Mrs. Swenson. She has a case all night. I heard Stan Sobieski going home and I thought of the flowers. He was singing loud."

"Close that lower door," ordered Mr. Brownlee. "Then make the rounds with your flashlight. When you come back, bring yourself a chair."

"The lowest is now above forty-eight," reported Jennie a few minutes later.

"Sit down, Jennie," said Mr. Brownlee. "Now tell me again how you happen to be here."

"I vas" — excited and embarrassed, Jennie spoke rapidly — "I vas studying mine lesson by Hilda Yonson, and I was coming past so I could see the flowers." Then she recovered her English. "There was no one in the office, but a newspaper was lying all mussed on the floor. When I was in bed I heard Stan going home."

"He wasn't here," said Brownlee. "He never came.

I was shoveling coal when this attack of lumbago caught me. It's happened before. All I could do was lie down on Stan's couch. It'll take a stretcher to get me home. My sister is in New York; otherwise she would have been here long ago. Now go on. So you heard Stan going home?"

"Then I came," said Jennie.

"Then you came," repeated Mr. Brownlee. "You got up in the middle of the night in a blizzard and you came."

"I saw the newspaper in the same place," she explained, "and I felt something was wrong."

Again Mr. Brownlee covered his eyes. "Better make another round, Jennie, and you might fetch my overcoat along."

"It's now fifty at the lowest," she reported on her return. "I'll cover you up. I can hear water bubbling in the pipe. I could take a few of those bottles, fill them with hot water, and put them behind you."

"Why so you could! Open that spigot and you can fill them. Do you go to school?"

"Yes." Jennie sat down in her chair. "But I'm not good at Latin and algebra and geometry. I don't know if I can graduate in June. And I don't know if I can find a" — this time Jennie knew that she had made a slip — "a yob. I'm strong, but I'm not bright."

"No?" said Mr. Brownlee. "Will you kindly take another look at the thermometers?"

"Fifty-two everywhere," she told him jubilantly. "It's three o'clock now, not long till daylight."

"At five-forty my sister's train is due. She'll see the light in the office as they come into the station. Whatever has been our pain and anxiety, Jennie, we shall have the fun of seeing her come down those stairs. While I was at war, you know, the Government shut down on luxuries. We couldn't use our own coal to run our own greenhouse, and we lost sixteen thousand plants in one night."

"I have heard of that," Jennie wept.

"You've got to keep the houses fifty-seven at night and fifty-five by day. Below forty-eight there is blight and mildew. Will you please put more coal on, and make another round?"

"Sure!"

At six o'clock that morning the outer door opened, and there was a brisk tap of feet on the linoleum.

"Dick!" called a frightened voice. "Where are you?"

Already Miss Brownlee was on the steps. At the bottom she stood looking from her brother to his guest. Jennie rose, the flashlight in her hand.

"You might take that flash, Alice, and read the thermometers," said Mr. Brownlee in a tired voice.

Like an old woman, Miss Brownlee crept up the steps. Then she ran.

"It's fifty-seven everywhere," she cried, returning. "Have you lumbago? You've been shoveling coal! Where's Stan? What's the matter?"

"Alice, this is Jennie Swenson, Harriet Swenson's daughter," said Mr. Brownlee. "Last night at one o'clock, lying in her bed, she heard Stan going home, singing as he went. Now Jennie is something of a prowler herself. She comes here — has been coming for a good

many years — to peer in at our windows. She looks at
the roses; she doesn't handle them, she doesn't even
smell them. She has never been in the greenhouse. But
hearing Stan yelling, she dressed and came down, just to
look in and see that everything was all right. She says
that she's dull, but she observed that my newspaper was
lying exactly where she had seen it at nine-thirty."

"I'll put on a little more coal," offered Jennie.

Miss Brownlee looked hard at her. "You certainly
have common sense, and you're certainly strong, and you
certainly love flowers," she said at last. "Would you come
here and work as an assistant? I would teach you all I
know."

"When school closes, you mean," put in Mr. Brownlee.
"In the meantime, we'll help her with her Latin, her
Greek, her Hebrew, her calculus, and her what-not."

If he thought Jennie would laugh, he was mistaken.
She lifted her hand to cover her trembling lips.

"Sure I'd come!" said she.

At half past six Jennie went up the street. The snow
was whirling through the air. Traveling was uncertain,
because you stepped now on bare, slippery flagstones, now
into deep drifts. Jennie had a box on her arm; she carried
it as though it were a baby.

Jennie opened the kitchen door of her home. The light
was burning, and her mother sat before the fire, taking
off her shoes. She turned with a start. She had pleasant,
tired eyes and a braid of thick, light hair.

"Why, Yennie!" she exclaimed. "Where were you
out in the night? What have you?"

Jennie sat down, the box in her arms.

"I've got roses in this box," she said. "Red and pink and white and yellow. They have long, long stems. And — moder — oh, moder! I've got a yob!"

Questions for Self-Testing

1. After Jennie was in bed and had decided not to open her eyes again, what startled her into opening them?
2. Why was there no one to prevent her going out at night?
3. How had Mr. Brownlee come to be raising roses in a mining town?
4. To what size had his business grown at the time of this story?
5. Why did Jennie feel it so important that she should graduate from high school?
6. What had happened to Jennie's father?
7. What change took place in Jennie's English when she became excited?
8. Seeing Mr. Brownlee's coat on the hook and knowing he was there, why did Jennie not go home content?
9. Why had Mr. Brownlee's sister not come to his rescue?
10. When Jennie first saw Mr. Brownlee on his couch, what sprang to her mind as the probable reason for his not being able to get up?
11. When Jennie said to Mr. Brownlee, "I'm strong, but I'm not bright," by what little sign in Mr. Brownlee's answer does the author let us know that Mr. Brownlee did not believe her?
12. When Miss Brownlee, just back from New York, ran to look at the thermometers, how does the writer show us without telling us that she was afraid of what she might see?
13. Is there evidence anywhere in the story that Jennie, even though she was "not bright," had picked up some knowledge of nursing from her mother?

14. Before Jennie found Mr. Brownlee in the furnace-room, had the author warned us anywhere that Mr. Brownlee could not look out for the flowers by himself?

15. What shows us that Miss Brownlee really wanted Jennie for an assistant and was not asking her merely as a reward for what she had done?

TOPICS FOR THEMES OR DISCUSSION

1. Jennie says she is "not bright." Do you believe her?

2. Are there different kinds of brightness? If there are, are there any qualities which go with all the kinds?

3. Picture the mining town in which Jennie lives.

4. Write the dialogue which occurs between Stan and Miss Brownlee when Stan returns, sober, the next evening.

5. Apart from being strong and willing and fond of flowers, are there any other qualities Jennie has which would make you feel safe in employing her?

6. If you wanted to make a one-act play out of this story and could have only one stage set for it, what should you choose to have?

7. Show some situation in the greenhouse after Jennie has gone to work in which she shows that, though she is "not bright," she is capable of meeting an emergency.

FOR WHAT WE HAVE JUST RECEIVED

By Josephine Daskam Bacon

Making a living is the occupation which fills most of the hours of most of the days of most Americans. Even those Americans who have enough to live on without working usually do work, either because they really like to or because everybody else works. In this story, two of the four young people concerned have to make their own living and two do not, but all four are eager for the excitement of doing it. As the rich girl explains, "I like business," and in the course of the story the reader finds out why.

"For What We Have Just Received," though it appeared first as a short story in St. Nicholas, *has since been made part of a mystery novel for girls,* The House by the Road, *appearing as a serial in* The American Girl. *Josephine Daskam Bacon, the author, has written many well-known stories and novels for young people. Some of them are* The Girl at the Window, The Room on the Roof, *and* Girl Wanted.

Angelica was seventeen, and the image of her dad. This would have been all right if she had been a boy; but square, strong, dark eyebrows and the nose of a successful locomotive-builder do not look so well under floppy, garden-party hats — and that's what her mother wanted her to wear.

On the morning of Thanksgiving Day, long before anybody else was up, she threw herself into her car and dashed off aimlessly. The morning was mild and clear, with just enough tang in the air to remind a healthy young stomach of breakfast, and Angelica, following a dim recollection, nosed about till she found "Ye Olde Englysshe Tea Shoppe." Old enough the house certainly was: run-down, but not picturesque, with a big printed sign:

MEALS A LA CARTE OR TO ORDER!
TEA! DINNER! LUNCH!
SANDWICHES!

But nobody answered her impatient ring, and she pushed through, with her father's brisk, hectoring stride, straight into the kitchen.

At a littered table sat a dark girl, perhaps a year or two older than Angelica, elbows on the table, her chin propped on clenched fists, and such a hopeless stare on her face as made Angel's morning sulks look like mere nursery temper.

"Can I get some breakfast here?" asked the visitor curtly.

"Everybody's gone," the girl answered in a tired, even resentful voice, without turning her head. "What did you want?"

An untidy jersey dress and a loose knot of heavy, dark hair helped to conceal the fact that she was much the same type as her impatient guest. Angelica's barber and Angelica's tailor would have given you a handsome pair of discontented, boyish brunettes; but as it was, there was one sport-girl and one household drudge. They faced each other doubtfully.

"What do I want?" Angelica repeated. "Why, just some breakfast!"

"If you want coffee," said the girl brusquely, "I guess there's some here. The woman who was helping just left — I can't do everything."

"How do you mean?" Angelica asked, interested, somehow, in this sullen, despairing creature. "Isn't this a regular tea-house?"

"It was going to be," said the girl, "but I guess it's all off now. Joe always said it wouldn't work. Well, if you want coffee, I'll get you some."

She got up, reached for the coffee-pot, and began to pile some fresh rolls on a plate.

"I'll bring it out," she said in a low voice, and as she turned her back Angelica saw her rub furtively at her eyes.

"Never mind," Angel burst out uncomfortably, "I'll take it here — what's the difference? Don't bother!" She poured herself a cup of steaming brown nectar, sniffed hungrily, and fell upon a fluffy roll. Both food and drink were surprisingly delicious.

"What happened here, anyhow?" she asked, her eyes roaming disdainfully over the slipshod kitchen.

The girl flushed, but her answer was as pointed as the question.

"If you want to know," she said sharply, "my brother Joe and I thought you couldn't lose on food. I know how to cook, all right, but I don't know anything fancy, so I thought I'd learn. Joe says the things have to have French names nowadays, or people won't pay for them."

"That's all rot," Angelica interrupted. "My father says if he could ever find a place where the cook had never heard of a sauce, he'd go there and board!"

"Oh, well," said the girl. "But I'm talking about rich people. Joe knows. He's lived in New York."

Angelica's quick temper rose.

"I don't know anything about Joe," she replied curtly, "but my father happens to live in New York, too — his name is Grant."

"There's lots of Grants, I suppose," the girl agreed listlessly. "Joe works in Grant's Pittsburgh office —

James J. Grant, you know. He gets three weeks' vacation, so he came on here, to help me start."

"I see," said Angelica, amused at the idea of this obstinate creature's surprise if she knew that she was talking to the daughter of Joe's boss. "But the summer's over, isn't it? Aren't you late?"

"That's what Joe says. But he had to take his vacation late, and I couldn't begin all alone. And I had ten people promised for lunch — there, I must call that man up and tell him I can't take care of them!"

"Ten people!" Angelica repeated. "That is hard luck! How'd you get them?"

"Some man at the Braeview Inn," the girl answered on a long, sighing breath. "He came by in a big car and saw the signs Joe made, and he asked us if we could take a party of ten for lunch on Thanksgiving Day. He said he didn't care what we gave them so long as it wasn't turkey. He said if he saw any cranberry sauce, he'd cry like a child. He told Joe he'd like to poison every turkey in the egg."

Angelica grinned.

The girl scowled.

"Squabs were what I'd thought of," she went on. "Joe and I planned out a real swell dinner, like you'd get in a New York hotel, with six courses, and we thought maybe he'd tell his friends at the Inn, and that would be a start."

"Well?" Angelica shot out impatiently.

"Well," the girl answered, "that's all! The Reilly girl went back on me, and the butcher sold the squabs to the Inn by mistake, and they sent me codfish instead of fillet of sole, and Joe's gone off to get the ice-cream salt, and I don't know when he'll be back. And even if the squabs had come, who'd wait on the table? I could get the woman across the road to help in the kitchen, but she's no cook, and she weighs about two hundred, I should think — she couldn't go into the dining-room!"

"Gosh!" Angelica breathed. "Haven't you anything to give them? Not anything at all?"

The girl shook her head.

"There's a big chunk of corned beef in the house," she said. "I always get it for Joe, to make Grandma's wet corned-beef hash — he loves it. But that's no use, of course. And it's too late to get any chickens. I can make supreme of chicken as good as a chef —"

"Oh, forget it!" cried Angel impatiently. "It's just as Dad always says — American women have turned into French copy-cats and spoiled a lot of good cooks! I don't know what 'wet corned-beef hash' is, but Dad's always yelling for it. What do you do, pour water over it?"

"Water!" the girl repeated scornfully. "The idea! There isn't any crust on it, that's all. It's moist. You wet it up with the water the beef boils in, and a little stock — any kind. Then you put in chopped raw apples. Grandma taught me."

"Why don't you give them that?" said Angelica abruptly. "I'll bet they don't get that at the Inn!"

"You're crazy," the girl said coldly.

"Oh, am I?" Angel cried. "Now you listen to me, Miss —"

"My name's Gray, Frances Gray," the girl murmured sulkily.

"All right; now listen! Americans go motoring all over France, raving about the lovely little inns and the grand food — why? Do they get a long bill of fare, with fifty different things that nobody could afford to keep in stock but the big hotels? They do not. They get what there is that day (they call it the *plat du jour* — the dish of the day) and you can take it or leave it. If it's veal, all right. If it's omelet, all right. And good bread and butter, a plain salad, and coffee. Then they all say: 'How cheap! How delicious! Why can't we eat like this at home?'"

Angelica waved her hands with her dad's impatient gesture. "Do you know what I'd do, if I ran a place like this? I'd serve that wet beef thing, and one or two other good, plain dishes like that, one day; something else another day; and so on. No choice — take it or leave it, and if the stuff was good they wouldn't leave it!"

The girl sat up and stared, unconvinced, but longing to be.

"Do you mean that you'd dare to give a crowd like the one I was expecting corned-beef hash? Hash?" she breathed.

Angelica's eyes snapped. "I certainly would! Didn't he say 'anything so long as it isn't turkey'? Call his bluff!"

"But the fillet of sole! It's only codfish!"

"Can't you make anything good out of codfish?"

"Well, I was going to make a fish-chowder for Joe. I told him to bring back a few hard clams for flavor. Then, if your salt pork is good, and you don't overcook the potatoes, and you have the real old-fashioned pilot-biscuit, and brown the onion first, Joe says it has clam-chowder screaming for help."

"Well, maybe he's right, at that," Angelica allowed. "Why don't you start them on fish-chowder? I would."

Frances pushed back her hair and sat up straight.

"I could give them Waldorf salad, anyway," she said, "or fruit with mayonnaise?"

Angelica scowled. "Not if Dad was coming, you couldn't," she warned. "He says Americans think the French national anthem is The Mayonnaise! He swears that if he ever got a piece of banana with mayonnaise on it into his mouth, he'd spit it out then and there!"

"Grandma always said red cabbage cole-slaw with boiled dressing went best after corned-beef hash," Frances suggested doubtfully, "but she was old-fashioned, of course, in her ideas."

"Well, so is this luncheon," said Angelica. "Stick in the red cabbage and let it go at that."

"All right!" Frances was on her feet and moving to the stove. "I will! They can't kill me, I guess, even if they don't like it. I see what you mean — all old-fashioned. But then — I ought to have pie, and there isn't time to make pie-crust now."

Angelica's eyes narrowed and she chewed at her lips, just as her father did when he was planning something really notable.

"Cut out the pie," she ordered. "They'd feed them pie anywhere they went on Thanksgiving Day. Can't you think of something tricky?"

Frances pondered. Then a twinkle came into her deep-set brown eyes and she nodded shrewdly.

"I'll bet I could fool 'em on Mother's bread-pudding!" she said, and at Angelica's horrified face, she smiled for the first time, showing strong white teeth.

"I was only twelve when Mother died," she explained, "but Joe and I were so crazy about her bread-pudding that she taught us how to make it. The minister always asked for it when he came. It isn't soggy, you see, nor even stiff. The bread's soaked in milk, with an egg in it; no raisins, and not too sweet. Then it all puffs up, like a soufflé, you know, and the top is brown — quite crispy. You serve boiled molasses sauce with it."

"Oh," Angelica murmured doubtfully.

"That's the secret," Frances added seriously. "The sauce. It won't do just to heat the molasses — old-fashioned, dark molasses, of course — or even just to boil it a long time. You put butter in, and sugar, and you boil it till it almost hardens in cold water. Then it's done. It's lovely, really."

"All right, go ahead," Angelica agreed. "And coffee after, of course."

Suddenly the other girl's face fell; her voice, when she spoke, had lost its interested ring.

"Oh, what's the use?" she said. "I can't cook this stuff and serve it too! And there's not a soul around here — I tried."

"Look here," Angelica cried, "I'll serve that luncheon for you! I couldn't help if it were dinner, but I can for luncheon."

Frances stared. "Honestly?" she cried. She was between laughing and crying for a moment, but Angelica's brusque answer turned the scale.

"For Pete's sake, why not?" she said curtly. "But what'll I wear? I can't look this way."

Frances hurried into the long, old-fashioned dining-room, and returned with a bright flowered dress and a high mob-cap.

"I thought this would be nice," she said. "You have to have your waitresses dressed up nowadays — like that place in New York."

Angelica chewed at her lip and glared distrustfully at the costume.

"What's the idea of the fancy-dress ball?" she demanded.

"But — but we called it 'Ye Olde Englysshe Tea Shoppe,' you see," the other girl pleaded. "I thought it was cute — don't you?"

"If you ask me, I think it's rot," said Angelica. "Why not dress like a waitress?"

"But then, where does the 'Olde Englysshe' come in?"

"It doesn't." Angel's jaw set firmly. "It goes out! What's the name of the place, really?"

"Oh, it hasn't any," Frances said scornfully. "It's just 'Gray's Corners.'"

"If I were running this place," Angel declared, "I'd have a sign — I know someone who would make it for me, too — like this: GRAY'S CORNERS. THREE GENERATIONS OF AMERICAN COOKING! LUNCH AND TEA ALWAYS READY. DINNER TO ORDER. MISS FRANCES GRAY'S PERSONAL SERVICE.

"That's the real stuff. They can get hot dogs, or chicken à la king, or ice-cream with nuts all over it, or fruit salad, anywhere. Dad says he'd pay five dollars

for a steamed huckleberry pudding with hard sauce, but
nobody can make it. He says you boil it in a lard-pail —
can you do that?"

"Can I?" The soft brown eyes opened wide. "I had
one last Sunday for Joe. You bring your father over
here, will you? But — but — five dollars! He was joking,
wasn't he? Even a — a rich man wouldn't pay that!"

"Oh, well, he just meant he liked it a lot, that's all,"
Angelica answered guardedly. "I'll bring him, all right,
only not today. Now I'll have to telephone Bun — my
friend — and you'd better get things going!"

At half past ten an amazed but docile Bunny deposited
a suitcase on the veranda and received instructions as
to sign-painting. Frances' brother had little faith in
the shockingly humdrum meal so eagerly outlined to
him, but the girls were so enthusiastic, Mrs. Reilly was
lumbering so efficiently about a clean, workmanlike
kitchen, this slim, blond "Bunny" boy was so matter-
of-fact in his acceptance of any orders issued by the
mysterious dark creature who had dropped on them from
the skies, that Joe followed suit, and filled in the leaves
of the old-fashioned walnut dining-table under her direction, though he could not restrain a few objections as he
worked.

"We'd better put a pumpkin or something on the
table, in the middle," Joe suggested. "I hear they're
having 'em at the Inn. What do you say?"

"No!" Angelica snapped at him. "This man doesn't
want any of that Thanksgiving stuff — can't you get
that? Bunny, hop in the car and find us some chrysan-
themums, can't you? And make it snappy — it's nearly

twelve. You'll both have to help with the dishes — there aren't enough for four changes for ten people, Frances says."

"Sure, anything you say," agreed Bunny, the grand-nephew of Henry Huntington Bliss, the sugar emperor. His uncle would have rubbed his eyes distrustfully at the sight of his lazy nephew sweeping the cracked boards of a narrow veranda, bringing chairs from one room to another, framing a neatly lettered sign, and welcoming politely, at one o'clock, two shining carloads of hungry guests.

And Mrs. Grant would have been very near to tears if she could have seen Angelica, trim and demure in her white apron and cap, changing the brown fish-chowder plates for the blue ones destined for the famous wet corned-beef hash, and pressing them excitedly into the hands of Joe, behind the kitchen door, while Bunny, in a white duck jacket borrowed from a friendly soda-water clerk, assisted with the most surprising tact at all crucial moments.

"I think I'll make my whole meal of this," said Mr. Butts, the organizer of the "anything-but-turkey" move-ment, "if this young lady will be so kind as to give me another plateful —"

Angelica was on the point of gratifying this harm-less wish, but to her surprise, Bunny, who until now had done nothing but follow out her slightest wish, inter-vened.

"Beg pardon, sir," he said, politely but firmly, "we recommend the corned-beef hash very strongly. The luncheon is — er — rather filling."

"Corned-beef hash? Sounds good," Mr. Butts agreed, "but you see, this chowder —"

"We serve this lunch every Thursday, sir," Bunny reminded him. "Won't you come again?"

"It's — it's a wet corned-beef hash!" Angelica added politely, and Mr. Butts gave way.

"A weakness of mine," he explained to the lady at his right. "I'll come next Thursday; you can depend on me!"

"Tell 'em we'll have music next week," hissed Joe, as the busy waitress dashed past him. "I know a fellow that has a three-piece band —"

"Hush!" she warned him, and as she returned to the dining-room Bunny was leaning over the shoulder of Mrs. Butts, a nervous little woman.

"Oh, no, madam," he was saying reassuringly, "nothing of that kind! No music, no dancing! Good cooking is our specialty!"

"Thank Heaven!" said Mr. Butts. "Mother, we'll come over Saturday night — shall we? What's the menu Saturday night, young man?"

"I — I'll ask the cook, sir," Bunny replied smoothly, and in a moment a young woman in a businesslike apron, with a close white cap over her dark hair, was at his elbow.

"This is Miss Gray herself, sir," said Bunny. "Just what had you planned for Saturday, Miss Gray?"

"Don't tell me it's chicken!" Mr. Butts implored. Frances drew a long breath and changed her plan.

"No, sir," she answered firmly, "no chicken. We will have stuffed beef hearts with gravy, and plain baked potatoes; and steamed suet pudding with hard sauce for dessert."

"Beef hearts? Honestly, do they have them any more?" cried a tall, lean man across the table. "My mother always bought one when the butcher killed. Count on my sister and me for Saturday, will you?"

Two golden brown puddings, puffy and delicate, had been placed at either end of the table; two bowls of dark, foamy, molasses sauce had been served to ecstatic consumers, and the guests now sat in the comfortable, commonplace parlor, drinking freshly made black coffee in a happy, digestive silence. Mr. Butts beckoned to Angelica and laid a five-dollar bill on her tray.

"I didn't contract for any price, young lady," he said, "but this is for you, understand? And I want to say here and now what my grandfather used to say after meals, for it seems to fit in with the meal we've just had: 'For what we have just received, the Lord make us truly thankful!' We're all of that."

Angelica had taken part in charity bazaars before, and she was about to accept the bill with a smile, when a white-jacketed arm prevented her.

"Sorry, sir," came the unexpected voice of Bunny, "but it's against the rules of the house. The lunch is two dollars, and we go on a ten per cent tipping basis. Thank you just as much."

Angelica could hardly believe her ears. What had happened to Bunny? How Frances would have liked that five dollars!

"Oh, I didn't know," Mr. Butts answered, impressed. "Still, it's Thanksgiving Day, you know. Holidays don't count."

"I understand you wanted to forget the day, sir!"

Bunny retorted quickly, and the laughter that followed convinced Angelica that he had been right.

"If you like the system, we hope you'll recommend us," he added, and retired with honors and twenty-two dollars, over which he and Frances went into minute financial calculations.

"That fat little man is bringing five tomorrow," said Bunny proudly. "I suppose we can give him those fish-cakes? Not too greasy, you know, on account of his mother."

"I know something better than that," Frances assured him. "Grandma always had it for Father, because he had indigestion, too. You shred the codfish all fine, with a silver fork, and then you mix it with the boiled potato, while it's hot, all dry, and toss it up together. You put it in a heap on a platter, and then pass drawn-butter sauce, with a lot of hard boiled eggs chopped up in it, and then pour the sauce over the codfish. It tastes grand."

"What's the name of it?" Bunny asked thoughtfully.

"We always called it 'Grandma's codfish,'" said Frances.

"Fine!" he approved. "That'll get 'em!"

"I'll bring my father over Saturday," Angelica interrupted eagerly, "but of course I can't very well wait on the table then."

"No, I suppose not," Frances agreed. "What shall we do about that, Bunny?"

On Saturday morning Bunny appeared at the door and pulled Angelica into his car.

"Hurry up, for goodness' sake," he begged. "And can't you get another of those black dresses? We'll have to have two tables — Joe's going to rig one up on trestles for the parlor. We can put your father, and a party that made reservations after you left on Thursday, in the dining-room, and Frances and Joe can handle them. Then you and I can take the other eight in the parlor, and your father won't see us — get it? Does he like nutmeg on his hard sauce, do you know? Frances grates it over, fresh, she says."

"Yes, he does," said Angelica. "I'll get another dress. You seem to be going into this."

"I am, rather," he answered absently. "We're going to give 'em black bean soup boiled with a ham bone, to begin. She had popovers yesterday — I thought they'd bust, they ate so many. Joe says the suet pudding will knock 'em for a goal; it's made with bread crumbs, so it's light, but it tastes rich as Rockefeller, he says."

It was very exciting in "Gray's Corners" kitchen that evening. Angelica passed the beef hearts and the succulent, mealy potatoes, whose skins she herself had carefully brushed with butter as they roasted; but though her hands and feet were busy in the parlor, her ears were strained to catch her father's voice in the dining-room. His acclamations over the suet pudding floated across the hall: he was calling for the cook.

"They're a great set of kids, Mr. Grant," came the voice of Mr. Butts, "and you ought to see the other two — that dark, good-looking sister of yours is all right, believe me!"

He nodded at Joe and Frances.

"Where is she? I'd like Mr. Grant to see her," he went on, "and the other young man; he's the business

head of the whole shooting-match. Go and get him, will
you?" he demanded of Joe. "And — could I talk to you
a moment, Mr. Grant? We have a little proposition here
that might interest you."

Angelica, glancing at Bunny, saw a strange confusion
in his face.

"Gosh! Oh, my good gosh!" he murmured.

"What's the matter now?" she whispered nervously.
"Hadn't we better beat it? Where did you leave the
car?"

"We — we can't, I'm afraid," he whispered back.

They slipped behind the door just as J. J. Grant,
escorted by Mr. Butts, came in.

"Fine!" said Mr. Grant. "It's a pleasure to find two
girls with the sense to capitalize a real talent like sound,
tasty cooking! I'm in on that lunch club, Mr. Butts, like
a shot. How much do you want?"

Angelica gasped, and Bunny squeezed her arm warningly.

"Why, you see, young Bliss had the sense to realize
they couldn't begin on a shoestring," Mr. Butts explained.
"When I suggested their coming to town and starting a
Down-town Luncheon Club, I agreed to bring 'em a
dozen patrons, to begin, but he said that wouldn't be
enough. So we worked out a sort of guaranty fund, and
I said I'd put up fifty per cent of the cash, if he'd find the
rest. Last night he phoned me that a relative of his was
good for a quarter more, and when I heard you were
dining here, I wondered if, as a satisfied patron —"

"Absolutely," said Mr. Grant. "I'll take the last
quarter."

"The other girl is a friend of his," Mr. Butts explained.
"She's to be the dining-room manager. He'll do the
buying and keep the books, and Miss Gray is the cook.
I think they'll make a go of it, Grant. They're sharp and
snappy and right up on their toes, all three of 'em. You
see what the food is. Great youngsters we have nowadays. Independent. A clever, well-educated girl like
that dark one — where is she, I wonder? — wouldn't have
gone into this sort of thing in our day."

"Absolutely," said Mr. Grant. "And they've got a
fine winter and summer business."

"I shouldn't wonder," agreed Mr. Butts. "Who's
that?"

For Angelica simply had to sneeze, and the door swung
back while she was still there.

"There she is!" cried Mr. Butts.

Mr. Grant saw the scarlet cheeks, the cap, the apron.
His mouth snapped shut like a trap.

"Oh," he said, "so it's you!"

"Yes, Dad," Angelica replied.

"Waitress, eh?" said Mr. Grant. "Well, let's settle
this right here! Take off those things and come home.
You know you can't do this, Angie; it's impossible.
Bliss, I'll talk with you later."

Mr. Butts withdrew tactfully. Angelica glanced doubtfully at Bunny, but he only held his head higher and
looked seriously at her father.

"I'm sorry, Mr. Grant," he said, "but I'm afraid we're
all set. Angel will be through school next year. I'll
have a good business, I think, when I graduate. I've
always wanted to do something like this. I suppose you

won't care to put up the money, now, but someone else will, I'm sure, and Angel and I know we can put this through."

Mr. Grant's chin shot forward.

"You're a couple of idiots," he said shortly. "The idea!"

"You seemed to think pretty well of the idea before you knew it was us, Dad," Angelica put in. "I want to do something! And I thought of this idea before Bunny ever saw it — this kind of an eating-place, I mean. I hate charity stuff — I like business!"

"Oh, you like business!"

"Yes, I do. I'm like you. I want to make something go! You said it was a pleasure to find two girls who had the sense to capitalize cooking! Well, I'm one of those two girls. Do you think it's fair to turn us down? You made your money — can't I make mine?"

"Attagirl!" said Bunny cheerily. "Honestly, isn't she right, Mr. Grant?"

It was not the first time Angelica's father had saved his face by a quick roundabout. He looked searchingly into the brown eyes that snapped like his own, and measured the strong, square chin appraisingly.

"Well," he said slowly, "times have changed. It's hard to say, nowadays. I must say that you've made an impression on Butts, here. It'll stand a little discussion, I imagine, but as far as the money goes —"

Angelica smiled trustingly at him. "Oh, come on, Dad, you couldn't go back on Mr. Butts very well, could you? You agreed to put up a quarter of the guaranty, you know."

Mr. Grant pursed his lips, then straightened them. "I suppose the real fact of the matter is that you should have been named Jim, Junior," he said. "Come on home!"

Questions for Self-Testing

1. How does the author account for Angelica's having so large an amount of initiative and business sense?
2. What was one idea about the food to be served that Angelica made Frances give up?
3. Why was Angelica out looking for breakfast away from home?
4. Angelica's mother does not enter this story at all. Do you get anywhere an idea of what she was like?
5. Which one of the dishes Frances was serving her guests should you choose to eat?
6. Why did Angelica object to decorating the table with a pumpkin?
7. How did Bunny try to make certain Mr. Butts would come again?
8. What did Angelica's father think of the enterprise of feeding people before he knew Angelica was concerned in it?
9. What did he think after he found out what she was doing?
10. How did Angelica persuade him to let her continue?

Topics for Themes or Discussion

1. Does it seem to you natural that Angelica and Bunny, who had been brought up with money, had so much more sense about how to make money than the two who had always been poor?
2. Angelica made Frances discard her idea of putting the waitresses into fancy costumes. Invent one other wrong

idea — one not given in the story — for Frances to express and Angelica to decry. Show why the idea is a poor one.

3. Not using any of the kinds of food named in this story, make up a menu which is distinctively American.

4. Make up a menu which belongs distinctively to another nation.

5. Does this story have a moral? If so, what is it?

6. If you had been Angelica's father, should you have acted as he did?

7. When the author has Frances call her inn "Ye Olde Englysshe Tea Shoppe," of what is she making fun?

8. Is food really as important as this story makes it seem?

Questions on
"MR. BROWNLEE'S ROSES" and "FOR WHAT WE HAVE JUST RECEIVED"

1. The differences in these two stories are very easily seen. What likeness do you see in them which has caused them to be paired?

2. Have you found in this book another story to put with either of these, which would make a better pair?

3. If you like one story decidedly better than the other, explain why.

4. Which character, out of all those in both stories, seems to you the most natural?

5. Write out the single sentence or phrase in either story which tells you most about a character. You are limited to one.

6. A great educator once said that genius consists of getting the world to pay you for what you want to do anyway. If that were true, which of the characters in these two stories would be geniuses?

AFTER TWENTY YEARS

By O. HENRY

Not many people in the United States spend their lives in one spot. Probably nowhere in the world do people wander away from the places in which they grew up as often as they do in America. Because this is so, there are hundreds of American stories which deal with the return of the wanderer to his native town. Sometimes he comes back rich and honored, sometimes he comes back poor and forlorn, but very seldom indeed does he come on the kind of errand or meet the kind of reception that is described in "After Twenty Years."

The author, O. Henry (whose real name was William Sidney Porter), is the writer of nearly a dozen volumes of short stories. Almost all his stories are lightly and flippantly worded, and almost all end, as this one does, in a surprise. Some of the most popular of them are "The Gifts of the Magi," "The Third Ingredient," "The Hiding of Black Bill."

THE POLICEMAN on the beat moved up the avenue impressively. The impressiveness was habitual and not for show, for spectators were few. The time was barely ten o'clock at night, but chilly gusts of wind with a taste of rain in them had well-nigh depeopled the streets.

Trying doors as he went, twirling his club with many intricate and artful movements, turning now and then to cast his watchful eye adown the pacific thoroughfare, the officer, with his stalwart form and slight swagger, made a fine picture of a guardian of the peace. The vicinity was one that kept early hours. Now and then you might see the lights of a cigar store or of an all-night lunch counter; but the majority of the doors belonged to business places that had long since been closed.

When about midway of a certain block the policeman suddenly slowed his walk. In the doorway of a darkened hardware store a man leaned, with an unlighted cigar in his mouth. As the policeman walked up to him the man spoke up quickly.

"It's all right, officer," he said, reassuringly. "I'm just waiting for a friend. It's an appointment made twenty years ago. Sounds a little funny to you, doesn't it? Well, I'll explain if you'd like to make certain it's all straight. About that long ago there used to be a restaurant where this store stands — 'Big Joe' Brady's restaurant."

"Until five years ago," said the policeman. "It was torn down then."

The man in the doorway struck a match and lit his cigar. The light showed a pale, square-jawed face with keen eyes, and a little white scar near his right eyebrow. His scarfpin was a large diamond, oddly set.

"Twenty years ago tonight," said the man, "I dined here at 'Big Joe' Brady's with Jimmy Wells, my best chum, and the finest chap in the world. He and I were raised here in New York, just like two brothers, together. I was eighteen and Jimmy was twenty. The next morning I was to start for the West to make my fortune. You couldn't have dragged Jimmy out of New York; he thought it was the only place on earth. Well, we agreed that night that we would meet here again exactly twenty years from that date and time, no matter what our conditions might be or from what distance we might have to come. We figured that in twenty years each of us ought to have our destiny worked out and our fortunes made, whatever they were going to be."

"It sounds pretty interesting," said the policeman.

"Rather a long time between meets, though, it seems to me. Haven't you heard from your friend since you left?"

"Well, yes, for a time we corresponded," said the other. "But after a year or two we lost track of each other. You see, the West is a pretty big proposition, and I kept hustling around over it pretty lively. But I know Jimmy will meet me here if he's alive, for he always was the truest, stanchest old chap in the world. He'll never forget. I came a thousand miles to stand in this door to-night, and it's worth it if my old partner turns up."

The waiting man pulled out a handsome watch, the lids of it set with small diamonds.

"Three minutes to ten," he announced. "It was exactly ten o'clock when we parted here at the restaurant door."

"Did pretty well out West, didn't you?" asked the policeman.

"You bet! I hope Jimmy has done half as well. He was a kind of plodder, though, good fellow as he was. I've had to compete with some of the sharpest wits going to get my pile. A man gets in a groove in New York. It takes the West to put a razor-edge on him."

The policeman twirled his club and took a step or two.

"I'll be on my way. Hope your friend comes around all right. Going to call time on him sharp?"

"I should say not!" said the other. "I'll give him half an hour at least. If Jimmy is alive on earth he'll be here by that time. So long, officer."

"Good night, sir," said the policeman, passing on along his beat, trying doors as he went.

There was now a fine, cold drizzle falling, and the wind

had risen from its uncertain puffs into a steady blow. The few foot passengers astir in that quarter hurried dismally and silently along with coat collars turned high and pocketed hands. And in the door of the hardware store the man who had come a thousand miles to fill an appointment, uncertain almost to absurdity, with the friend of his youth, smoked his cigar and waited.

About twenty minutes he waited, and then a tall man in a long overcoat, with collar turned up to his ears, hurried across from the opposite side of the street. He went directly to the waiting man.

"Is that you, Bob?" he asked, doubtfully.

"Is that you, Jimmy Wells?" cried the man in the door.

"Bless my heart!" exclaimed the new arrival, grasping both the other's hands with his own. "It's Bob, sure as fate. I was certain I'd find you here if you were still in existence. Well, well, well! — twenty years is a long time. The old restaurant's gone, Bob; I wish it had lasted, so we could have had another dinner there. How has the West treated you, old man?"

"Bully; it has given me everything I asked it for. You've changed lots, Jimmy. I never thought you were so tall by two or three inches."

"Oh, I grew a bit after I was twenty."

"Doing well in New York, Jimmy?"

"Moderately. I have a position in one of the city departments. Come on, Bob; we'll go around to a place I know of, and have a good long talk about old times."

The two men started up the street, arm in arm. The man from the West, his egotism enlarged by success, was beginning to outline the history of his career. The other, submerged in his overcoat, listened with interest.

At the corner stood a drugstore, brilliant with electric lights. When they came into this glare each of them turned simultaneously to gaze upon the other's face.

The man from the West stopped suddenly and released his arm.

"You're not Jimmy Wells," he snapped. "Twenty years is a long time, but not long enough to change a man's nose from a Roman to a pug."

"It sometimes changes a good man into a bad one," said the tall man. "You've been under arrest for ten minutes, 'Silky' Bob. Chicago thinks you may have dropped over our way and wires us she wants to have a chat with you. Going quietly, are you? That's sensible. Now, before we go on to the station here's a note I was asked to hand you. You may read it here at the window. It's from Patrolman Wells."

The man from the West unfolded the little piece of paper handed him. His hand was steady when he began to read, but it trembled a little by the time he had finished. The note was rather short:

"BOB: *I was at the appointed place on time. When you struck the match to light your cigar I saw it was the face of the man wanted in Chicago. Somehow I couldn't do it myself, so I went around and got a plain clothes man to do the job.*

JIMMY"

QUESTIONS FOR SELF-TESTING

1. Where do you find out that the man from Chicago was prosperous?
2. What action of his gave the policeman a chance to see his face?
3. What was unusual about his face?
4. When the policeman moved on, how did he know the man in the doorway would stay there?
5. What first makes the reader suspect that the stranger who came up and called the man from the West by name was not the one he was waiting for?
6. What first made the man from the West suspicious?
7. Why did Jimmy Wells not make the arrest himself?
8. Where do we learn what Jimmy Wells' occupation was?

TOPICS FOR THEMES OR DISCUSSION

1. Explain in what ways the characters in this story do or do not act as you would expect real people to act.
2. Was Jimmy Wells right in using the appointment made twenty years earlier to catch his former friend?
3. If the stranger from the West had been poor and forlorn, should Jimmy Wells still have acted as he did?
4. Supposing that the stranger from Chicago recognized who the policeman was as soon as he addressed him, write the scene which would then have taken place between the two.
5. Find the exact phrases by which the author makes sure that our sympathy shall not go out to "Silky" Bob.

MISS LETITIA'S PROFESSION

By Lupton A. Wilkinson

In the last twenty or thirty years, magazines in the United States have multiplied until now hundreds are published every month — some excellent, some good, some silly. In "Miss Letitia's Profession," the writer is not only telling a surprising story, but he is also poking fun at those magazines which are filled by "true confessions" about crime or love or whatever. As Rodney explains to his sister in the course of this story, most of the supposed authors of crime confessions "couldn't write a pardon letter to the governor." Their imaginary careers are invented by busy hacks, not many of whom are so painstaking as is Miss Letitia, and very few indeed of whom manage to have such an exciting adventure.

Lupton A. Wilkinson, the author, has written a wide variety of articles and stories, ranging from "thrillers" for pulp magazines to fiction for The Atlantic Monthly *and* The North American Review. *He is also the author of two books of verse,* Interludes *and* Blood and Silver.

Miss Letitia Mallow's profession and her appearance were utterly incongruous. The only comparable example is the trite one of the hirsute male who chews a black cigar and curses through ginny breath as he edits "Advice to the Lovelorn."

Miss Letitia's mind, this bright afternoon, was not on her source of income. Her thoughts seldom dwelt there, except when she was actually at work. Her professional self was a sort of gold-paying Letitia Hyde to a very delicate Miss Jekyll.

It would be difficult to exaggerate that impression of delicacy as the slight figure bent over a glowing petunia bed. Petunias were a good deal like weeds, Miss Letitia decided, grubbing among the roots with a tiny white hand; next year she would have less of them. The sunny garden looked like a color print of some New England yard; it had variety of color, yet all the lush rows were prim, geometrical, old-fashioned.

Somehow this garden had got itself transplanted, as it were, to Long Island, where it warmed the left lawn of a large, modern, pleasant house.

Miss Letitia's silvery curls, as she bent over the petunias, hung a little forward, to either side of a face of which the skin was white like incredibly thin china. Her gray silk dress, with a skirt that widened at the bottom and ruching at the sleeves, resembled a cut from that old arbiter of fashion — *Godey's Ladies' Book.*

The truth was, since the doctor had talked to her so plainly, Miss Letitia expended decreasing attention on the big house, the coupons that the bank clipped and entered in her passbook, and the recent newspaper hubbub over the work that remained so easy and took so little out of her. Her garden and her friends, in the new knowledge, seemed more important.

Studies of herself in her rosewood mirror had failed to alarm. The added pallor she had lately acquired caused her, she concluded, to look more and more becomingly fragile.

"Feeble" was the word in John the gardener's mind as he approached on a green inner path and coughed. The word would have made Miss Letitia delicately furious; the cough flustered her.

"Why, John," she exclaimed, straightening up, "I thought you had gone downtown." She had given the yard man and both the house servants the afternoon off, so she could putter among the flowers.

She did look absurdly fragile, standing with garden

soil on her hands, as if a housemaid had neglected to tidy one of the parlor ornaments.

"I was just going," said John, shiny with pressed serge, clean shoes, scrubbed face and Sunday hat. "But, Ma'am, you won't find a mite o' grass in them petunias. No later than Tuesday morning —"

"I know," Miss Letitia confessed apologetically. "I was only — fiddling."

"The doctor —" began John. He had tended that garden, and the rose arbor on the other side, for ten years, and had privileges.

"I know," Miss Letitia surrendered. "I know."

She stepped past a perennial border, seated herself in a twisted wood seat under a Japanese maple and watched the gardener depart virtuously among the flowers — out a white gate flanked by a fence supporting honeysuckle.

Over the blossoms John could be seen tilting his hat to a holiday angle.

II

Miss Letitia's choice of her incredible profession had come about in a circuitous way, impinged by the irony life dealt to her brother, Rodney Mallow.

Rodney was Yale '90; he was thin, anaemic-looking, wore spectacles and blinked through them. He lacked the alertness that ambushed behind Miss Letitia's gentle blue eyes.

Rodney piddled at writing six years, but his futility did not matter, for Rodney, Sr., had left his children a moderate income, a chest of silver from England, and a cottage in Connecticut.

Miss Letitia saw the panic of 1897 wipe the investments as blank as the paper that reposed so long in her brother's typewriter. Shuddering a little, she took in sewing. She petted Rodney firmly into the ranks of job-seekers. He trod countless literary avenues and bypaths, wandering finally into the building owned by a very large company that published many magazines on rough paper. The editor-in-chief wanted to save five dollars on a salary; Rodney took the job at twenty-five a week. The name of his particular charge was *Hot Clues*.

Miss Letitia sewed in and sewed out. The cottage sprouted a lopsided mortgage. In 1907 Rodney's salary was raised to thirty dollars; in 1916 to thirty-five.

One day — it must have been about 1920 — the editor commuted home in disconsolate mood.

"I'm afraid I'm going to be discharged," he announced gloomily. "*Hot Clues* is losing circulation every month."

Miss Letitia knew at once, with woman's instinct for direct thinking in a crisis, that what he feared must not happen. It must not be permitted to happen.

"What's the matter, dear?" She laid down her sewing.

"It's this true story craze," Rodney explained. "Only a few writers have the knack of it yet, and they're in great demand. I can't buy the product at the rate Doag and Hart permit me to pay authors, and our competitors are just eating us up."

Miss Letitia, mind grappling with this alien problem, recalled a full-page advertisement she had seen in the newspaper, heralding a new magazine.

"You mean," she asked, blushing at the phrase, "*Confessions of Love?*"

"No, no. We use crime material only. Reminiscences of crooks is what we need. But it's the same principle."

"Why, Rodney!" Miss Letitia was alarmed. "Will you have to — to seek out criminal individuals and persuade them to write their memoirs?"

"Most of them couldn't write a pardon letter to the governor," Rodney deprecated. "Trained hacks invent and write the material and the magazines sign likely names."

"I shouldn't think it would be very difficult," Miss Letitia observed, "if you can just make it up."

There followed a time of secret but keen excitement. The very next day the little woman from the cottage, whom everybody liked, walked down to the railroad station and persuaded the newsstand proprietor to let her have his left-over magazines, the very cheap ones, of which he had only to send back the torn-off covers to secure refund credit. Later, she discovered to her joy that there existed glossaries of criminal slang. When points puzzled her, she wrote sacheted, handscript letters to prison wardens and chiefs of police, who chuckled and replied. She made all-day trips to New York and browsed in the Public Library.

Miss Letitia read hundreds of thousands of words on tawdry subjects. The words fascinated her; the topics did not distress; these true stories were evidently fairy tales for adult readers with an odd turn of mind.

She decided to try her hand first at a career of safe-robbing (as she called it then), inspired by a news item detailing a local merchant's misfortune. Quickly she learned that nitroglycerine was "soup"; that a safe was a "pete," and the criminal specialist involved was a "peterman." Her investigations were drawn far afield. She found that safe-blowers began as "punks," or "apprentices to hoboes," and here was a whole new language. "Dinging" for begging. "Bugs," "jiggers," "saps," "high heels," "splints," "dummy gags," and "throw-me-outs"; all devices for faking physical ills and arousing sympathy. She was the first purist to write "yeag" instead of "yegg," tracing the word to the German *jeager*, a hunter.

All this in the realm of fancy. Her Dr. Jekyll self, the real Miss Letitia, never believed that actual human beings manufactured wounds with lye to draw tears and roast beef from housewives.

"The writing part is simple, just as I thought," she explained at the necessary time to Rodney. "You give the boy a drab background, city or small town, to show that fate was against him. Then you conduct him through a long series of crimes. No connecting thread is needed — no plot. You spice the narrative by relating it in slang and interposing frequent physical conflict. After two or three prison sentences, the hero reforms, and is telling the story of his life to warn others. That's the formula."

Rodney blinked through his spectacles, amazement bordering on horror.

Soon Miss Letitia was supplying the magazine with as many as three true stories in a single issue. She grew accustomed to seeing her work under such signatures as "Mike the Dip" or "Daggers Moran." When, in 1925, gangland stories leaped to popularity, she made the transition easily, becoming the amanuensis of imaginary gunmen, hijackers, and narcotic racketeers. Always the research for new vocabulary fascinated her, maintained enthusiasm, and nourished facility of pen.

Through the years Miss Letitia's enterprise garnered cumulative results. The circulation of *Hot Clues* returned to vigor; Rodney Mallow was permitted to raise the rate of pay from half a cent a word to three-quarters, then munificently to a cent. His own salary increased, by driblets, to fifty dollars a week.

Other editors learned of the diminutive penmaiden to crime. It became advisable to live on Long Island, so they could confer with her readily. In 1927 she received her first check at a five-cent rate. Even though she never neglected *Hot Clues* she maintained a three-cent average during the new depression! The Doag and Hart people paid Rodney a hundred a week, to hold his sister.

Early in 1934 success proved embarrassing. A metropolitan newspaper, learning Miss Letitia's story, sent out a pert young woman and a freckled photographer. Details of the Long Island house, from Miss Letitia's curls to the Mallow silver's interlaced monogram, were blazoned in Sunday supplements.

It all seemed a little childish, in view of what the doctor said. The scales told Miss Letitia she was growing smaller; her mirror said paler; more than ever as she grew weaker she seemed fragile, gentle, utterly out of congruity with the springs of the restored Mallow fortunes.

III

Sitting in the twisted wood seat under the Japanese maple Miss Letitia saw the big Lugano cabriolet of Mrs. Elmore Bacon glide to the porte-cochère of the white house. She liked Mrs. Bacon very much and she stepped a short way across the garden's bright bands. Her voice had always been low, slight; to call out loudly now would be one of those exertions the doctor forbade. The gray dress, though, was easily discernible against the patterned flowers, and Mrs. Bacon traversed the lawn to join her.

They chose a more comfortable seat, in the sun, and fell to talking of the forthcoming charity bazaar.

"I don't think people just ought to give money," Miss Letitia voiced opinion. "They ought to do something. I'm working some petit point table covers. They're old-fashioned, but they're rarely seen now and I hope someone will want to buy them."

"I'm sure they will," Mrs. Bacon approved. "You're wonderful, dear. So many activities. . . ." Her mind was busy with the Sunday supplement flare, but she couldn't devise a reasonable way to mention it to such a porcelain figurine.

For the better part of an hour they conned affairs social, religious, and charitable, in that section of Long Island; then Miss Letitia, animated, walked with her visitor to the big Lugano, watched the blue magnificence roll away, mounted steps and entered her wide, old-type hall. She felt cheered but tired; it seemed a good idea to go upstairs and sleep a while before dinner.

Foot on the second step, she paused. The big house seemed empty, lonely; she wished she were back in the Connecticut cottage. A positive weariness oppressed her.

Miss Letitia had been reared a good church member and her view of alcohol remained rigorous. Neither the concoctions of Prohibition nor the raw distillations of repeal had sullied her lips. But there was in the house — had been since its building — a residue of fine sherry, imported long ago by Miss Letitia's father.

A mental image bloomed of the pre-Revolutionary, cut-glass decanter, warmed by the brown glow of the wine. A small sip of that would be grateful: one could feel, it seemed, too fragile.

The little figure stepped down, as if the past curtsied to the twentieth-century front door. Miss Letitia walked softly through an opening to her right and across the deep pile of the sitting-room rug. Thus she reached the folding doors that she had had placed between there and the dining room, to remind her of Connecticut.

The doors were partly open. Miss Letitia gasped.

A man who had been standing at the sideboard, stowing the Mallow silver silently in two suitcases, whirled and drew from inside his coat an automatic pistol.

Miss Letitia was startled — out of reality, not into it. The stranger seemed the figment of a familiar dream. She had described him so often: black, partless hair that lay back as if glued; lithe, quick hands; skin a muddy olive; cruel mouth; rattiness gleaming in hot eyes.

A sentence in Miss Letitia's last true story came naturally to mind: " Joe's automatic seemed to leap from

nowhere into his hand." Even the name coincided, but
the author did not know that.

"Not a sound!" the man ordered, but the rattiness
faded, the cruel look softened, as he looked at Miss
Letitia. The late afternoon light, lemon pale, more like
sunrise than evening, slanted through the dining-room
windows. The soft hues of the gray dress and the silvery
curls gave a pastel effect, but the small face, very white,
more nearly resembled an old cameo.

"Drop that rod, gimmick!" Miss Letitia said. "If
you gat me, you'll fry in the hot seat."

Gentleman Joe's mouth opened to a round "O"; his
nostrils trembled; over his eyes flashed the look of a
man convinced of hallucination.

He did exactly what Miss Letitia had told him to; the
automatic fell from a nerveless hand.

Miss Letitia picked it up. She regarded it curiously,
the first she had ever seen. But how many times she had
described it: blunt, stub, blue, ugly.

"Don't hand me any tough luck patter," she warned.
"You can't beat this rap."

"G-gwan!" stammered Gentleman Joe. "One of us
is nuts."

"Don't crack wise." The gentle voice held its even
modulation. "You're no big shot. You've probably
been sniffing joy-powder to hop you up for this haul.
You're a — an ump-chay!"

Gentleman Joe could stand no more. The gun had
become the least of the terrors confronting him. He
stared a last moment, incredulous. With a strangled cry
he ran headlong across the room, plunged through a

French window and sped across the lawn, trampling flowers, as if all the fiends clattered behind him.

Miss Letitia, grieved for the flowers, stood a long minute holding one hand over her heart, which hurt.

She had forgotten about the sherry. She placed the automatic gingerly on the sideboard. Then she returned to the sitting room, wavering a trifle, and there pressed a button, bringing rose-glow to electric coals. She lowered herself into a comfortable chair before the fireplace and picked up a small hoop, drum-tight with embroidery. Unconsciously her fingers began to work but the needle and thread shook.

Presently she looked up, face white, wistful.

"He took it on the lam," Miss Letitia sighed. "No guts."

Unusual Words

amanuensis — (becoming the amanuensis of imaginary gunmen) the writer-down of material for imaginary gunmen

anaemic-looking — (he was thin, anaemic-looking) looking as though he did not have enough red blood corpuscles

arbiter — (that old arbiter of fashions) that decider of fashions

figment — (the figment of a familiar dream) something which appeared over and over again in dreams

hallucination — (the look of a man convinced of hallucination) convinced of seeing something which had no real existence

hirsute — hairy

impinged — (impinged by the irony) touched by the irony

narcotic — (narcotic racketeers) racketeers dealing in drugs

perennial — (a perennial border) a border growing each year without replanting

porte-cochère — carriage entrance

Questions for Self-Testing

1. What formula did Miss Letitia invent for the writing of her crime stories?
2. Had she known many criminals?
3. In what part of her writing had she usually taken the most interest?
4. Why was she now taking less than her usual interest in her house and her bank account and her other worldly affairs?
5. Where does the writer warn us that Miss Letitia was to be entirely alone in her house on the afternoon of the story?
6. Why could Rodney piddle at writing for six years without having to face the fact that he could not write?
7. What crisis forced him into hunting work?
8. How rapid was Rodney's advance in the job he found?
9. Why was Rodney's job finally endangered?
10. Why did the prison wardens and chiefs of police to whom Miss Letitia wrote take the trouble to answer?
11. How did Rodney at first feel about his sister's writing?
12. What did Miss Letitia look like as she faced the burglar?

Topics for Themes or Discussion

1. "Her professional self was a sort of gold-paying Letitia Hyde to a very delicate Miss Jekyll." Explain the reference and show why, and how far, it is appropriate.
2. Detail the steps by which Miss Letitia succeeded in launching herself in her profession.
3. "She petted Rodney firmly into the ranks of job-seekers." Write one of the dialogues between sister and brother in the course of which Rodney is being urged to find a job.
4. Helping yourself as much as you can by means of the

vocabulary given in the story, write the burglar's account to one of his friends of why he did not bring away the silver.

5. Is this story intended to teach anything? If so, what?
6. Make a list of the titles of all the magazines with which you are familiar, and choosing the one you read most often, explain why you like it.

QUESTIONS ON
"AFTER TWENTY YEARS" AND
"MISS LETITIA'S PROFESSION"

1. Does the criminal in "After Twenty Years" or the one in "Miss Letitia's Profession" seem to you the more life-like? What are some of the reasons for your decision?
2. "After Twenty Years," like most of O. Henry's stories, is of the surprise-ending variety. Is "Miss Letitia's Profession" a surprise-ending story?
3. What would "Silky" Bob have done if he had been faced by Miss Letitia while he was in the act of taking her silver?
4. From one story or the other, copy the warnings of the writer as to how the story is to end.

PAGE REFERENCES FOR ANSWERS TO QUESTIONS FOR SELF-TESTING

GROWING UP

Question 1, p. 4; 2, p. 6; 3, p. 3; 4, p. 10; 5, p. 10; 6, p. 14; 7, p. 11; 8, p. 15; 9, p. 12; 10, p. 17; 11, pp. 17–18.

THE NIGHT HUNTER

Question 1, p. 25; 2, pp. 27, 28, 36; 3, p. 26; 4, p. 29; 5, p. 29; 6, pp. 29–30; 7, p. 32; 8, p. 33; 9, p. 39; 10, p. 39; 11, p. 39.

THE SILVER SNUFFBOX

Question 1, p. 45; 2, p. 45; 3, p. 47; 4, p. 49; 5, p. 50; 6, p. 50; 7, p. 52; 8, p. 48; 9, p. 53; 10, p. 54.

FOR PEACE AND CONCORD

Question 1, p. 59; 2, p. 59; 3, p. 60; 4, p. 61; 5, pp. 65, 67; 6, p. 65; 7, pp. 69, 70; 8, p. 73; 9, p. 74; 10, p. 75; 11, p. 80; 12, p. 81.

SHANTY BOY

Question 1, p. 89; 2, pp. 89, 90; 3, p. 90; 4, p. 90; 5, p. 101; 6, p. 91; 7, p. 91; 8, p. 92; 9, p. 93; 10, p. 94; 11, p. 100; 12, p. 101.

A TALE OF THREE TRUANTS

Question 1, p. 113; 2, p. 114; 3, p. 117; 4, pp. 118–119; 5, p. 119; 6, p. 120; 7, p. 122; 8, p. 121; 9, p. 121; 10, p. 122.

GUESTS IN THE SMOKEHOUSE

Question 1, p. 128; 2, p. 129; 3, p. 132; 4, pp. 133, 134; 5, p. 137; 6, p. 140; 7, p. 144; 8, p. 144; 9, p. 143.

QUITE SO

Question 1, pp. 150, 151; 2, pp. 151, 152, 153; 3, pp. 148, 149;

4, p. 159; 5, p. 153; 6, p. 153; 7, p. 153; 8, p. 155; 9, p. 156; 10, pp. 163, 164.

THE RIP VAN WINKLE MAN-O'-WAR

Question 1, p. 171; 2, p. 171; 3, p. 171; 4, p. 172; 5, p. 176; 6, p. 177; 7, p. 178; 8, p. 180; 9, p. 178; 10, p. 179; 11, pp. 181, 182; 12, p. 185; 13, p. 186; 14, pp. 186–187.

THAT SPOT

Question 1, p. 193; 2, p. 193; 3, p. 194; 4, p. 195; 5, pp. 196, 197; 6, p. 198; 7, p. 199; 8, p. 200; 9, p. 200; 10, p. 203.

THE 'COON AND DOG LOGAN

Question 1, p. 208; 2, p. 208; 3, p. 210; 4, p. 211; 5, p. 210; 6, p. 212; 7, p. 213; 8, p. 215; 9, p. 216; 10, p. 219; 11, p. 219; 12, pp. 219, 220.

BINGISM

Question 1, p. 228; 2, p. 224; 3, p. 227; 4, pp. 229, 230; 5, pp. 232, 233; 6, p. 233; 7, p. 233; 8, p. 235; 9, p. 238; 10, pp. 239, 240; 11, p. 242; 12, p. 243; 13, pp. 244, 245; 14, p. 245.

SNAPSHOT OF A DOG

Question 1, p. 250; 2, p. 251; 3, p. 251; 4, p. 252; 5, pp. 252–253; 6, p. 253; 7, p. 254; 8, p. 255; 9, p. 255; 10, p. 250.

OCEAN GOLD

Question 1, pp. 268–269; 2, p. 269; 3, p. 275; 4, pp. 271, 272; 5, pp. 282, 283; 6, pp. 272, 273; 7, pp. 266, 267, 269; 8, p. 274; 9, p. 275; 10, pp. 277, 278; 11, pp. 266–269, 272–273, 277, 279–281; 12, p. 283.

THE WHITE DOGS OF ARRAN

Question 1, p. 286; 2, p. 287; 3, pp. 287, 288; 4, p. 288; 5, p. 293; 6, p. 291; 7, p. 293; 8, pp. 294, 295; 9, pp. 296, 297; 10, p. 298; 11, p. 299; 12, p. 299.

TAMERLANE

Question 1, pp. 305–306; 2, p. 304; 3, pp. 304–305; 4, p. 305; 5, p. 307; 6, p. 305; 7, p. 307; 8, pp. 307, 308; 9, p. 308; 10, pp. 308, 309; 11, p. 309; 12, p. 309; 13, p. 311; 14, pp. 311–312; 15, p. 313.

MR. BROWNLEE'S ROSES

Question 1, p. 325; 2, p. 322; 3, p. 321; 4, p. 321; 5, p. 322; 6, p. 323; 7, p. 322; 8, p. 326; 9, p. 329; 10, p. 327; 11, p. 329; 12, p. 330; 13, p. 329; 14, p. 321; 15, p. 331.

FOR WHAT WE HAVE JUST RECEIVED

Question 1, pp. 336–337; 2, p. 338; 3, p. 336; 4, pp. 336, 346; 5, pp. 341–343; 6, p. 345; 7, pp. 346, 347; 8, pp. 350, 351, 352; 9, pp. 352, 353; 10, pp. 353, 354.

AFTER TWENTY YEARS

Question 1, pp. 359, 360; 2, p. 359; 3, p. 359; 4, p. 360; 5, p. 361; 6, p. 362; 7, p. 362; 8, p. 362.

MISS LETITIA'S PROFESSION

Question 1, p. 371; 2, p. 371; 3, pp. 370, 371, 372; 4, p. 367; 5, p. 367; 6, p. 368; 7, p. 369; 8, p. 369; 9, p. 369; 10, p. 370; 11, p. 371; 12, p. 375.